7/6net

# MAN AND THE ATTAINMENT OF IMMORTALITY

'They saw afar off the day of the Lord Christ, and were glad.' (From the frieze by John Sargent in Boston Public Library, U.S.A. By permission.)

*Frontispiece*

# MAN
## AND THE ATTAINMENT
## OF IMMORTALITY

BY

JAMES Y. SIMPSON, M.A., D.Sc., F.R.S.E.

PROFESSOR OF NATURAL SCIENCE

NEW COLLEGE, EDINBURGH

ILLUSTRATED

THIRD EDITION

HODDER AND STOUGHTON
LIMITED          LONDON
1923

*First Edition December 1922*
*Second Edition Revised May 1923*
*Third Edition December 1923*

Made and Printed in Great Britain.
T. and A. CONSTABLE LTD., Printers, Edinburgh.

TO

H. H. D. S.

WHO MAKES THE BEST EASILY CREDIBLE

'Then, if that is his motive, he will not be a statesman.

'By the dog of Egypt, he will! in the city which is his own he certainly will, though in the land of his birth perhaps not, unless he have a divine call.

'I understand; you mean that he will be a ruler in the city of which we are the founders, and which exists in idea only; for I do not believe that there is such an one anywhere on earth?

'In heaven, I replied, there is laid up a pattern of it, me-thinks, which he who desires may behold, and beholding, may set his own house in order. But whether such an one exists, or ever will exist in fact, is no matter; for he will live after the manner of that city, having nothing to do with any other.

'I think so, he said.'

PLATO, Republic, 592 (tr. Jowett).

## PREFACE TO THIRD EDITION

APART from a few verbal alterations this edition is the same as the second.

J. Y. S.

*November* 1923.

## PREFACE TO SECOND EDITION

ADVANTAGE has been taken of the issue of a new edition to make several minor corrections, and in particular on p. 296 to give a fairer appreciation and fuller criticism of the counter-arguments referred to there.

J. Y. S.

*March* 1923.

# PREFACE

THIS book may be considered as a development of, or sequel to, an earlier volume entitled *The Spiritual Interpretation of Nature*.[1] Like the previous work it contains little for the specialist in science, philosophy, or theology, but as an attempt to consider as a whole certain of the principal facts relating to the past history, present situation, and ultimate destiny of mankind, it may commend itself to some of those who feel the imperative need for themselves of a synthetic view of the world process, which shall cover not merely the story of man but the stages antecedent to his appearance. The mere scope of the investigation must necessarily involve partial and incomplete treatment at many points; at the best it is no more than an endeavour to approach some outstanding questions in terms of the dominant category of this generation.

Where the writer is conscious of so much indebtedness, it is difficult to make full acknowledgment, but in addition to the references in the footnotes he would particularly wish to thank Professors Sir Richard Lodge, T. J. Jehu, David Waterston, J. H. Ashworth, H. A. A. Kennedy, and H. R. Mackintosh, for their kindness in reading the chapter or chapters dealing with subjects upon which they are recognised authorities, so saving the writer from some pitfalls and in addition making positive suggestions of great value; as also Dr.

[1] Third and revised edition 1923.

A. H. Freeland Barbour, who has essayed the task of reading the whole book, and to whose wise counsel the writer owes a life-long indebtedness. At the same time, this acknowledgment does not necessarily imply their agreement with the positions developed in the book.

The thanks of the writer are further due to the following individuals and publishing houses for permission to make use of the illustrations cited:

The Director of the Boston Public Library, U.S.A. (frontispiece).

Dr. A. Smith Woodward and the Trustees of the British Museum (figs. 10, 11, and 15).

Mons. A. Rutot (figs. 8, 12, 14, 20, and 24).

Messrs. Oliver & Boyd (figs. 13, 16, 17, and 18 from James Geikie's *Antiquity of Man in Europe*, and figs. 21, 22, and 23 from R. Munro's *Palaeolithic Man and Terramara Settlements in Europe*).

G. Bell & Sons, Ltd. (figs. 3, 4, 6, 9, and 19 from H. F. Osborn's *Men of the Old Stone Age*, and figs. 25, 26, and 27 from J. M. Tyler's *The New Stone Age in Northern Europe*).

Messrs. Macmillan (fig. 1 from T. H. Huxley's *Man's Place in Nature*).

The Open Court Publishing Co. (fig. 2).

Williams & Norgate (fig. 5 from Sir A. Keith's *The Antiquity of Man*).

The Cambridge University Press (fig. 7 from R. A. S. Macalister's *Text-book of European Archaeology*).

Edward Arnold (fig. 28 from Weismann's *Evolution Theory*).

Constable & Co. (fig. 29 from A. Dendy's *Outlines of Evolutionary Biology*).

Swann Sonnenschein & Co., Ltd. (figs. 30, 31, and 32 from A. Sedgwick's *Student's Text-book of Zoology*).

The writer also desires to thank the Directors of the Religious Tract Society for permission to use in the Introduction some passages from a pamphlet entitled *Some Thoughts on the Relations between Science and Religion*, being one of their series of 'Tracts for the Day.'

J. Y. SIMPSON.

NEW COLLEGE, EDINBURGH.

# CONTENTS

## CHAPTER I

INTRODUCTION . . . . . . . 1

PAGE

## CHAPTER II

MAN'S PLACE IN NATURE . . . . . 27

## CHAPTER III

THE ANTIQUITY OF MAN . . . . . 47

## CHAPTER IV

THE ORIGIN OF MAN . . . . . 67

## CHAPTER V

PALAEOLITHIC MAN . . . . . 90

## CHAPTER VI

PALAEOLITHIC MAN (*continued*) . . . . 119

## CHAPTER VII

MESOLITHIC AND NEOLITHIC MAN . . . 147

## CHAPTER VIII

THE PLACE AND FUNCTION OF NATIONALITY . , . 179

## CHAPTER IX

PAGE

THE EVOLUTION OF INDIVIDUALITY . . . . 197

## CHAPTER X

THE METHOD OF EVOLUTION . . . . . 216

## CHAPTER XI

EVOLUTION AS THE WINNING OF FREEDOM . . . 234

## CHAPTER XII

GOD AND THE WORLD . . . . . . 263

## CHAPTER XIII

THE SCRIPTURAL DOCTRINE OF IMMORTALITY . . 275

## CHAPTER XIV

THE HISTORIC JESUS AND THE COSMIC CHRIST . . 302

# ILLUSTRATIONS

Sargent frieze from Boston Public Library, U.S.A. *Frontispiece*

FIG.                                             PAGE

1. Skeletons of gibbon, orang, chimpanzee, gorilla, and man . . . . . . . . . . . 33
2. The grasping power of infants . . . *facing* 43
3. Evolution of the lance-point . . . . . 55
4. Map—Europe in the period of maximum continental elevation . . . . . . . . . 59
5. Suggested genealogical tree of man and anthropoid apes 64
6. Evolution of the brain . . . . . . 75
7. Types of Kentian eoliths . . . . . . 83
8. Restoration of *Pithecanthropus*, after Rutot *facing* 85
9. Discovery site of Heidelberg jaw . . *facing* 92
10. Side view of skulls of *Eoanthropus*, Neanderthal and modern man . . . . . . . 94
11. Side view of lower jaw of chimpanzee, *Eoanthropus*, Heidelberg and modern man . . . . 97
12. Restoration of *Eoanthropus*, after Rutot . *facing* 98
13. Types of coup-de-poing or hand-axe . . *facing* 100
14. Restoration of Neanderthal man, after Rutot *facing* 106
15. Front and side views of skull of Rhodesian man *facing* 109
16. Types of Mousterian and Aurignacian implements *facing* 112
17. Succession of deposits in Cave of Sirgenstein . . 129
18. Types of Solutrean and Magdalenian implements *facing* 132
19. Engraved reindeer on reindeer antler, from Kesslerloch, Switzerland . . . . . . . 135

FIG.                                                          PAGE

20. Two bison modelled in clay, from Tuc d'Audoubert cave

*facing* 137

21. Examples of Magdalenian art   .   .   .   *facing* 138

22. Bison from Niaux Cavern, with four arrow marks   .   141

23. Examples of Campignian pottery and flint implements

*facing* 152

24. Restoration of Neolithic man, after Rutot .   *facing* 155

25. Reconstructed lake-dwellings   .   .   .   *facing* 159

26. Crouching burial, menhir and dolmen   .   *facing* 164

27. Map—Migrations of peoples   .   .   .   .   .   170

28. *Volvox aureus*—Type of colonial Protozoan   .   .   203

29. Early stages in development of primitive vertebrate

*facing* 205

30. Branch of typical Coelenterate colonial form   .   .   206

31. Dividuality in Planarian worm .   .   .   .   .   208

32. Dividuality in Polychaete worm   .   .   .   .   210

# CHAPTER I

IT is a matter of common observation that the great trends of philosophic thought have been in some measure a reflection of the social and political conditions of the periods in which they were dominant. Thus those ages in which the sense of law and order and authority was supreme, were on the whole characterised by ascendancy of the idea of the unity of thought, while those in which the human race took to experimenting with its destiny, or breaking new ground in the social, political, and economic fields, were marked by systems of thought whose leading conception was that of multiplicity, or in some sense, pluralism. That the decade covered by the Great War, the even more significant movement of the Russian Revolution—the ground swell of which was felt more widely than that of the war itself—and the subsequent phase of world-wide economic depression, and social and political unrest, should have been without effect on contemporaneous philosophic thought is inconceivable, although it is still too early to attempt an estimate. Of the character of that decade, however, as a period of testing and revaluation, of discovery and readjustment, there can be no question. No feature stood out in greater relief throughout these days than the scrap-heaps of the war. They were noticeable everywhere—in factory and foundry, inside the dockyard and the aerodrome, in the filed designs of the naval constructor, at headquarters of the military strategist, or hard by the shrine of the political economist—everywhere there was evidence of the worn-out implement, the super-

A

seded mechanism, the discarded method, the exploded theory. It is not entirely a coincidence that these were also the days of an Einstein and a Freud.

That this period of stress and of fierce challenge should have been without its influence on that whole range of thought and activity which may be covered by the word Religion, was not to be expected. If some were persuaded by the very course of things that the world in which they found themselves was indeed God's world, there were many on the other hand whose contribution to the scrap-heaps of the war was religion, or what they deemed to be religion. In addition to the moral issues that were involved in the question of what kind of a world it could be in which such a cataclysm was possible, there was the circumstance that the whole conduct of the war was a matter of exact science in a degree which was true of no previous war in history. The mathematician won greater victories than the musketeer : the engineer had everywhere laid the basis of success. If there were branches of science that were put under heavy contribution in the saving and restoring of human life, there was no corner of the known that had not been ransacked for the wherewithal to destroy it. It was science—ordered, tested, exact, organised knowledge—that was the sign in which men had conquered ; blessed be Science which gave us the victory ! She it is that alone can guarantee certitude, and what goes counter to, or transcends the limits of, her achievements, either of statement or construction, may well be looked at askance. There is a realm of hard and fast fact, of things that can be known, and that with certainty, in a way to which there is nothing comparable in the whole field of religion. A ' life of faith ' all up in the air, so to speak, and unrelated to everything else that is known, is not a matter for serious consideration in an age of continuously menacing realism. Such have been, and are, the thoughts consciously and subconsciously at work in the minds of many to-day, and with ample reason.

Nevertheless the fact remains that investigation of the long history of mankind has disclosed no period in which the most distinctive thing about him has not been his sense of Powers or a Power, expressing itself in the universe, with which he instinctively wished to come into some sort of a satisfactory relationship. There is in man a sense of need and dependence on something without him ; there is that in his being which goes out to something in the universe which he feels secures his place in it, and with which he desires to be at one. Challenged from the dawn of intelligence by the world order external to him, and impelled by his sense of need, he has committed himself to that world order in one way or another. As the initial acts of self-committal proved to be justified, man with his awakening mind made ever greater demands upon that order, and in turn began to feel its demands upon himself.

Man, that is to say, whether he likes it or not, is distinctively the religious creature. Man, constituted as he is, cannot help being religious, however different the expressions and form of the sense of the relation that religion represents. Thus the Bible did not make religion : rather did religion make the Bible, and the Koran and the Indian Vedas also, for that matter. The word Religion has had to cover an immense range of experience, from primitive man's tremulous response to lightning and thunder, or the feelings associated with the hesitant yet expectant sowing of his scant seed in the earth, up to conscious fellowship with Jesus Christ. Religion is a capacity and character—a higher awareness and responsiveness—that have developed with man's mental and spiritual progress, of which the growing revelation of God to man has been the converse side. In short, it is the last and highest expression of that *élan vital* that has characterised the whole history of life from the beginning—that reaching out towards a richer, completer, more harmonious life which was all unconscious until it became aware of itself in a human mind.

A sense of need, effort to satisfy that need in some new relationship to the stimulating and challenging environment, with, as a result, change in the organism, are elements in the Neo-Lamarckian conception of Evolution which is again slowly in the ascendant. Indeed, Lamarck's own word for his theory—'Appetency'—is very suggestive as a theory of all life—the idea of striving to satisfy a desire. A sense of need issuing in some fresh act of trusting self-committal has been the mainspring of all organic progress, mental and material : without it there had been no experience, no fuller and more abundant life. It is in the nature of all living beings thus to strive for betterment, and the striving has been historically justified. If the factors have been different, yet the method of Organic Evolution has been one throughout, whether regard be had to the development of the amoeba to-day, the saurian of Secondary time, or the physical and spiritual nature of man.

When this reaching out and self-committal attain that conscious level to which the term *faith* can be strictly applied, we are in presence of an activity which is fundamental, and a function of the whole man. Into this act enters every aspect of his being, intellectual, emotional, and volitional, varying in the degree of their intensity according to the aspect of Reality which is being envisaged at the time. A man's faith in the railway timetable may seem different from his faith in the stationmaster's word : but the attitude is fundamentally the same. There may be a difference in emotional degree as, in ordinary circumstances, the faith elicited by a person will be more rich and living than that developed by a bald statement in black and white ; especially so will it be when the object of faith is God. The difference lies not so much in the faculty itself as in the exciting object. There is no religious faith different in *kind* from faith as that term is rightly and ordinarily understood, any more than there is a peculiar religious consciousness differing from consciousness in the regular acceptation of that term. In every case the basal attitude is the same—an act of self-committal to that which challenges our need of satisfaction and ultimately justifies our trust. It is, of course, possible to work out points of distinction between the secular and religious conceptions of faith, but to hold them as absolute can only be done at the expense of truth and with disastrous results for religion. Thus it is easy to underestimate the character of scientific faith, and speak of it as if it were totally without moral content. But the faith of the man of science is no mere easy assumption of a postulate, or indifferent assent to a general view of things. His faith in the uniformity of Nature, that is to say, in the ultimate rationality, the absolute soundness and solvency, of Nature, is a central dominating motif of the man's activity *qua* man of science. Religious writers are serving neither the cause of truth nor of religion when they make statements to the effect that ' our religious affirmations, unlike those of science, are morally conditioned.' Both are morally conditioned, although in differing degrees. They are, both of them, affirmations of the whole man ; we believe alike in science and religion, with all that we are. In religious faith undoubtedly the emotional and volitional factors may play a greater part than the intellectual factor. The data are more often experiences of self-conscious states than mere sense impressions, while the challenge to action is more insistent in religious faith. Faith differs in content and object, and that naturally affects the intensive or quantitative character of the state, but in a psychological regard there is no deep-lying or fundamentally qualitative distinction. In religious and scientific experience alike, the fundamental attitude is the same.

If, however, this attitude of self-committal has been historically justified as the method of progress throughout the ages, and if it is clearly fundamental in human life, it is difficult to understand why in its most conscious and highest form—in something so ultimate and vital as religion—it does not control the whole of human life. If, indeed, it can come to mean the consciousness of a divine Power and Presence ' as the ultimate reality of the world and of our life,' [1] it is remarkable that the results of reflective thought upon it should not influence all other constructive thinking in some way or another. So, indeed, it was in the days of the Schoolmen.   Theology could not be for them simply one science amongst others, or something in any degree unrelated to the rest of knowledge ;  it was for them at once ' a wisdom of God ' and ' a wisdom of the world.'   Indeed, it is just as we endeavour to make clear to ourselves the method and degree wherein we have made progress upon the outlook of that mediaeval age, that we realise the measure of our loss.  For the sheer grip and mastery of Nature that have characterised the intervening ages, have resulted at the same time in an increased specialisation of study that tends to dull men's sense of perspective and of the whole, while their very insinuation into Nature, their significant success in becoming one with her, as they have understood and manipulated her into all sorts of relationship with human life, have in many cases made this world almost a prison for that which was never meant to be confined by it.  The pilgrim spirit of the mediaeval worker is gone ;  the man of the twentieth century has centred his thought and imagination upon the earth.   Over the whole there has been a loss of the sense of the unity of knowledge, and the dethronement of Theology as Scientia Scientiarum, that knowledge of the Whole, which it truly was for the Schoolmen, whence their hospitality of mind, their catholicity and their vision.  Much of modern systematic theology has no such boldness of conception as it had for them.  Separated alike from metaphysics and from those special sciences

[1] *The Study of Nature and the Vision of God*, by G. J. Blewett, p. 29.

that could illuminate and on occasion give it content, it has shrunk in grasp and vision and so in power, until the religious point of view is considered as absolutely unrelated to anything in politics or economics, science or law. Withdrawing for justification more and more into the realms of psychology and of a certain kind of mysticism that removes it from all contact with the world of thought, or dwelling in a sublimated region of values of its own determining, religious thought has in some forms confessedly sought a refuge in a region where it fondly hoped to be beyond, and uninfluenced by, the common thought of man, with unfortunate effects on the life and thought of the ordinary man ; for the religious attitude, which ought to be the most natural thing in the world, has come to be thought of as an excrescence and abnormality. For most thinking men in these days the ultimate question often is, What kind of a world am I living in ? Yet modern theology has been little enough interested to make them feel and see that the world in which they find themselves is God's world, and so they remain dissatisfied, or indifferent, or content to leave theology as an amiable diversion for minds of leisure. There is no challenging resounding argument from the age-long travail of a world which has issued in man, and which, by the pervading purposiveness of its process and the proved potentialities in man, hints both at the character of its Ground and the further possibilities of the individual human life. Instead, such theology has been too content with a forensic mechanical 'scheme of salvation' which has little relationship to the mind of Jesus as revealed in the Gospels, or to St. Paul's profound conception of the Eternal Christ as at once the very bond and ultimate explanation of the universe as a whole and the supreme revelation of the grace of God to mankind, however much it may have seemed real in the mental atmosphere of the generation who ingeniously pieced it together out of selected passages from his writings. It is this unrelatedness to the thought

and life of the day, as well, too often, to the social
aspirations of the times, that makes theology, and
religion, with which it is so often confused, a somewhat
unappealing thing in conditions when men were never so
religious, or desirous to be so.   One of the imperative
needs of this generation is the work of men with minds
like those of Albert Magnus or Thomas Aquinas, men
who shall see things steadily and see them whole, and who,
starting from that knowledge of the world which men
call Science, shall be able to lead up to that more ultimate
and comprehensive knowledge of the Whole, which rises
into Theology.

And most particularly is this true with regard to all
doctrine about man.   For if the concern of practical
religion be with ' the saving of the soul,' then no theology
can be content to-day with shallow, ambiguous answers
to the question, What is the soul ?   but must be first
driven into a fuller understanding of that world in which
the soul of man finds its place.   Yet to know and understand that world, we must know about its character and
ultimate Ground, and to understand aright the nature
of the soul's salvation, we must apprehend the nature
of its source which is God, and the nature of the end for
which He made it, the attaining of which *is* its salvation.
' So that theology, in order to be a wisdom of salvation,
must be a wisdom of the soul, a wisdom of the world,
a wisdom of God.' [1]   And this simply means that theology
to be of real service, must in some degree be a knowledge
of the world as an expression of God, and of Him as
energising in and through it.

Than the relation of God to the World and the Universe
of Worlds, no problem is, however, more difficult for
the human mind to set forth with any satisfaction to
itself.   Ordinarily the relation is covered by the term
Creation.   This process as a divine activity may be held
to be an expression of the divine nature.   Both with
regard to what we know of that nature and of the actual

[1] Blewett, *op. cit.* p. 41.

constitution of the Universe, Creation reveals itself increasingly as an eternal 'process. If, however, there never has been a time when there was no manifestation of God, that does not imply the eternity of matter except in so far as that which is, and has been, material owes its existence directly to the creative and sustaining will of God. Better than the ancient writer, the modern physicist realises that ' what is seen hath not been made out of things which do appear.'[1] Matter is for him simply a more or less stable form of energy. He resolves the atom into an ordered whirl of negative electrons, balanced by an equal distribution of positive electricity, possibly constituting the central nucleus. The electron in its turn, according to one famous theory, is purely electrical in origin—a strain or stress in the ether, that imponderable woof of the world. An electron, in Sir Oliver Lodge's words, is ' a peculiarity or singularity of some kind in the ether itself,'[2] and that which we perceive as matter is simply an aggregate of innumerable localised strains (electrons) at an enormous number of positions in the ether. The ether accordingly is not expressible in terms of matter, for it is prior to matter, impalpable, invisible, homogeneous in its smallest realisable parts or ultimate structure, and not necessarily possessing any of the properties of matter as these are ordinarily understood. Matter, then, as composed of electrons, is an electrical manifestation ; yet just as ultimately it is ethereal in origin, being a structure built up in and from the ether. That is to say, certain physicists trace everything back at last to the ether and an operation of energy—some Infinite Power of doing work. At this stage, indeed, the duality of matter and energy is resolved in terms of ether and ether strains, or even of energy alone,[3] which is for the physicist an ultimate ; the changes in energy—the strains and stresses, if not

---

[1] Heb. 11[3] (R.V.).  [2] *The Ether of Space*, p. 87.
[3] For an expansion of this point, reference may be made to *God and the Universe*, by G. W. de Tunzelmann, chap. iii.

its actual source—may, accordingly, in default of further guidance from the physicist, be ascribed, theoretically and ultimately, to the exercise of the Divine Will, and will is mind in action.[1]  Yet this relationship of God to the World, if it is to be true to the facts so far as we can understand them, must not be conceived in any purely external fashion.  God is ;  the World becomes :  He is the Being in the Becoming.  He is the World-Ground, the unifying principle of the process in all its phases. Yet He is not exhausted, so to speak, by this continuous work of creation and sustaining of that which has been created :  the relation is panentheistic rather than pantheistic.  The process of creation presents itself to us as the outcome of the application of Infinite Extended Energy accompanied by characters that suggest and yet transcend consciousness and will as we understand these words, and expressing itself in a progressive series of extended forms in Time and Space.  When we think of God in His creative activity, we are compelled to think of wisdom and fulness of power.

If now we examine a little more closely the actual process of events which resulted in a world capable of harbouring life, we gain from the study of inorganic evolution a profound impression of order and uniformity, and of the provision in this way of a necessary basis for the development of that which was to be assertive, and a localised centre of activity from the beginning, viz. Life.  By no one has this particular problem been so thoroughly investigated as by Professor L. J. Henderson, of Harvard, who in two books of exceptional brilliance [2] marshals an array of facts from the abstract standpoint of physics and chemistry indicating the unique fitness of the inorganic realm for life.  He shows how ' the very nature of the cosmic process and of the physical and chemical phenomena of matter and energy brings about

---

[1] See later, chap. xii.
[2] *The Fitness of the Environment* (1913) and *The Order of Nature* (1917).  Cf. also H. F. Osborn, *The Origin and Evolution of Life*.

not only stability of the solar system, but very great stability of land and sea.' [1] He explains how ' the temperature of the earth is far more equable than it could be if the composition of the surface of the earth were other than it is. Thus the alkalinity of the ocean possesses a constancy which is nearly perfect, and this depends upon certain unique properties of carbonic acid.' So also ' the currents of the atmosphere and of the ocean, the fall of rain and the flow of streams are almost ideally regular, and are so only because water is very different from any other substance.' Again, ' the properties of water cause a mobilisation all over the earth of most of the chemical elements in very large quantities, and no other substance could so effectively accomplish this result. Once mobilised, these elements penetrate everywhere, borne by water, and the penetrating qualities of water are unique.' In this manner vegetation is highly favoured, and the whole earth has become habitable.

Even more significant, however, are the properties of the three elements, hydrogen, oxygen, and carbon, from which water and carbonic acid are formed. In great detail Henderson shows in the earlier volume that if we take account of both intensity and variety of activity, ' these are the most active of all elements, their compounds are the most numerous, [and] the molecular structures which they form are incomparably the most complex and elaborate which have been brought to light. Moreover, the energy which they yield in their mutual chemical transformations is more than other elements can provide, yet, because of their manifold reactions, more easy to regulate, to store, and to release.'

In short, the primary constituents of the environment, water and carbonic acid—substances that have appeared upon this planet's surface under the action of evolutionary forces—' serve with maximum efficiency to make stable, durable, and complex, both the living thing itself and the

---

[1] *The Order of Nature*, p. 4, from the Introduction to which (pp. 3-9) these points in partial résumé of the earlier volume are taken.

world around it. With otherwise unattainable effectiveness they provide both matter and energy in many forms and in great abundance for growth and for repair, and in the ensemble of characteristics upon which these results depend they are unique. Nothing else could replace them in such respects, for their utility depends upon a *coincidence* of many peculiar and unequalled properties which they alone possess. It is therefore certain that in abstract physical and chemical characteristics the actual [inorganic] environment is the fittest possible abode of life as we know it, so far as the elements of the periodic system are concerned.' That is to say, ' fitness of the environment is quite as constant a component of a particular case of biological fitness as is fitness of the organism, and fitness is quite as constantly manifest in all the properties of water and carbonic acid as in all the characteristics of living things.'

But Professor Henderson goes much further; so far he has been dealing, in his own words, only with ' the surface of the problem.' The relationship although mutual is not symmetrical. ' It is something more than adaptation, for it involves great adaptability. In every case the particular characteristics of the organism fit a special environment, while the general physical and chemical properties of water and carbonic acid fit the general characteristics of life. But it may be shown that stability, mobility, durability, complexity, and availability of matter and energy are favourable not merely to life as we know it; they are favourable to any mechanism, to any possible kind of life in this universe. For it is not by chance that life needs to be stable, that it needs food, that it needs to be complex if it is to evolve. Accordingly it is not for any special or peculiar form of life, whether life as we know it or another form, that this environment is the fittest.

' Just because life must exist in the universe, just because the living thing must be made of matter in space and actuated by energy in time, it is conditioned. In so far as this is a physical and chemical world, life must manifest itself through more or less complicated, more or less durable physico-chemical systems. Accordingly it is possible to assert,' concludes Professor Henderson, ' and it will be presently demonstrated that the primary constituents of the environment are the fittest for those general characteristics of the organism which are imposed upon the organism by the general characteristics of the world itself ; by the very nature of matter and energy, space and time.' He believes that the facts that he relates prove that ' a hitherto unrecognised order exists among the properties of matter. For the peculiarities that make things what they are have been found not evenly distributed among the compounds of all the elements, nor in such manner as the laws of chance can explain, nor altogether in such manner as the periodic system of the elements describes. If the extreme values and unique properties be considered, very many are seen to belong to the three elements, hydrogen, oxygen, and carbon, in an arrangement that brings about stability of physical and chemical conditions, and diversity of phenomena, and, further, the possibility of the greatest complexity, durability, and activity of physico-chemical systems on the surface of a planet. This order is masked when the properties of matter are considered statically. It becomes evident only when time is taken into account, for this is the order that determines the later course of cosmic evolution.' In short, ' the whole evolutionary process, both cosmic and organic, is one, and the biologist may now rightly regard the universe in its very essence as biocentric.' [1] It becomes increasingly clear, then, that what we have to deal with in organism and environment is a single system undergoing change, the working up and out through that which is physical, to that which is ultimately spiritual. One of the ultimate problems, the ignoring of which by Naturalism really leaves many naturalistic conclusions in a rather question-begging

[1] *The Fitness of the Environment*, p. 312.

position, is just this fact of adaptation. The result of Henderson's work is to show that it is a fact in the inorganic as well as in the organic realm, and therefore a basal fact in the evolutionary process as a whole. The more general the interpretation that is put upon this fact, the more remarkable becomes the circumstance that the process has worked out in that particular way which we know. The more particular the interpretation, the stronger the probability of the correctness of a teleological basis to the process. As Henderson pertinently asks,[1] ' What are the physical and chemical origins of diversity among inorganic and organic things, and how shall the adaptability of matter and energy be described ? ' For even the molecules themselves and their activities have been moulded by a process of evolution, and in turn form part of the environment.

Much the same general impression follows the consideration of the actual methods and results of the working of the various geological agencies of change—all of them forms of energy—in the later stages of our planet's history. Reference has often been made to the relation that exists, for example, between geological uplift and denudation.[2] As a result of any considerable elevation of the land, whether by slow oscillation or folding, the agents of denudation are set increasingly hard at work. Streams flow more rapidly, frosts act with greater constancy and effectiveness, even glaciers may form. But as the height of the land is gradually reduced through the erosive interplay of the different agencies, the latter lose their power, and moderate altitudes prevail. Elevation and denudation thus balance one another in a truly remarkable manner, and to some purpose. For if the continental areas had been very high as a whole, they would have been too cold and the atmosphere too rarefied for the support of life. Had they, on the other hand, been too low, we should have had no variety of physical environ-

[1] *The Order of Nature*, p. iv.
[2] Cf. *e.g.* A. P. Brigham, *A Textbook of Geology*, p. 189.

ment—no beauty of landscape or of sea—a tendency
towards monotony of type throughout the organic world,
and a lessened measure of individuality amongst the
nations of the earth.    It is matter of historical observation that the highest progress has gone with a diversified
physical geography, and one great stimulus to organic
progress has just been the actual process of environmental
physical diversification. Yet that process has been
orderly from the beginning, dominated, in spite of everything that may seem catastrophic, by a principle of progressive unfolding, with the present-day result of ' lands
of moderate average altitude, great areas with genial
climate, rocks covered with soil, and soil supporting abundant life.' [1]    So that we can feel that the seer's exclama-
tion is no rhetoric, but a profound glimpse into the heart
of things—' For thus saith the Lord that created the
heavens; he is God; that formed the earth and made it;
he established it, he created it not a waste, he formed it
to be inhabited.' [2]

Further, it is interesting to note that those major internal readjustments, which are due to the continued
shrinkage of the earth as the result of the loss of heat
and molecular rearrangements, and may make themselves
visible at the surface as warpings of inconsiderable height
or in the slow emergence of a mountain range, are being
increasingly taken as the natural marks by which to
divide off the different geological eras.    These eras constitute immense periods of erosion, following a big uplift,
and end with continental areas lying in low relief.    The
progress of life throughout them has been a fact of
general recognition for many decades.    But apparently
also it is becoming clear to the geologist that a like
progress has characterised the purely physico-geographical evolution.    According to Professor Schuchert,
the earth has just passed through one of those periods
of major readjustment in which ' all of the strains
and stresses set up in the earth's mass by the

[1] Brigham, *op. cit.* p. 463.          [2] Is. 45 [18] (R.V.).

minor, incompletely adjusted shrinkages ' are brought into equilibrium. ' Accordingly we see all of the continents standing far higher above sea-level than has been the rule throughout geologic time, and in many of them rise majestic ranges of mountains. A grander, more diversified, and more beautiful geography than the present one the earth has never had ; this statement is made advisedly and with the knowledge that our planet has undergone at least six of these major readjustments of its mass. These greater movements are the " revolutions " that close the eras.' [1]

To nothing, then, does the progress of science contribute so much as to the sense of wholeness and of continuity in the evolutionary process. The steady filling up of gaps removes the difficulties that confronted former generations. It is not that we know exactly how things did actually occur, but by extrapolation of the curve of our knowledge we can reconstruct within the range of conceivability, if not of probability, the course of events. Thus to the mind that realises that the physical ultimate is of the nature of Energy, there is no hesitancy in facing the direct linkage of the organic with the inorganic. Life in its earliest manifestations was associated with matter in a colloidal condition,[2]—a condition peculiarly favourable to the action, reaction, and interaction of physico-chemical energies. When, however, we consider the chemical complexity of the food of even the simplest protozoa or bacteria, it is obvious that the latter cannot have been the first forms of life. Life in its initial forms was probably simpler even than the intracellular vital units known as chromidia ; possibly it was molecular.

[1] Prof. Charles Schuchert in *The Evolution of the Earth and its Inhabitants*, p. 71.
[2] Colloidal, from Latin *colla*, glue. ' A substance which will not diffuse through membranes and which forms with water a kind of tissue or gel.'—Albert P. Mathews, *Physiological Chemistry*, p. 11. ' The distinguishing feature of the colloid is that the molecular unions shall be of a feeble unstable kind with very little evolution of energy.'—Prof. Benjamin Moore, *The Origin and Nature of Life*, p. 130.

We may think with Professor Moore [1] of some very complex labile inorganic colloid, taking up water and carbonic acid, absorbing radiant energy, building up still more complex structures through interaction with nitrogenous inorganic matter, and finally in the course of the ages acquiring the power to convert radiant into chemical energy, and lo! the birthday of life, come without observation. Yet in the beginning, as all the way through, it is a process directly dependent on the Infinite Energy of the Universe. That is to say, while the above framework of conceptions corresponds only in a partial degree to what has been actually achieved or is still likely to be achieved, it leaves a justifiable impression of life as essentially an energetic phenomenon—the persistent progressive maintenance of a dynamic equilibrium between innumerable energetic activities in face often of totally new situations. The control expresses itself normally in an ordered process of successive states. The characteristic of life is seen essentially in the linkage and interaction between the countless energetic actions and reactions in the organism. Whether with Moore we think of ' biotic energy ' as a distinctive type of energy, [2] or believe with Macfarlane [3] in ascending phases of energy marked by increasing condensation, complexity, and perfection in work-transformation, or simply maintain with Woodruff as a working hypothesis that ' life phenomena are an expression of a complex interaction of physicochemical laws which do not differ fundamentally from the so-called laws operating in the inorganic world,' [4] yet it is indisputable that with life a new kind of relatedness appears which gives a particular direction and integration to energy transformations that are

[1] For a somewhat different estimate of primitive living energetic relationships, see Osborn, *The Origin and Evolution of Life*, p. 48.

[2] Prof. Benjamin Moore, *Biochemistry*, chap. i.

[3] Prof. J. M. Macfarlane, *The Causes and Course of Organic Evolution* chap. iv.

[4] Prof. L. L. Woodruff in *The Evolution of the Earth and its Inhabitants*, p. 87.

quite different from anything known in the inorganic world.

Just in proportion as it becomes more evident that we are dealing with a process that is a whole in the sense that life has issued from an inorganic womb under some intensive, transforming, and uplifting operation of Energy, and that thereafter its progressing forms were closely dependent at every stage upon the changes in the physical environment, so the impression deepens that just because of the intimacy of that relation of life with its environment, no stage could be repeated. Life does not return upon itself. No species once extinct has ever again appeared. It could not do so in a developing system, and it is only in the most superficial aspects of things that history can ever be said to repeat itself. A boy may commence to shave at the same time as his father, but the essential and vital fact, determinative, it may be, for history, is that the boy is not his father. What the energetic changes that ushered life in were, we do not know, although we can imagine and in part believe. Yet it is clear that the organic colloids came into existence after the inorganic at a definite period and stage in the history of our earth when many conditions were very different from the present, and absolutely irreproducible in their ensemble, if not individually. The ocean, for example, has grown colder and more saline since that era ; its reaction has changed from faintly acid to faintly alkaline. The amount of carbonic acid and aqueous vapour in the atmosphere has been enormously reduced since those days, and the sun is colder. In short, conditions of temperature, atmosphere, possibly even in some measure of chemical affinity and electricity, were greatly different, and in view of the peculiarly close relation and adaptation of every form of life to its environment, it seems unphilosophical to look for an origin of life at any other period than the precise phase of planetary development under which it first arose.

In this rediscovery of the world process as essentially a

progressive whole of more than merely physical character in that the ends achieved and the life forms by which the different stages are marked are objectively of increasing complexity of structure, progressively freer from the domination of the more proximate physical aspects of the Environment, and mentally an advance upon their predecessors, no feature has stood out with greater implication than the failure as yet to give a complete account of any organic function in terms of physics and chemistry alone. Metabolic change assuredly involves physico-chemical 'events' and transformations of energy, but these transformations are conducted in a distinctive way and to a specific end. In the fact of organisation, the fact that living matter has a structure and that ' each part of the structure not only bears a more or less definite spatial relation to the other parts but is actively maintained in that relation,' [1] we have something, as we have seen, to which there is no exact analogy in the inorganic. The structure is a definite expression of an activity which we call Life, and when the latter ceases to be in evidence or is withdrawn, the structure shrivels up and eventually disappears in accordance with the ordinary material and energetic relations of the physical world. The living organism is something, then, which resists the universal tendency to the degradation of energy; it affords a demonstration that the Second Law of Thermodynamics is not an absolute statement. There is something here resistant, assertive, self-regulative with a delicacy and persistence unknown elsewhere, self-reproducing, an historic being, carrying its past about with it in the form of memory and modifying its present experience in the light of that past. It is a suggestive fact in view of this assertiveness of life that while it is readily possible to stain differentially the ' fixed,' *i.e.* killed, cell, no success has as yet been achieved in staining cells *intra vitam*. In that newer biology which has really amounted to a rediscovery of the significance of life, the outstanding fact is the recog-

[1] Prof. J. S. Haldane, *Mechanism, Life, and Personality*, p. 77.

nition of the organism as an agent in its own evolution, unconsciously so below a certain level, but always through its own activities, creative or appeasing, exerting a direct influence upon the course of its development. The constraint of the physical environment is at a maximum in the case of the simplest forms, but even there life is not completely bound, just because it is life.[1]  On the psychical side there is a progressive integration which at the human level begins to be worthy of the name of personality, although even this characteristic is only yet in process of attainment.

Again, recent advances in biological thought, in their elucidation of the closely supporting and directive relation of the Environment, are in that measure tending to reestablish the supremacy of the Neo-Lamarckian as opposed to the Neo-Weismannian account of Evolution. With regard to the particular point of the transmission of acquired modifications, it is not suggested that modifications acquired or developed in one generation are reproduced in detail in the succeeding generation—only on an incredibly materialistic view of things could such a statement have ever found any support—but it is maintained that there is not sufficient reason for dogmatic assertion to the effect that such modifications are always totally without any kind of influence on progeny. Indeed, if the remarkable results obtained by Professor Guyer of Wisconsin are confirmed [2]—and they do not stand alone [3]— the extreme Weismannian position in this particular respect must be surrendered, and in any case the new knowledge about the action of internal secretions (*e.g.* hormones) supplies us with a means of reasonably postulating how changes in tissue due to environmental stimuli might affect germ cells and so the succeeding generations.

[1] See later, chap. xi.
[2] *Journal of Experimental Zoology*, vol. xxxi. 1920 : for a short résumé see Presidential Address to Zoological Section, *B. A. Report*, 1921, p. 81 ff.
[3] For other examples, cf. R. Semon, *Die Mneme*, pp. 74, 79 ;  W. Kidd, *Initiative in Evolution* ;  and J. T. Cunningham, *Hormones and Heredity*.

We believe that future developments will tend to make increasingly clear that living forms have not, so to speak, developed *in vacuo*, sorting out from some primeval germ-plasm various combinations of already pre-existing characters, but rather that at every stage there has been progressive creation of the new as the result of the commerce of living forms with an active Environment. Heredity in a sense is really ' potted ' Environment, and with the Environment the last word rests. An element in confirmation of this general position is sometimes concealed by the use of a misleading term, ' social heredity ' or the ' social heritage,' to express the influence exercised upon humanity by traditions and institutions, by literature and art. The determining influence of these factors is recognised by many authorities in different fields. Thus Professor J. Arthur Thomson in his masterly Gifford Lectures speaks of ' our *social heritage,* which is as supreme as our *natural inheritance* is fundamental,'[1] while Benjamin Kidd draws attention to ' the immense import of the fact that *since man became a social creature the winning variations upon which Power has rested in his evolution have been to an ever-increasing degree neither variations in the structure of his body nor in the size of his brain, but variations in the type of social culture to which he is being submitted.*'[2] These are impressive statements, presented, however, under a misleading figure, for the use of the phrase ' social heredity ' based on the insignificant circumstance that such tradition and culture are transmitted orally or in print or in institutions, obscures the fundamental fact that they form part—and the determining part—of the *Environment* into which each individual is born.

A further indication of the character of the process is disclosed when we regard it as a whole, for mechanism cannot in the end explain itself. There is, as we have seen, something about the ensemble or ' hang ' of the inorganic that at any rate looks very like purpose. If

[1] *The System of Animate Nature,* vol. ii. p. 497.
[2] *The Science of Power,* p. 262 (italics as in original).

to-day the physiologist prefers to speak of the function of an organ or adaptation, he is simply employing another word for the same idea.    The study of the historical series of the forms of life gives the impression that Evolution is, so to speak, getting somewhere.    The facts of adaptation, and of a changing Environment that has played upon adaptability in the interests of progress, are too big in implication to be mere accidents.[1]    Evolution that was once supposed to have given the death-blow to teleology, has really given us back a grander teleology that embraces the inorganic and the organic in one connected whole. The many convergences and anticipations of the future in Nature, organic or inorganic, the fact that the world process is capable of being understood, however imperfectly, *all along*, are at once data more easily explained on the basis that Intelligence of some kind is related to the Infinite Energy than in any other way.    We find ourselves in the midst of a process about which it is apparent that while the end, so far as it has been reached at any stage, can help to explain the beginning, the beginning can never explain the end, simply because it is a process of advance in the main line and of progressive result.    It is a process with a definite direction, irreversible, and issuing in fuller and more abundant life.    It is a process in which ends of increasing value become means to still higher ends, a process which is therefore intrinsically a whole :    or, as Professor Pringle-Pattison puts it, ' a teleological view of the universe means the belief that reality is a significant whole.' [2]    The idea of a preconceived

---

[1] Cf. H. F. Osborn : ' The Darwinian view, namely, that chromatin evolution is a matter of chance and displays itself in a variety of directions, is contradicted by palaeontological evidence both in the Invertebrata and Vertebrata, among which we observe that *continuity and law in chromatin evolution prevails over the evidence either of fortuity or of sudden leaps or mutations*, that *in the genesis of many characters there is a slow and prolonged rectigradation or direct evolution of the chromatin toward adaptive ends*. This is what is meant in our introduction by the statement that in evolution law prevails over chance.' —(*The Origin and Evolution of Life*, p. 146.)

[2] *The Idea of God in the Light of Recent Philosophy*, p. 330.

plan elaborated in detail is replaced by that of a purpose or desire on a clear yet broad scale, but a purpose can only be attained through the establishment of freedom. In organic life, and indeed in the evolutionary forms as a whole, we have a series of facts which apart from a teleological interpretation really mean *nothing*—a situation that in ordinary life is suggestive of mental vacuity or disorder somewhere. Things are because of their significance. An account, however detailed, of a human tear, in terms of the conception of it as a watery secretion from the lachrymal glands, would be incomplete to the degree of meaninglessness without some reference to the emotion of joy or sorrow of which it was an expression.

Accordingly, in view of the actual situation as a whole, and of the problems that Science does not touch, it is far from easy to maintain seriously that the one faculty by which man alone judges natural process has been derived in the course of the working of that process, and at the same time assert that the process itself shows nothing that is akin to mind, intelligence, or reason in it. This cannot be asserted in the sense that the process is less than rational ; in so far as it may be taken to mean that the process is informed by some Ground displaying intelligence vastly superior to the human mind, we come within hailing distance of theistic interpretation. ' Nature,' said Tertullian, ' is a rational work of God.' [1] A further knowledge of this Divine Mind will probably enable us to explain in terms of creative mind alone that which we have at present to describe in terms of mind and energy controlled by it, even as the duality of matter and energy may be resolved in terms of energy alone.

Of supreme value, however, has been the discovery of the direct implication of man in the evolutionary movement as a whole. For if it can be firmly established that he is an integral part of the world process, so integral that it almost looks as if it had required the whole long process from Cambrian days to the Pliocene to evolve him, the

[1] *De Anima*, 43.

conclusion will be difficult to resist that there must be
some great potentiality of value—some rare possibility—
associated with a being whose production has involved
such travail.  His arrival in the world will give meaning
to the previous stages of vertebrate advance.  Man thus
standing in direct organic relation with the world process,
will prove that there is something about it which is kin to
him.  If he is its growing point—that element or organ
by which Nature becomes conscious of, and best reveals,
herself—then everything that is characteristic of man at
his noblest is predicable of her in some kind of way.  Just
because of that very intimate relation of him to the process, it follows that his highest characteristics are not
altogether unrelated to the process itself, and it is at least
probable that the characters displayed in this highest
product are transcended in the producing Cause or Ground.
Thus to argue may seem to be illegitimate in the sense
that it is an inference from the part to the whole ; but the
criticism fails where that whole stands in a genetic relationship to the part.

The chief glory of the old apologetic lay in the belief
that it could think of man as unrelated, and indeed
opposed, to the rest of creation.  He was introduced as
something built to a specific type into a prepared Garden
of Eden, and in the same way the Son of Man was thought
of as coming into a world whose condition just at that
moment was as peculiarly fitted to His appearance as
Eden to that of man.  It was a world of abrupt discon-
tinuities, of intrusions from the outside into a scheme of
things prepared or gone awry.  It may have been that no
other views were possible, but it is quite certain that
these were neither the views on the one hand, of man
when first he began to reflect upon the meaning of human
life, nor on the other, of the Son of Man Himself.[1]  'Man
is organic to nature, and nature is organic to Man,' as
Professor Pringle-Pattison concisely puts it,[2] and even
more illuminating is the thought, as old as St. Paul, that

---

[1] See later, chap. xiv.                    [2] *Op. cit.* p. 177.

Jesus Christ is organic to Nature, and Nature is organic to Jesus Christ.[1] We know to-day, as we did not know before, that for long millennia previous to the year A.D. I, men and women have lived and loved and hoped and died, and we must reach a view of God and of the person and work of Jesus Christ that shall cover this long sweep of history. But it is just in proportion as we realise that man is the product of an evolutionary process in mind and spirit as well as in body, that we first begin to understand what he really is, and what are the possibilities associated with him. 'God became man,' describes one of those great historic moments in the evolutionary movement, after which, as at the birthday of life and in the dawning of self-consciousness, everything thereafter moved, as it were, on a higher plane. Yet, as a matter of fact, throughout the untold ages of organic history God *was becoming* man.

Now in the sphere of religious thought nothing more profound or challenging has ever been uttered by human lips than the statement that ' God is Love.' [2] It gives a complete philosophy of religion. For if God is Love, then since Love must needs express itself in action and have that to which it can go out in mutual fellowship, it would follow that the age-long process—that divine self-communication and impartation that constitute creation—began, in order to produce a plurality of human souls. It is therefore not one single act of divine Kenosis, or self-emptying and self-limitation, with which we have to deal, for all creation is a process of Kenosis. From the period marked by the dawning of self-consciousness, such self-communication in creation on the part of God would further assume the form of self-revelation to the minds that began to ponder on the meaning of things, in which case grace has been of the process from the beginning. But for reciprocating Love on the part of human souls to be spontaneous—to be Love—there must be the possi-

[1] Col. 1 [17]. ' And he is before all things, and in him all things consist.'
[2] 1 John 4 [8], [16].

bility of choice, and in the winning of freedom—that gradual liberation from the domination of the physical, and the lower self, in which consists the reality of spiritual life—there entered the possibility of human failure, and grace is supremely shown that in just such a world, God, Who throughout the whole process was becoming man, did so in a unique form in Jesus Christ, through fellowship with Whom men may come to know God in a perfect way, and attain to newness and wholeness of life.

The subject of our present investigation is whether any such religious interpretation can still be maintained as consistent with the actual history of man. But this involves, in the first place, a frank and fearless examination of some aspects of modern scientific knowledge in regard to the physical and spiritual evolution of man, and to this subject we may now turn.

# CHAPTER II

## MAN'S PLACE IN NATURE

THE modern answer to the question, What is man? is infinitely more impressive, and, for that matter, vastly more complicated than any that was given up to as late as the middle of last century. The difference is mainly due to the new viewpoint that has been supplied by the facts issuing in the doctrine of Evolution. From the older point of view man was placed on a pinnacle by himself and everything was explained in relation to him from above downwards. He was thought of as specially created in a definite locality, at a particular point in time not so very remote from the present, built as it were to a certain specificity of type, physical, mental, and moral, which had persisted unchanged through the intervening ages, and was to all intents and purposes represented in contemporary man. Reference was made to the rest of the animal creation in connection with man simply to emphasise the distinction between him and it. Man and the rest of Nature were held in marked contrast, and there was no idea of a genetic bond. The world of early scientific thought was a world of marked discontinuity. And the same outlook dominated its religious thought.

Modern discussion of the question, What is man? must commence with a threefold examination of him, physical, mental, and moral. Evolution, it has been said, is a jealous mistress; she will have all or nothing. Her claim, at any rate, must be impartially examined. Probably the generality of modern thought is more or less convinced of the truth of the doctrine of the physical descent, or, as Henry Drummond more truly worded it, the ascent of man. The difficulty is felt when the same claim is made for his mental and moral nature. At some point, it is felt, his apartness from the rest of creation must be preserved at all costs, else he is no better than the beasts that perish. It is apparently not realised that if man at his best and highest, in every aspect of his being, is a genetic result of natural process, then that process becomes transfigured for us, and must be reconsidered not merely in its working but in respect to what it is in itself. The more man, being what he is, is seen to be a part of Nature, not in a discrete and partitive, but in a genetic, relation, the more is Nature ultimately seen to possess in some transcendently physical and spiritual sense the highest characters that are reproduced in man. That which has achieved, however we may think of it, cannot be less than the achievement.

That man is an animal is no discovery of modern science: to the Schoolmen, even, he was *animal rationale*. At the same time, the title of Huxley's famous book of 1863,[1] published eight years before *The Descent of Man*, was significant in its indication that man's place was in Nature. What modern science has done is to give him his distinctive place amongst the other creatures, grouping him, for example, amongst the Primates, highest of vertebrate forms, yet further, with changing differentia, separating him from those other forms that most nearly approach him by reason of his peculiarities, amongst which the faculties of tool-making, of articulate speech, and of conceptual thought are immediately the most outstanding.

Man, physically regarded, accordingly finds himself a member of the vertebrate class Mammalia, the principal members of which, amongst other features, are warm-blooded and viviparous, possessed of a characteristic epidermal covering of hair, a diaphragm separating the chest and abdominal cavities, and suckle their tender young. Of Mammals there are three sub-classes, two of which have no direct relationship with man. These are

[1] *Evidence as to Man's Place in Nature.*

1) the Prototheria or Monotremes, a low oviparous group, represented by the Duckmole (*Ornithorhyncus*) and the Spiny Ant-eater (*Echidna*) ; and (2) the Metatheria or Marsupials, characterised in most cases by a marsupium or pouch to which they transfer their prematurely born offspring—a group of which the best known representatives are the Opossum (*Didelphys*) and the Kangaroo (*Macropus*). The third sub-class, the Eutheria or Placentalia, whose unborn young are connected with the mother by the characteristic placenta,[1] is by far the largest. It is subdivided into some ten orders, of which the highest is the Primates, consisting of two sub-orders, the Lemuroidea or Lemurs and the Anthropoidea or Apes.[2] The Primates are for the most part arboreal forms, with well-developed collar-bones (clavicles) and prehensile limbs. Usually five digits are present, the thumb (pollex) and great toe (hallux) being more or less opposable, and commonly bearing a flattened nail. The orbit, which lodges the eye, is surrounded by a ring of bone, and the stomach is simple, as compared with the complex chambered organ of Ungulates. Their ' primacy ' is essentially an expression of brain development. The Lemurs are interesting because of their antiquity, being known fossil in the Eocene rocks of Europe and North America, as also because of the cerebral development of some members of the group, which has led to their being allotted a very definite place in some hypothetical schemes of the ancestry of man.

The sub-order of the Anthropoidea is composed of five living families, of which the Hominidae is the fifth. Of the other families, two, the Hapalidae or Marmosets, and the Cebidae or American Monkeys, are confined to the

[1] Through this organ a vascular connection is maintained between mother and foetus upon which the nutrition and respiration of the latter depend.

[2] For full details on points of physical structure reference may be made to *An Introduction to the Study of Mammals Living and Extinct*, by W. H. Flower and R. Lydekker ; *The Orders of Mammals*, by W. K. Gregory ; and *Morphology and Anthropology*, by W. L. H. Duckworth.

New World.   They are together characterised by a broad
nasal septum (whence the name Platyrrhine, usually given
to this group), and by a non-opposable and sometimes
reduced thumb.   The next two families, the Cercopithe-
cidae, comprising the Old World Monkeys and Baboons,
and the Simiidae or Anthropoid Apes, inhabit tropical
and temperate regions of the Old World.   They, and for
that matter the Hominidae, are characterised by a narrow
septum between the approximated downward directed
nostrils (whence the name Catarrhine, usually given to
this group), and by thirty-two teeth ; [1] the non-prehensile
tail which is found in some of these forms is rudimentary,
or entirely absent in others.   The great toe is opposable,
except in the case of man ; the thumb, while differing in
the degree of development, is always opposable.   It is,
then, necessary to note that Man has points of contact
with all of these families, but in such a special way with
one of them that Flower and Lydekker state that ' the
differences between Man and the Anthropoid Apes are
really not so marked as those which separate the latter
from the American Monkeys.' [2]   Hence we reach the
following scheme of relationship, which shows the basal

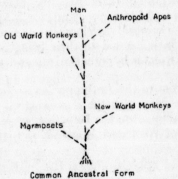

Common Ancestral Form

[1] These are arranged after the formula, incisors $\frac{2}{2}$, canines $\frac{1}{1}$, pre-
molars $\frac{2}{2}$, molars $\frac{3}{3}$, or more briefly $\frac{2}{2}\frac{1}{1}\frac{2}{2}\frac{3}{3}$, where the figures in either case
represent the dentition in one half of the jaw above and below.

[2] *Op. cit.* p. 740.

error in the popular fancy that Man on the evolutionary theory is descended from a monkey. What is maintained with confidence on the strength of the evidence is the conclusion that he and the Anthropoid Apes are descended from some common stock.

The whole question of animal classification, morphologically considered, however, has in it little that is settled beyond dispute. If we attempted a classification on psychical lines, nothing but dire confusion would result. What is worthy of remark is that from the morphological point of view man has not a sub-kingdom to himself, not even a special order. Many taxonomists indeed make *Homo sapiens* but a genus of the family Simiidae.

But further, this family of the Simiidae [1] which shows the closest resemblances to man, is distinguished by well-marked characteristics. As a whole, these apes are less like quadrupeds than the others, while they have no externally developed tail or cheek pouches. In every case the arms are longer than the legs, the thumb is opposable to the other fingers, the sternum or breast-bone is broad, and the caecum has a vermiform appendix. The dentition is like that of man—$\frac{2123}{2123}$. It is of particular interest to note how each of these forms has certain definite peculiarities in which it more closely resembles man than the others.

Of the four genera into which the Simiidae are divided, the Gibbons (*Hylobates*) are probably on the whole the most primitive. Their present range is Indo-China and the Malay Archipelago, but all four genera of the Simiidae once extended far beyond their modern limits : thus an extinct gibbon has been described from the Middle Miocene of France. There appears to be little doubt that in the earliest Primates the main axis of the body was horizontal. The gibbon shows the earliest and most complete adoption of the upright posture amongst the Simiidae, which therefore *in itself* was not a characteristic

---

[1] The exact meaning of the term is doubtful, and may be either ' flat-nosed ' (Latin, *simus*) or ' mimic.'

that led to ' humanity ' ; indeed, it is also found in other classes of animals (*e.g.* penguins, amongst birds). They are the only apes that habitually move in an upright position, but their land gait is rather akin to a rapid waddle than to the stately human progression. The arms are so long that the knuckles reach the ground. Their true element is amongst the trees, where acrobatic arm-swung springs from one branch to another, sometimes over distances said to vary from twelve to forty feet, call for a wide range of subconscious calculation. With this may be correlated a marked development of the brain centres of sight, touch, and hearing. The gibbon rarely exceeds three feet in height, yet has a prodigiously strong voice with a peculiar wailing note and double call—' hoo-lock.' In their possession of small ischial callosities the gibbons show resemblance to baboons, and they have nails only on the thumb and great toe. The skull is small and smooth, having neither the great supra-orbital or eye-brow ridges nor the sagittal crest [1] of the other Simiidae, and thus showing a more human profile than any other Simiidan skull, an effect which is increased by the presence of a rudimentary chin. The gibbon feeds on fruits and young shoots, insects, and birds' eggs.

The Orang-utan (*Simia*) is confined to Borneo and Sumatra, where it lives in gloomy, swampy forests near the coast. F. E. Beddard describes it as ' a large and heavy Ape with a particularly protuberant belly and a melancholy expression.' [2] It is of a yellowish-brown colour, and the males are seldom much over four feet in height, but they are very bulky creatures : they also have a markedly developed sagittal crest and very prominent canines. The eyes are set peculiarly close together with an almost Mongoloid suggestion about them. The orang is even more closely adapted to arboreal life than the

---

[1] A vertical ridge of bone that runs along the middle of the top of the skull, and provides additional attachment for the muscles working the lower jaw.

[2] *Mammalia*, p. 582.

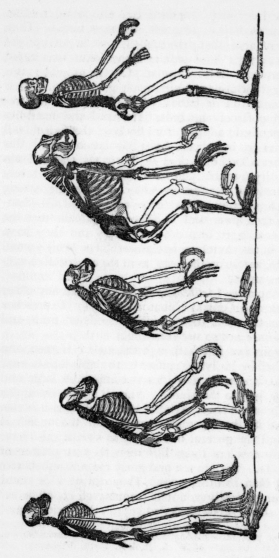

FIG. 1.—Skeletons of the Gibbon, Orang, Chimpanzee, Gorilla, and Man. (Photographically reduced from diagrams of the natural size, except that of the Gibbon, which was twice as large as nature. After T. H. Huxley, by permission of Messrs. Macmillan.)

*Page 32.*

C

gibbons, and descends from the tree-tops only at night. On account of its size this anthropoid is not nearly so agile in its movements as the gibbon, but the great length of its arms permits of its walking along downward sloping branches without inconvenience.   On the ground it is a very clumsy performer, shuffling along, with bent knees, on the knuckles of its hands, while the soles of the feet are turned obliquely inwards.   Its hand and hand-like foot are peculiarly adapted for climbing, the four fingers in particular having a very hook-like appearance.   The orang makes a kind of nest or shelter in the trees, changing its locality frequently in search of its food, which is of an exclusively vegetarian character.   The orang is very intelligent and shows a high degree of maternal solicitude. According to Flower and Lydekker the brain ' is more human-like than in any other Ape ' : [1]   the ear also is somewhat human in its size and gracefulness, being placed, however, higher up on the head, as in the case of the South African Bushman.

The Chimpanzee (*Anthropopithecus*) is to-day restricted to Western and Central Equatorial Africa.   Unlike the members of the other three families, the male and female chimpanzee are not so very dissimilar in their size, which never exceeds five feet, although the male can always be distinguished by his larger canine teeth.   Black in colour, the chimpanzee in its activities is comparable rather to the gibbon than to the orang.   When it stands erect, the arms reach only a short distance below the knee ; in this respect, as in the sigmoid curvature of the vertebral column, and the general uniformity in size of the teeth, the chimpanzees are more like man than any other of the Simiidae.   The thumb and great toe are also better developed than in other apes.   They can walk or stand in the upright position, but in running go on all fours. The skull shows well-developed supra-orbital ridges and

[1] *Op. cit.* p. 733.   This particular claim is, however, also advanced on behalf of the gorilla :   cf. W. L. H. Duckworth, *Morphology and Anthropology*, p. 89.

sagittal crest : the forward sloping teeth and receding chin present an appearance suggestive of Neanderthal man. The chimpanzees live in families in the forest, and frequently build nests in the trees like the orang : they are more arboreal than the gorilla. They appear to feed on fruits, and are the gentlest and possibly the most intelligent and sociable of the Simiidae.

Although inhabiting roughly the same area, the Gorilla (*Gorilla*) offers a contrast to the chimpanzee at many points. Of great size and weight—a specimen 'mounted in the museum of the Academy of Natural Sciences in Philadelphia stands 5 feet 1½ inches in height, and weighed in the flesh 418 pounds ' [1]—the gorilla is ferocious and brave. If the legs were developed in the human proportion to the rest of the body, this anthropoid would supply everything that could be most exactingly demanded in the giant of fairy lore. The skin is black, as is also the hair, which turns greyish in ageing individuals. Other features of the male chimpanzee are carried by the gorilla to an extreme—the prognathous muzzle, supra-orbital ridges, sagittal and occipital crests, and tusk-like canines. On the other hand, the skull of the young female, lacking these excrescences, is much more human in its general appearance. The gorilla has, perhaps, a more human hand and foot—the heel is especially well developed—than any other anthropoid, but its crouching progression is mainly by the use of all four limbs. Structurally, however, the chimpanzee and gorilla are really very much akin, the differences suggesting that the gorilla is the more primitive of the two. The gorillas live in families in the forest, feed on fruits, and are the most terrestrial of the anthropoids. It is said that the young and the female sleep up in the tree, while the male lies in watch at the foot.

We are free to pass to the consideration of the fifth family of the Anthropoidea, viz. the Hominidae. It has no specific divisions, but three primary varieties may be recognised. These are all connected by endless inter-

[1] Prof. R. S. Lull, *Organic Evolution*, p. 651.

mediate forms or sub-varieties, and have spread over most of the habitable world during and since Pleistocene times.  These ordinary varieties are : [1]

I. *Homo Aethiopicus*—inhabiting most of Africa and Australasia—the Black or Woolly-haired (Ulotrichus) Man.  The Negroid races are characterised by a dark skin ; short, black, or reddish brown, frizzly hair, flattened-elliptical in cross-section ; dolichocephalic skull ; broad flat nose ; low orbits ; prominent eyes ; thick everted lips ; prognathous jaws ; large teeth ; a narrow pelvis, and long forearm.  This group comprises (*a*) African or typical Negroes, Negrilloes, and the Bushmen of South Africa, and (*b*) the Oceanic Negroes of the Western Pacific, including Negritoes, Tasmanians, Melanesians, and Papuans.

II. *Homo Mongolicus*—inhabiting most of Asia and Malaysia, North and South America aboriginally, and parts of Europe—the Yellow or Straight-haired (Leiotrichus) Man.  He is characterised by long, black, coarse, straight hair, round in cross-section ; skull mostly mesocephalic ; broad flat face with prominent anteriorly-projecting cheek-bones ; small nose ; high round orbits and narrow, sunken eyes ; jaws mesognathous with moderately sized teeth.  The principal sub-divisions are (*a*) the Northern Mongols, including, amongst others, the native Siberians, Japanese, Koreans, and Turki peoples ; (*b*) the Southern Mongols, including, amongst others, the Chinese, Burmese, and Thibetans ; (*c*) the Oceanic Mongols, including, amongst others, the aboriginal and modern Malays, and some Polynesian groups ; and (*d*) the native Indian population of the New World, whose colour is, however, copper brown, and who are further distinguished by a special form of the nasal bones

[1] For a full description see A. H. Keane, *Man, Past and Present.*

producing a large and high-bridged nose, and with only moderately prominent cheek-bones. In this last group there is great diversity in the shape of the skull, and more than twelve hundred languages past and present are known.

III. *Homo Caucasicus*—distributed throughout most of Europe, parts of Asia and Africa originally, later everywhere—the White or Wavy-haired Man (Cymotrichus). This section has as special features soft, straight, or wavy hair, elliptical in cross-section; retreating cheek-bones; narrow and prominent nose; orthognathous jaws; small teeth; broad pelvis, and short forearm. The sub-divisions here, according to Keane,[1] should be (*a*) the pre-Dravidians, including, amongst others, certain jungle tribes of South India, the Veddas of Ceylon, and the native Australian, who is particularly difficult to classify as showing various negroid characters without the distinctive woolly hair, and probably directly represents a very primitive human type; and (*b*) the 'Caucasic' peoples. This sub-division contains the following groups : (i) Southern Dolichocephals — Mediterraneans, Hamites, Semites, Dravidians, Indonesians, Polynesians in part; (ii) Northern Dolichocephals — Nordics, Kurds, Afghans, some Hindus; (iii) Brachycephals — Alpines, including the short Cevenoles of Western and Central Europe, and tall Adriatics or Dinarics of Eastern Europe, and the Armenians of Western Asia.

Now, between Man and the Simiidae there are certain broad lines of physical resemblance. The general anatomical structure is alike in the two families. They are all, as it were, built on the same general plan, and the five types approach one another in different points in differing degrees. In both families the tail is absent,

[1] *Op. cit.* p. 39.

nothing remaining of it except a few caudal vertebrae, which are invisible in the living subject. The dentition is the same in regard to the number and sequence of the teeth. The ear is well developed in all members of both families, but it is lobeless in the case of the Simiidae—and for that matter the South African Bushman—with the exception of the gorilla, which alone shows a rudiment of the human lobule. The brain with regard to form and general structure is much the same in man and ape. The various organs of the different systems do not differ in either case in any very important respect.

The community of physical structure is paralleled by a remarkable community of function ; in detail there are numerous physiological points of resemblance between Man and the Simiidae. Of these perhaps the most important is the proof of literal blood-relationship between man and the anthropoid apes that is furnished by the blood serum tests of Uhlenhuth and Nuttall. By this means it has been found possible to attempt the definite determination of the degree of relationship of the various Primate groups. The character of their diseases and reactions to drugs indicates a certain fundamental similarity in the nervous system to that of man. In the same way it is important to note that the Primates are as a rule gregarious forms, with the rudiments of social and family life already developed.

Indeed, so great is the measure of physical community that it becomes a matter of considerable difficulty to formulate well-marked lines of difference. They have been thus briefly summarised by Flower and Lydekker. ' The distinctions between the Hominidae and Simiidae are chiefly relative, being greater size of brain and of brain-case as compared with the facial portion of the skull, smaller development of the canine teeth of the males, complete adaptation of the structure of the vertebral column to the vertical position, greater length of the lower as compared with the upper extremities, and greater length of the hallux or great toe, with almost complete

absence of the power of bringing it in opposition to the
other four toes.   The last feature, together with the small
size of the canine teeth, are perhaps the most marked and
easily defined distinctions that can be drawn between the
two groups.' [1]   In one or two cases they might be perhaps
more sharply drawn.   For example, the brain is absolutely as well as relatively much smaller in all apes than
in man.   Thus ' the highest cranial capacity of Orang and
Chimpanzee, which in this respect approximate nearest
to the human, (is) 26 and $27\frac{1}{2}$ cubic inches respectively ;
(the) lowest normal in man (is) 55.' [2]   In particular, the
cerebral hemispheres are very greatly developed in man,
both in bulk and in the complexity of the convolutions.
Then, again, the development of the erect posture brought
with it a series of morphological modifications—e.g. increased length in the hind limbs as compared with the
fore limbs, greater structural adaptation of these hind
limbs to bear the weight of the body—whose cumulative
effect in general poise and efficiency of the body is really
greater than is implied in their individual accomplishment.   In this connection, Flower and Lydekker lay
stress on the distinction that in man the great toe is not
opposable to the other digits.   But this is really not a
strong zoological character inasmuch as it depends on a
slight change in the form of a single tarsal bone, and it has
been shown that in the human embryo the hallux is
opposable till the fourth month.   Further, as Keane
points out,[3] the great toe is still somewhat opposable
among the Annamese, who, from this circumstance, have
always been known to the Chinese as Giao-Chi or ' Cross-
toes.'   Further, we may note in man diminished proportions of the maxilla, its early and complete fusion with the
pre-maxilla, and the circumstance that the teeth are much
more uniform than in any ape, and form an uninterrupted
horseshoe-shaped series without conspicuous canines or
diastema.   This fact is correlated with the reduction of

[1] *Op. cit.* p. 740.          [2] A H. Keane, *Ethnology*, p. 25.
[3] *Op. cit.* p. 26 n.

the maxillary apparatus due to the circumstance that, owing to the development of the grasping hand, the jaws were largely relieved of their prehensile function. The uniformity and simplicity of the teeth, together with the lack of bony ridges on the skull, and the large nasal bones, may be considered as primitive characteristics in man. The true chin may also be said to be a distinctively human characteristic, although there are approximations in some of the apes, notably in the gibbons.

The same conclusions of kinship and community of descent are suggested even more strikingly by consideration of certain facts in the individual development (ontogeny) of man. Bearing in mind the Recapitulation Theory or Biogenetic Law that the individual organism passes through stages in its developmental history corresponding to stages in its ancestral history, we would expect to find that the study of human embryology will shed light on the past history of man. The Recapitulation Theory simply gives expression to the conviction that the organism is a historical being, and finds an explanation of data in terms of that conviction which otherwise are inexplicable. In the case of a form which *ex hypothesi* has the whole of progressive animal history behind it, the résumé can only be of the briefest, and we can also understand that the farther off the stage be in time, the shorter will be the reminiscence of it. Now, as a general statement, it may be said that the results of embryology indicate the ascent of man from an initial unicellular stage through invertebrate phases, and later stages characterised by features that are now permanently associated with certain of the lower groups, until a form is reached difficult to distinguish from the corresponding form in the anthropoid apes, which finally slowly develops into the distinctively human individual. The human embryo both in the method of its attachment to the maternal tissues and in the manner of its nutrition, as well as in what is known concerning the earliest developmental stages, while following the general lines of mammalian or even vertebrate development, shows in particular the closest correspondence with the Anthropoidea. Further, as W. L. H. Duckworth puts it:[1] ' Of the peculiarities observed (*i.e.* in anthropoid, as opposed to mammalian, development in general), it happens that in several instances the characteristic feature is precocity of the formation and appearance of certain structures, which are acquired more slowly by other mammals. And the explanation offered for this characteristic precocity seems a valid one, viz. that where so high a specialisation in certain respects has to be attained, there will of necessity be a tendency to abbreviation of the earlier phases, which are more protracted in such forms as have not to travel the same distance beyond those early stages. . . . But while we find the closest approximation between Man and the Anthropoidea, in respect of early embryology, the chief evidence in those portions of the history thus studied, of the close association between Man and the Simiidae, is that discovered by Strahl in the characters of the histological structure of the placenta.' Such a minute correspondence testifies very strongly to affinity.

Further, distinctively, towards the end of the fourth week, the human embryo has a form which closely corresponds in shape, size, and internal structure with a chick embryo at the end of the fourth day, or a rabbit embryo at the end of the eleventh day. At this period the tail is considerably longer than the limbs, which have the form of ' flattened buds, with rounded margins ' : [2] later, it gradually becomes incorporated in the body, owing to the growth of the adjacent parts. At this stage also may be noted the presence of visceral gill clefts, four in number, which appear as early as the third week, but do not, as such, usually persist after the second month.

Again, the Simiidae, as mammals, are covered with hair over the entire body with the exception of the palms

[1] *Morphology and Anthropology*, p. 211.
[2] A. Milnes Marshall, *Vertebrate Embryology*, p. 496.

of the hands and the soles of the feet. In the case of the human embryo, during the fourth month a downy covering of hair appears, which, by the sixth month, is definitely developed all over the body with the exception of the parts that are hairless in the apes. By the seventh month these hairs (*lanugo*) attain a length of 5 or 6 mm., but latterly disappear before birth. 'At one stage of human embryonic development the arm is longer than the leg—a typically arboreal Primate feature ; later the two members are equal, and then the leg outstrips the arm in relative growth.'[1] Once again ; in a very common type of the deformity known as clubfoot, the sole is turned inwards and upwards, and the heel is raised. This is a normal prenatal phase in the development of all children, but in some cases the development is arrested at that point, and unless relieved by the surgeon, they are permanently clubfooted. Now this particular form of the abnormality is the normal condition of the foot in the adult gorilla and orang-utan.

The linkages are not less marked after birth. If there is a direct relationship between man and the anthropoid apes, and if the Recapitulation Theory is a true interpretation, we would expect that the resemblances would be more marked in the young, rather than in the adult, forms. Now Selenka in particular has shown that the skulls of the various young anthropoids not only resemble one another more closely than they do later on, but are much more human in their characters than the adult skulls. Yet ' as soon as the teeth begin to appear, the individual characters are assumed so rapidly, and become so marked, that, in the absence of the intermediate stages, it would be difficult to establish the kinships.'[2] The skulls of young anthropoid apes show no brow ridges, sagittal or temporal crests, which are in any case peculiarly a feature of the males, and it can confidently be predicted on the basis of evolution that when a skull

[1] F. Wood Jones, *Arboreal Man*, p. 203.
[2] For references, see E. Metchnikoff, *The Nature of Man*, pp. 46-48.

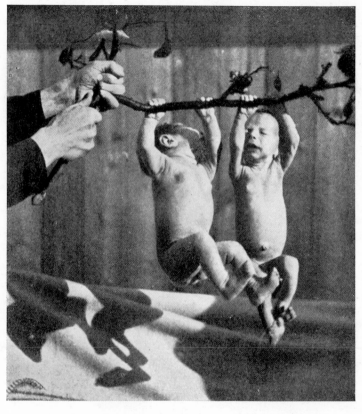

FIG. 2.—The grasping power of infants. (After Dr. L. Robinson, by permission of the Open Court Publishing Co.)

of any ancestral anthropoid form is found—hitherto such remains although definitive have not comprised a skull—it will prove to be without either crests or ridges. The same relation holds in psychical development. ' Young orang-utans in their " talk " as well as in their actions, are the counterparts of human infants. . . . But how pitiless is the inevitable change of the next few years ! ' [1]

Again, in the new-born infant, the flatness and wideness of the nose, the imperfect power of opposition of the thumb (shown by its peculiar mode of grasp), the straighter lumbar column, the imperfectly extensible hip and knee, the incurved soles—' turned inwards so completely that they can be pressed flat against each other ' [2]—all betoken points of contact, particularly with the gorilla and chimpanzee. Further, there are differences in the relative positions of various internal organs from those in the human adult, which are found to correspond to the positions of the corresponding organs in adult Simiidae. Once more, we may find physiological points of contact when we reflect why it is that the human infant, unlike all other creatures, crawls before it walks, and why when it begins to walk, it puts its weight on the outer side of its feet ; both traits are elements in the progression of the adult gorilla. Dr. Louis Robinson made a series of interesting experiments to test what Henry Drummond called ' the awful grasp of a baby.' [3] Robinson experimented with thirty less than an hour old : each of them, with two exceptions, was able to hold on to a horizontal stick and sustain the weight of its body for at least ten seconds. Twelve less than an hour old held on for thirty seconds, while three maintained their grasp for almost a minute. One infant of three weeks supported the weight of its body for two minutes thirty-five seconds—more than most adults could do. The thighs meanwhile were drawn up in the characteristic anthropoid attitude. And this Dr.

---

[1] C. W. Beebe, quoted in R. S. Lull, *Organic Evolution*, p. 660.
[2] F. Wood Jones, *op. cit.* p. 205.     [3] *The Ascent of Man*, p. 101

Robinson explained as a vestigial instinct and capacity persistent from the days of ancestral arboreal life, when the life of the young individual depended on its ability to cling round its mother's neck as she made her way through the tree-tops.[1]

Further, from any other point of view of man's origin, the eighty or so vestigial structures in his various systems are likewise totally inexplicable. The fact that the human body is an old curiosity shop is meaningless apart from the interpretation that these vestiges (e.g. appendix, muscles for moving the skin, ears, etc.) testify to a stage in the evolution of man when these organs were functional, and when the muscles were in regular use. So also, a detailed study of the variations in the different human organs would show that many of them approximate to the conditions in lower forms. They are intelligible as arrested development ; from any other point of view they are meaningless. It is this rehearsal of the story of the race within the limits of the individual life, not merely in the initial phase of intra-uterine development but likewise in the stages of childhood and adolescence, that gives such content to the saying, 'Unter jedem Grabe liegt eine Weltgeschichte.'[2]

But if the human body in its development thus bears within it a résumé of its past history, if the one fact that it bears witness to is that of change, then it is not probable that such change has even now come to an end. Instances of the continuance of physical evolution in man may be seen in the fact that nearly 10 per cent. of Europeans have no more than twenty-eight teeth, the formula being, in their case, $\frac{2122}{2122}$: this loss of wisdom teeth is an advantage because their power of mastication is feeble, and their absence does not seem appreciably to interfere therewith. It is an example of what Metchnikoff called 'disharmony,' because these teeth are usually a centre of decay or accident, and they appear to have no

---

[1] *The Nineteenth Century*, November 1891.
[2] Under each grave lies a world-history.

useful function that can be set against the disadvantage of possessing them. It was our remote ancestor masticating hard food who had the advantages of these additional teeth. Further, there are indications that go to show a progressive reduction in the size of the little toe. It is also probable that certain forms of rupture and uterine displacement should be construed as expressions of still imperfect adaptation to the erect attitude.

In face of the above considerations, the impartial observer finds himself forced to two conclusions : first, that man cannot possibly have ascended from any of the living anthropoid apes ; second, that the only tenable explanation of the measure of community of physical structure that exists between the two groups, is their origin by a process of natural evolution from a common ancestor. In Gregory's words, ' at least one great result, the derivation of Man from some as yet undiscovered Tertiary Primate, may be considered to be as well established as any of the great postulates of geology.' [1] The other alternative is Special Creation, which, unless supplemented by evolution, bars the way to all further inquiry, and, as Keane rightly remarks,[2] turns ethnology into mere ethnography. Now the special-creationist view does not affirm that all the different varieties of the Hominidae were independently created, but, so to speak, one alone. Hence the development involved in such extreme types as Homo Caucasicus (white man) and Homo Aethiopicus (negro), whatever the starting-point, must have been the result of some evolutionary process ; from this, for the creationist, there is no way of escape. But here is a range of evolution not so very far short of that which is covered in the differences between gibbon and orang or chimpanzee. Huxley indeed, with a certain exaggeration, even maintained that ' men differ more widely from one another than they do from the Apes ; while the

[1] William K. Gregory, ' The Orders of Mammals ' (vol. xxvii. of Bulletin of the American Museum of Natural History), p. 321.
[2] Op. cit. p. 28.

lowest Apes differ as much, in proportion, from the highest, as the latter does from Man.'[1]  On the other hand, the suggested origin of the human race from two or three discontinuous variations in mental equipment from the ancestral common stock presents a reconciliation of the older and newer views that possibly corresponds to the truth.  But whatever the place of Man in Nature be, he is distinguished as man from the rest of the animal creation by his knowledge that he has a place in Nature, by his saving discontent with life on a purely animal plane, by his power to communicate his ideas in speech and writing to his fellows, by his ability to fashion tools, and by what may be termed his capacity for God—in short, by a whole series of psychical qualities which make it immediately clear that it is in his spiritual rather than his physical nature, however derived, that his real significance lies.

[1] *Op. cit.* p. 78.

# CHAPTER III

## THE ANTIQUITY OF MAN

To the evidence for Evolution derived from the individual or ontogenetic history of man there must now be added the rapidly accumulating data that relate to his phylogenetic or racial history. Even when we include the lost years of the War, the fact remains that in the first two decades of the twentieth century we have learned as much as in all the previous years of a science which may be said to have been born in 1847, when Boucher de Perthes published his story of the worked flints that he had found in an old buried bank of the Somme, dropped mayhap a quarter of a million years before by Palaeolithic man, and so succeeded, after a struggle, in making the scientific world for the first time really sympathetic to the idea of the possibly great antiquity of man.[1] Already that period of antiquity has been subdivided into Eolithic, Palaeolithic, Mesolithic, and Neolithic Ages, peopled each year by an increasing number of representatives to whom names have been given, and of whose manner of life and thought we are coming to know more and more. When the earliest remains of Neanderthal man were found it was always possible to explain his peculiarities as something pathological, but now that the bones of at least two dozen of his contemporaries are known, all showing his distinctive characters, he is no longer left in peculiar

[1] Several discoveries antedated this year, notably the Gray's Inn Lane flint ' weapon ' found towards the close of the seventeenth century, the similar implements found by Sir John Frere in 1797 in brick earth at Hoxne in Suffolk, and the Engis skull discovered in 1833 by P. C. Schmerling in a Belgian cave ; but Boucher de Perthes was the first to produce any general conviction.

isolation but has to be reckoned with as a real element in the history of mankind. And we can be sure that a hundred years from now the Stone Age in all its stages will be as well known as the Bronze Age, which succeeded it, is known to-day. The widening of outlook in this respect has been so enormous that the continued retention of the date B.C. 4004 opposite the first chapter of Genesis in at any rate one edition of the English Bible constitutes a gloss, contrary to the whole spirit and intention of the Book.[1] The written records of Babylonia and Egypt go back at any rate to the fifth millennium before Christ, and it is obvious that if there are indubitable evidences of man in Pleistocene, not to speak of Pliocene deposits, we would then need to go back into Miocene times to look for the generalised ancestor that on the evolutionary theory was the common precursor of man and the anthropoid apes.

Prior even to a theoretical consideration of the antiquity of man, it is advisable to learn the state of modern expert opinion upon the question of the probable age of the earth. As is well known, this problem was for long the source of fruitful disputation between physicist and geologist. The latter demanded anywhere from thirty to about a hundred million years for the changes in the earth's surface since the azoic period, and in the various forms of life that inhabited it. The older physicists for good reasons of their own—definite calculations connected for the most part with the radiation of heat from a self-cooling body, such as the earth was supposed to be—rejected these demands as impossible, and cut down the figures to twenty or even ten million years.[2]  ' We have

---

[1] ' Dr. John Lightfoot, Vice-Chancellor of the University of Cambridge, and one of the most eminent Hebrew scholars of his time, declared, as the result of his most profound and exhaustive study of the Scriptures, that man was created by the Trinity on October 23, 4004 B.C., at nine o'clock in the morning.'—(Andrew D. White, A History of the Warfare of Science with Theology in Christendom, vol. i. p. 9.) We may smile—as men will smile one hundred years hence at many of the equally dogmatic statements of to-day.

[2] P. G. Tait, Recent Advances in Physical Science, p. 169.

now good reason,' said Lord Kelvin,[1] more than a quarter of a century ago, on the basis of certain definite premises, ' for judging that the consolidation of the earth was more than twenty and less than forty million years ago ; and probably much nearer twenty than forty,' and many similar statements could be quoted from the scientific literature of that period. It is obvious that the span which could have been allocated to man, the relative moment of whose appearance in the process of life is approximately known, could not have admitted of great antiquity if the whole process had had to be fitted into a scale of ten to twenty million years.

The discovery of radio-activity and the methods of estimation based upon it have, however, wholly altered the position, and decided the issue in favour of the geologists. In 1906 Professors Strutt (now Lord Rayleigh) and Joly proved that the most ordinary rocks contain on the average perfectly determinable quantities of radium and of its original parent uranium. The amount, small as it is, has yet been shown in the case of an assumed crust of rock of 20 to 25 miles in thickness, to be sufficient in thermal output to supply the whole of the heat lost by radiation into outer space. That is to say, the earth has had, and still has, within itself a source of energy sufficient to maintain the existing conditions of temperature over a period equal to the most extreme geological demands. The earth is certainly a self-cooling body, but the implications of radio-activity show that it is also to some extent a self-heating body. In Lord Rayleigh's words,[2] ' the upshot is that radio-active methods of estimation indicate a moderate multiple of 1000 million years as the possible and probable duration of the earth's crust as suitable for the habitation of living beings, and that no other considerations from the side of physics or astronomy afford any definite presumption against this estimate.'

[1] *Trans. of the Victoria Institute*, vol. xxxi. p. 20.
[2] *Report of British Association for the Advancement of Science*, 1921, p. 414.

This conclusion depends, however, on the assumption of uniformity in the disintegration of uranium, an assumption against which there appears to be some evidence.

Man being the crown of creation, it is within the latest of the geological successions that we shall naturally expect to find the evidence of his presence. These are known collectively as the Quaternary Era, including the Pleistocene,[1] and Holocene Systems. The Quaternary may be described compendiously as The Age of Man, just as the preceding Tertiary (Cainozoic) Era is sometimes spoken of as The Age of Mammals, the Secondary (Mesozoic) as The Age of Reptiles, and the Primary (Palaeozoic) as The Age of Fishes, from the dominant forms of these eras. If the whole evolutionary process of the earth be thought of in terms of a day of twenty-four hours, the Quaternary would have occupied about four minutes, from the point of view of comparative duration.

The relation of the different eras and systems may be seen from the following table. It should, however, be carefully remembered that there is no absolute discontinuity in Nature such as is represented by the use of separate words to express the different systems in the various formations.

| Era. | Systems. | Characteristics. |
|---|---|---|
| PSYCHOZOIC or QUATERNARY | Holocene<br>Pleistocene<br>(Ice Age) | Age of Man. |
| CAINOZOIC or TERTIARY | Pliocene<br>Miocene<br>Oligocene<br>Eocene | Age of Mammals and Flowering Plants. |
| MESOZOIC or SECONDARY | Cretaceous<br>Jurassic<br>Triassic | Age of Reptiles, Cycads and Conifers. |

[1] The terms Eocene (Dawn of the New), Oligocene (Few of the New), Miocene (Minority of the New), Pliocene (Majority of the New), Pleistocene (Most of the New), and Holocene (All of the New), by which the successive systems of the Tertiary and Quaternary Eras are designated, were originally based on these proportions of shells of molluscs found in them, but are true of all the forms of life in them.

| Era. | Systems. | Characteristics. |
|---|---|---|
| PALAEOZOIC or PRIMARY | Permian (Ice Age in S. hemisphere) Carboniferous | Age of Amphibians and Club-mosses. |
| | Devonian Silurian | Age of Fishes. |
| | Ordovician Cambrian | Age of Molluscs. |
| PROTEROZOIC | (Glacial conditions at commencement and close) | Age of Primitive Marine Invertebrates. |
| ARCHAEOZOIC | | Age of Protozoan and Protophytal Life. |
| COSMIC | | Age of Inorganic Preparation. |

An outstanding feature of the Quaternary is that in the Pleistocene it included an Ice Age, of which there probably had been at least three others previously. An Ice Age is essentially a periodic phenomenon both as a whole and in its phases. Its causation is a complex problem which has not yet been completely elucidated. Croll's Theory, depending upon changes in the eccentricity or elongation of the earth's orbit round the sun, together with other changes due to the precession of the equinoxes, may possibly account for the periodicity, but it is certain that the regions principally affected—Northern Europe, North America, and the Himalayas—stood at a greater elevation in Pleistocene time than they do to-day, a circumstance which, as it came into being, would greatly assist in the production and maintenance of glacial conditions. Of this elevation there is clear proof in the fiords or half-drowned river valleys of Norway, Scotland, and North America. These are the result of the subsequent depression which at the close of the Pleistocene made Great Britain, hitherto joined to the European Continent, an archipelago of islands. The data go to show that at several different intervals during the Pleistocene practically the whole of Great Britain and Ireland, together

with the northern half of Europe, was covered by a vast sheet of ice of great thickness that had its chief centre of flow in Scandinavia, east of the present watershed.  Out over the shallow basin of the North Sea it flowed, carrying Scandinavian boulders and depositing them in England, where conditions were much as in Spitzbergen or Greenland to-day.  The Alps were the location of enormous fields of ice above which projected the isolated tops of the highest mountains, and of glaciers with which those of to-day are mere pigmies in comparison.  These glaciers descended far to the south in France, the town of Lyons being built on the terminal moraine of the Rhone glacier of this period.  Other centres of glacial extension in Europe were the Pyrenees and Carpathians, while evidences of contemporary ice action on a grander scale even than in Europe are found in North America, as also in the Caucasus and Himalayas.

The characteristic deposits of the Pleistocene in the Alpine region have been made the subject of intensive study,[1] with the result that it is now possible to reconstruct to a large degree the conditions of the Great Ice Age.  It was a period of marked vicissitudes—of phases of glacial conditions alternating with genial interglacial epochs long enough to allow of the widespread development of a temperate and even semi-tropical fauna and flora.  Of these alternations four have been made out in the region of the Alps, and the following nomenclature, taken from the names of rivers in association with whose courses the phenomena have been studied, is commonly employed to indicate the glacial phases, beginning with the oldest—Günz, Mindel, Riss, and Würm.  Thus a lowering of temperature and gradual elevation of the land surface over the definite areas already indicated took place towards the close of the Pliocene and throughout the beginning of the Pleistocene ; this culminated eventually in the Günz glacial phase.  Thereafter the ice-

[1] Cf. *Die Alpen im Eiszeitalter*, by Profs. Penck and Brückner, and Prof. James Geikie's *Antiquity of Man in Europe*.

sheets gradually retreated toward their sources, thus
ushering in the Günz-Mindel interglacial phase, which
gradually reached its zenith of geniality, and then in turn
became overshadowed by the imminent Mindelian glacial
phase. And so on until the Würmian climax, and thereafter through two minor alternations (Laufen and Achen)
within the Würmian period, and three subsequent smaller
variations comprising the so-called Post-glacial phase,
into the Holocene or Post-Pleistocene days, in the later
of which we live, and which, for all we know, may be
part of one more interglacial phase.

It is confessedly difficult to express these different
phases in terms of solar years, yet with this determination
in great part is bound up the question of the antiquity of
man, for Palaeolithic man is eminently Pleistocene, while
Neolithic man corresponds to the Post-Pleistocene. The
Günz glaciation appears to have been the longest, and
the Mindel, perhaps, the most extensive, while the
moraines of the Riss period, when the snowline was some
1300 metres below the snowline of to-day, are particularly
well preserved. The Würmian period was apparently
not so severe as its immediate predecessor. The three
smaller variations which eventually led to the conditions
of modern times have been designated Bühl, Gschnitz,
and Daun respectively by Penck and Brückner, who
consider that the Daun ' stadium ' ended about 7000 B.C.,
and the Bühl ' stadium ' about 20,000 B.C. When to
these considerations we add the opinion of these investigators that the Günz-Mindel interglacial period was
approximately three times the length of the Post-glacial
phase (*i.e.* about 60,000 years in all), that the Mindel-
Riss interglacial period extended over twelve of the same
unit (*i.e.* about 240,000 years), that the Riss-Würmian
interglacial period was not less than the Günz-Mindel,
and that allowance has still to be made for the duration
of the actual glacial phases, we realise that in the case
of the Pleistocene we are dealing with an immense
section of time. Whatever the criterion adopted for the

attempted determination of Pleistocene chronology, the general impression is the same. ' When we reflect,' wrote Professor James Geikie, ' on the many geographical changes that man has witnessed—the submergence and re-elevation of enormous tracts—the erosion of valleys and general lowering of the surface by denudation ; when we consider that he has lived through a succession of stupendous climatic revolutions ; that he has seen widely contrasted floras and faunas alternately occupying our Continent—tundras, steppes, and great forests succeeding each other again and again—we must feel convinced that the few thousand years that have elapsed since the downfall of Babylonian, Assyrian, and Egyptian empires are as nothing compared with the long aeons that separate the earliest times of history from the apparition of Palaeolithic Man in Europe.' [1] Professor Geikie's own estimate for the duration of Pleistocene time was ' a minimum period of 620,000 years.' [2] Everything will, of course, depend on the precise association which can be demonstrated between the location of human remains or implements of human workmanship and definite horizons in the Pleistocene, or even, it may be, Pliocene deposits. But when we realise that flints of indubitable human handicraft are found in the drift gravel of the Somme at a distance of 100 feet above the present level of the river, and then consider how slowly the bed of the river is being lowered by erosion, we begin to have some sense of the vast period that has elapsed since man first dropped these implements by the water's edge, and are ready to believe that 400,004 B.C. is a more approximate date to his appearance than 4004.

The precise correlation of the geological phases of the Great Ice Age with the cultural phases that are recognised by the archaeologist is a matter of extreme intricacy on which no degree of certainty has yet been reached, nor is this likely to be the case for a considerable time to come. The different culture phases take their

---

[1] *The Antiquity of Man in Europe*, p. 300.    [2] *Op. cit.* p. 302.

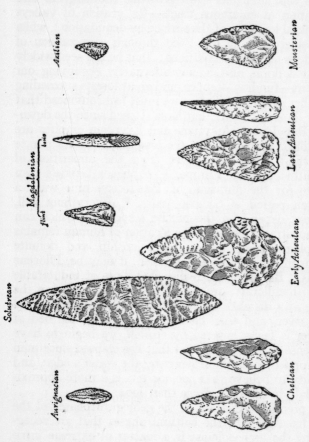

FIG. 3.—Evolution of the lance-point, spear, or dart head. Note the increasing symmetry and skill in the flaking and retouch as the types pass in ascending order through the Chellean, Acheulean, Mousterian, and Aurignacian into the perfected symmetrical Solutrean implement, and thereafter decline in the Magdalenian and Azilian stages. (From H. F. Osborn's *Men of the Old Stone Age*.) Page 56.

names, as will be described in greater detail in the next chapter, from the stations or deposits where they were first found and described. Without, at this stage, definitely attempting to allocate either particular human remains or characteristic implements to any special deposit, it may be stated that within the period covered by the Pleistocene of the geologist, there lie the following phases of Palaeolithic culture, beginning with the oldest—Chellean, Acheulean, Mousterian, Aurignacian, Solutrean, and Magdalenian. The precise difficulty lies in attempting to correlate them with the Günz, Mindel, Riss, and Würmian glacial phases and their connecting interglacial periods. Both Penck and Geikie agree in placing the Günz or first glaciation within the Pliocene, corresponding to the time of the Norwich Crag formation in England. The succeeding interglacial period which lies at the base of the Pleistocene is held to correspond to the early Eolithic phase designated Reutelian, whose delimitation is due to the work of M. Rutot, who devoted long years to the study of the Pleistocene deposits of the river valleys of Belgium. He maintained that a certain thick bed of clay that occurs in the Belgian Lower Pleistocene represents the work of enormous floods that followed the break-up of the second (Mindelian) and most severe glacial phase of the Pleistocene : it is held to correspond to the Chalky Boulder Clay of East Anglia. In this post-Mindelian interglacial period he placed the Mafflian, Mesvinian, and Strepyan cultures, all of them Eolithic, the last of which preceded the Chellean during the same phase. After the Riss glacial phase came an interglacial period which is represented in Belgium by a deposit of fine sand and clay (' ancient loess ') : this probably corresponds to the upper loam of the ' 100-foot terrace ' in the valley of the Thames. In this Riss-Würmian interglacial phase are found implements of the Acheulean stage of culture, and towards its close, of the Mousterian culture, which reached its zenith during the Würmian glacial phase. This was in turn followed by the Post-glacial phase during which great thicknesses of ' recent loess ' were accumulated : these are synchronous with the Aurignacian culture, and succeeded by loams and brick earth that correspond to the Solutrean and Magdalenian cultures. More particularly the Aurignacian is generally considered to synchronise with the Achen oscillation, and the Magdalenian with the Bühl glacial ' stadium ' of some 20,000 years ago. It ought to be added, however, that recently opinion has been tending towards a regrouping of these different phases which would relate them to two principal glacial advances, Günz-Mindel and Riss-Würmian, each composed of several oscillations. Of these the former was on a much more extensive scale. Under this rearrangement the Günz-Mindel interglacial phase sinks into insignificance, but the Mindel-Rissian interglaciation becomes increasingly important.[1]

It may be remarked at this point that the varying surface characters pictured in the words ' tundras, steppes, and great forests ' quoted above, can be taken to represent definite stages in the amelioration of regions that either once skirted or were actually under the ice-sheet in Europe. With each stage were associated its distinctive fauna and flora, and it is the development in the order named, as well as in the reverse direction as the climate changed again towards another glacial phase, that also compels the recognition of long periods of time for the replacement by one another of the corresponding definite faunal and floral series, the records of which are preserved in the interglacial deposits. It is not necessary to suppose that the glacial phases were characterised by unusual extremes of cold. The contrast between them and the interglacial periods lay rather in the shortened summers and lengthened winters, and in the gradual effect of the solidification of moisture in snow and ice in drying the air and so assisting the loss by radiation, of heat derived from the sun. With the natural assumption that as we proceed farther north towards the main source of flow in

[1] Cf. *e.g. Man*, vol. xxii. No. 5.

the Scandinavian backbone, we are less likely to find
clear evidence of interglacial periods, nothing occurs to
indicate marked divergence in any region from the general
characters of the Ice Age as a whole. Professor Geikie
successfully correlated the evidence for glacial and interglacial phases in Great Britain with the corresponding
evidence from the Alps.

Again, the slow movements of elevation—these secular
land oscillations—that were characteristic on the whole
of preglacial and interglacial periods and were a factor
in the causation of glacial phases, necessarily resulted in
readjustments of the surface lands and water, which had
a great bearing on the migration of plants and animals.
Thus we may think, in the Günz and even as late as the
Würmian phase, of land bridges across the Mediterranean
at Gibraltar, and by way of Southern Italy and Sicily,
which definitely connected Europe and Africa and transformed the Mediterranean of these days into two inland
seas. In the same way Great Britain and Ireland formed
part of a western prolongation of the Continent that ran
out to the north-west in peninsular fashion beyond Ice-
land. The larger part of the shallow North Sea was a
plain through which flowed a greater Rhine, receiving
the tribute of the Elbe, as well as of the Thames, the
Forth, and other rivers of the East Coast of Britain. The
area of the English Channel formed in part the bed and
valley of a great river, which, with the Somme and Seine
as tributaries, debouched into the Atlantic on a meridian
of longitude to the west of Ireland. It should also not
be forgotten that the North European rivers of these days
were larger than their modern representatives, since they
carried off the drainage from higher mountains that had
not in the beginning of the Pleistocene yet undergone the
scouring and reducing process of the passage of an ice-
sheet over their flanks. Glacial phases were apt on the
whole to end in various degrees of submergence of the land,
owing in part to the enormous weight of the ice-masses.

Once again, in the actual delimitation of the various

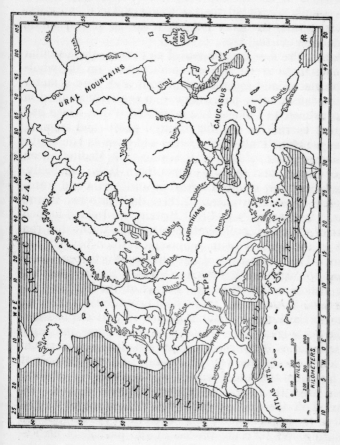

Fig. 4.—Europe in the period of maximum continental elevation. (After Obermaier, from H. F. Osborn's *Men of the Old Stone Age*.)
*Page 58.*

phases of the Great Ice Age, incalculable assistance is
derived from the fossil remains of plants and animals
found in the deposits that are associated with these
phases. The more completely it is realised how close is
the adaptation of distinctive forms of life to a definite
environment, the more reliability can be placed on the
deduction of conditions from the presence of distinctive
fossils. The associated remains in a stratum of what are
known to be arctic and subarctic types can confidently
be taken to be complete demonstration of the conclusion
suggested by other indications, that the stratum in question belongs to a glacial phase, and correspondingly with
regard to the interglacial phases. Such environmental
change meant a selective process which could be avoided
to some extent by migration, but which in the case of the
less adaptable forms—which often means the most
specialised and adapted forms—spelled extinction. New
finds in previously unstudied deposits, therefore, can be
dated, and other deductions checked, by the presence or
absence in them of characteristic forms whose association
with well-marked geological stages has already been
determined. Thus it is found, to mention but a few examples, that forms like the Arctic Fox (*Canis lagopus*), the
Banded Lemming (*Cuniculus torquatus*), the Obi Lemming
(*Myodes obensis*), the Wolverene or Glutton (*Gulo*), the
Marmot (*Arctomys*), the Reindeer (*Rangifer tarandus*),
and the Musk-ox (*Ovibos moschatus*) are generally associ-
ated with glacial or tundra conditions, as may also be the
Woolly Rhinoceros (*R. tichorinus*) and the Mammoth
(*Elephas primigenius*), which are, however, in addition
found under steppe conditions. Forms such as the
Souslik (*Spermophilus*), the Jerboa (*Alactaga*), the Tailless
Hare (*Lagomys*), the Saiga Antelope (*Saiga*), and the
Kiang or Wild Ass (*Equus hemionus*) are characteristic of
steppe conditions, although many others, such as the
Wolf (*Canis lupus*) and Fox (*Canis vulpes*), the Brown
Bear (*Ursus arctos*) and the Wild Boar (*Sus scrofa*), which
prefer a genial climate, are found associated with them.

Finally, the Apes and Monkeys (*Primates*), Lion (*Felis leo*), Leopard (*Felis pardus*), Hippopotamus (*H. amphibius*), the Broad-nosed Rhinoceros (*R. mercki*), various species of Elephant (*E. antiquus, meridionalis*, etc.), and the Spotted Hyaena (*H. crocuta*) definitely favour a warm climate. Closer study shows that in a peculiar degree the small arctic rodents (forms like *Myodes, Lagomys*, etc.), the Elephant, Reindeer, and Horse are important in connection with Pleistocene comparative chronology : [1] indeed, for a long time the three main periods of the Palaeolithic Age (Early, Middle, and Late) were often known as the Hippopotamus, Mammoth, and Reindeer periods respectively.

The blighting and impoverishing effect of an Ice Age as a whole upon the forms of life that struggled under and against it can be seen by a comparison of the fauna and flora of the Pleistocene system with those of the systems immediately preceding or succeeding it. Thus the Pliocene fauna and flora of Europe were rich and varied, the latter including many tree forms that are limited to America to-day. The climate was warm and genial over a continental area greater than that of the Europe of to-day, Africa and Britain being joined to it as the result of the gradual elevation that was a factor in the development of the cold of the Ice Age. Yet there was a temporary return to milder conditions after the first suggestion of the approaching Pleistocene, before the conditions of the Günz phase developed. Generic forms like the hyaena, bear, hippopotamus, tapir, rhinoceros, and elephant were common throughout Europe and partly migrated to the south only to return in the subsequent interglacial period, and partly were thinned out : the flora suffered more severely. The Mindel glaciation, longer and more relentless in its effects upon the fauna and flora, was ' the turning-point in the development of the later aspects of European fauna. It was a time of

[1] See Prof. R. A. S. Macalister, *A Text-book of European Archaeology*, vol. i. chap. iii. *passim*.

deadly slaughter.' [1]   The Rissian glaciation was a period
of invasion of Central Europe by a definitely arctic fauna
that was well adapted to the particular tundra conditions.
The reindeer appears wandering as far south as Spain,
together with the woolly rhinoceros, mammoth, wolverene,
and numerous small rodents.   The cave lion, cave bear,
and cave hyaena are especially distinctive.   It is in the
fauna and flora of the interglacial phases that the gradual
approximation to modern conditions is best marked.
Towards the close of the Riss-Würmian interglacial phase
forms like the broad-nosed rhinoceros (*R. mercki*) and
the straight-tusked elephant (*E. antiquus*) appear for the
last time.   The Würmian glacial period is much like
the Rissian in fauna except for a marked increase in the
numbers of reindeer.   The mammoth seems to have
survived in Europe until the Bühl stadium, and the
Irish elk (*Cervus giganteus*) until the Gschnitz.   At this
time also the reindeer withdrew from Central Europe
to the north.   The European Neolithic fauna and flora
differ little from those of to-day, which in their
richness and variety contrast favourably with those of
Pleistocene times.

The probability of a great antiquity for man is further
suggested as the result of certain theoretical considerations.   The most cursory physical examination of the
three principal modern varieties of the human species
serves to disclose a very great range of variation.   The
typical negro and white man are separated by marked
physical characteristics, yet inasmuch as they are both
specialised forms neither can be said to represent the
ancestral form.   Possibly the nearest modern representative of such a primitive stock—although not therefore to be
considered as a contemporary ancestor—is the Australian
aboriginal.   He combines characters of the negro and of
the white man, and at the same time has certain characteristics that recall the mid-Palaeolithic (Mousterian or
Neanderthal) type.   Taking him for the moment as a

[1] Macalister, *op. cit.* p. 89.

theoretical starting-point, we should then have to find an answer to the question, How long must it have taken for the modern negro and modern white man to evolve from such a common ancestor ? Now definite data are at hand to assist in the solution of this problem. Professor Elliot Smith had occasion to study certain mummified Egyptian remains, dynastic and predynastic—a succession covering some 6000 years at least. He and his fellow-workers found ' evidence of an infiltration of foreign blood both from the north and from the south ; they noted minor alterations in the configuration of the head and in the state of the teeth and jaws, but they could not say that the men at the end of that period were in any respect a higher or more specialised type than the inhabitants of the Nile Valley at the beginning of that period.' [1] When to this we add the fact of the general similarity of Neolithic man, so far as he is known, to the man of to-day, we realise that a process of evolution such as has been sketched above requires time. Sir Arthur Keith thinks that it took the whole length of the Pleistocene—a period whose duration he variously estimates from 300,000 to 500,000 years.[2] ' I am thus postulating,' he adds, ' in order to explain the differentiation and distribution of modern races, that mankind, at the beginning of the Pleistocene period, had reached a physical condition which has its best modern representation in the aborigines of Australia.' [3] But if, further, as he believes, human fossil remains from the Lower and Middle Pleistocene represent in more than one instance distinct species of the human race, if indeed some of the former are actually of Pliocene age, then his conclusion is conceivable that ' man had reached the human standard in size of brain by the commencement of the Pliocene period . . . a period of about one million years ' ago.[4]

---

[1] Prof. Arthur Keith, 'Modern Problems relating to the Antiquity of Man,' *B. A. Report*, 1912, p. 755.
[2] *The Antiquity of Man*, pp. 226, 308, 500.
[3] *B. A. Report*, 1912, p. 756.     [4] *The Antiquity of Man*, p. 510.

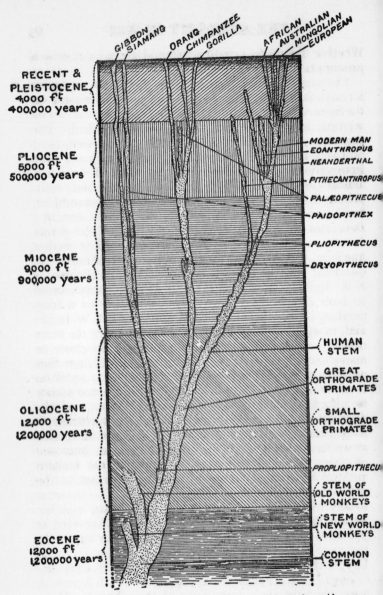

GIBBON
SIAMANG
ORANG
CHIMPANZEE
GORILLA
AFRICAN
AUSTRALIAN
MONGOLIAN
EUROPEAN

RECENT &
PLEISTOCENE
4,000 ft
400,000 years

PLIOCENE
5,000 ft
500,000 years

MIOCENE
9,000 ft
900,000 years

OLIGOCENE
12,000 ft
1,200,000 years

EOCENE
12,000 ft
1,200,000 years

MODERN MAN
EOANTHROPUS
NEANDERTHAL
PITHECANTHROPUS
PALÆOPITHECUS
PAIDOPITHEX
PLIOPITHECUS
DRYOPITHECUS

HUMAN
STEM

GREAT
ORTHOGRADE
PRIMATES

SMALL
ORTHOGRADE
PRIMATES

PROPLIOPITHECUS

STEM OF
OLD WORLD
MONKEYS

STEM OF
NEW WORLD
MONKEYS

COMMON
STEM

FIG. 5.—Suggested genealogical tree of man and the anthropoid apes.
(From Keith's *Antiquity of Man*. By permission.)

Whether the facts actually substantiate so extreme a presumption is another matter.

The same theoretical conclusion of a great antiquity for man is once again suggested by the data bearing on the history of the anthropoid apes, the degree of whose relation to man is now fairly well established. The existence of such fossils as *Pliopithecus* (*antiquus*), most probably a gibbon, represented by upper and lower jaws from various Miocene deposits in Europe ; *Pliohylobates*, almost certainly a gibbon, of which the remains, comprising a single femur and portions of three mandibles, have been found in the Miocene of France and Germany ; *Dryopithecus* (*fontani*), probably ancestral to the gorilla or orang, represented by about four mandibles and a humerus from Upper Miocene strata of France (S. Gaudens) and three forms from the Siwalik Miocene of N.W. India ; *Palaeopithecus sivalensis*, probably related to both chimpanzee and orang, represented by a fragmentary upper jaw, from the Upper Miocene in N.W. India ; and, most interesting of all, *Sivapithecus* from the same deposit, recognised by several authorities as closer to man's ancestral stock than any other ape—all show that we have to go back very early to find the form ancestral to them and man. The data are still much too scanty to afford any completely satisfactory account of the derivative relationship of these remains ; nevertheless, it is clear that if we wish to represent to ourselves the period at which the Primate forms ancestral to man branched off from the stock common to him and the modern anthropoid apes, we have to place it previous to the earliest known forms that could be thought of as ancestral to any of the Simiidae. Now, to quote again from Sir Arthur Keith, ' the earliest traces we have discovered as yet were described by Dr. Max Schlosser in 1910. In the very oldest Oligocene formation of the Fayoum, Egypt, the teeth and jaws of three Primates were discovered. Two of these are allied to the South American apes, the other is a forerunner of the gibbons. These

E

Fayoum fossils are of the highest importance to the solution of our problem. Their discovery assures us that at such an early date in the evolution of mammals the South American apes and the pro-gibbons were already in existence. They are highly evolved forms, and it is not unlikely that they appeared at a much earlier date. . . . Here, then, we have the assurance that an animal which springs closely from the stock giving rise to man has come down to us with but little change through the leagues of time marked by the Miocene, Pliocene, and Pleistocene formations. By the middle of the Miocene we know the great anthropoids were in existence ; it is most unlikely that the traces we have discovered mark their first appearance. With the evolution of the great anthropoids the appearance of a human ancestry as a separate stock is possible. From every point of view it is most probable that the human stock became differentiated at the same time as the great anthropoids. On the evidence afforded by our very imperfect knowledge of fossil forms of apes, we are justified in assuming that a very primitive form of man may have come into existence during the Miocene period—at the very latest during the early part of the Pliocene.' [1] It is the same extreme view reached along a slightly different line, although Sir Arthur, like every earnest gold-seeker, pegs out a larger claim than can be worked in the meantime, in the hope that it may contain something, or because he thinks it will contain something, rewarding. Nevertheless, it is obvious that the general trend of theoretical argument calls for great human antiquity.

[1] *B. A. Report*, 1912, pp. 756, 757.

# CHAPTER IV

## THE ORIGIN OF MAN

In endeavouring to trace more exactly the history of the relationship of man to the anthropoid apes, and even in attempting to postulate those earlier stages in the process of evolution by which the ancestral Primates came into being, we are not entirely in the dark. That which is most distinctive of man is in some kind of a way connected with his brain structure and capacity, and accordingly it is probable that the most fruitful line to pursue will be that which is marked out by increasing complexity in cerebral development. No one has followed this trail more closely than Professor Elliot Smith, upon whose work the immediately following paragraphs are based.[1]

Now that which distinguishes mammals from lower vertebrates, *e.g.* reptiles and fish, is the fact that they are able to unify, correlate, record, and recollect sensory impressions from *all* the senses in a way and to a degree which is not true of these lower forms. Their lives are therefore more of a whole—in a less degree bundles of disconnected moments—than is the case with the lower vertebrates. They are more active and alert, mentally and physically, and are better learners. The graduated advance upon the reptiles is clear, whose dominant sense is smell, with which they can to some extent correlate taste, and this progress continues within the class of the Mammalia. It is connected with the development of the cerebral cortex proper, or neopallium, as Professor Elliot

---

[1] Cf. especially *B. A. Report*, 1912, pp. 575-598 ; Morison Lectures, Royal College of Physicians, Edinburgh, 1922. The same point of view is adopted by F. Wood Jones in his *Arboreal Man*.

Smith terms this area.  ' The consciousness which resides, so to speak, in this neopallium, and is fed by the continual stream of sensory impressions pouring into it and awakening memories of past sensations, can express itself directly in the behaviour of the animal through the intermediation of a part of the neopallium itself, the so-called motor area, which is not only kept in intimate relation with the muscles, tendons, and skin by sensory impressions, but controls the voluntary responses of the muscles of the opposite side of the body.' [1]  This function of regulating skilled movements of the whole body, *i.e.* ' such actions as are possible only when there is a highly developed tactile information-bureau to render nicely adjusted movements possible,' [2] has been associated with the neopallium from its earliest appearance.

Amongst the mammalian order of Insectivora (moles, hedgehogs, and shrews) there is a very ancient and generalised family of lively, agile, squirrel-like creatures, the Tupaiidae or tree-shrews, which show points of kinship in habits and structure with the most primitive of the Lemurs, *Tarsius* or the Spectral Tarsier.[3]  Particularly on the strength of the relationships in brain structure, Professor Elliot Smith maintains that ' the brain of the Primates was derived from some Insectivore-like type, the cerebral hemispheres of which attained a precocious development,' and inasmuch as '*Tarsius* possesses at once the most generalised and the most pithecoid brain of all the Lemuroidea,' [4] lemurs and apes were certainly derived from a common stem.  Now in the case of primitive mammals the sense of smell, both in connection with the search for food and recognition of friend or foe, was dominant, and the olfactory lobes were particularly well developed.  But in arboreal life there are distinct limita-

[1] Sectional Presidential Address, *B. A. Report*, 1912, p. 581.
[2] Prof. G. Elliot Smith, 'On the Origin of Mammals,' *B. A. Report*, 1911, p. 427.
[3] For the evidence, cf. W. K. Gregory, *The Orders of Mammals*, pp. 268-280.
[4] Quoted in Gregory, *op. cit.* p. 500.

tions to the value of the sense of smell, and a greater necessity for the development of sight and touch and hearing. Accordingly we find in arboreal forms like the tree-shrew a reduction in the olfactory regions of the brain, and a greater development of the areas in the neopallium concerned with sight, touch, hearing, and motor functions, as also with the unifying of the effects of the different impressions passing into the brain through the senses. That is to say, there is less of sensory specialisation and more of a general balance in relation to the physical environment, which reacts on the body as a whole, and leaves these creatures free to develop that agility which was and is a dominant survival factor in mammalian arboreal life. Further, towards the close of the Cretaceous period, some shrew-like animal, suggestive of *Tarsius*, freed from the domination of the sense of smell through the continued reduction of the olfactory lobes in reaction to the new environment, developed to a very remarkable degree the sense of vision, aided by the circumstance that with the shortening of the snout and the flattening of the face, the eyes were brought from the sides to the front of the head, so that the creature was able to look straight ahead. Images of the same object were impressed upon both eyes, and a wide range of co-ordinated movement was now possible. In the case of the diminutive *Tarsius*, sight predominates over smell, and in the ancestral history of man this dominance first came into existence at this Tarsian stage. But with this development of sight went a corresponding development of the sense of touch, for better vision meant heightened curiosity and a quickened desire to examine : the eyes could also now better guide the fore-limbs, and so aid in the establishment of more precise and skilled movements. This meant the gradual replacement of the jaw by the hands as instruments of prehension. Accordingly, not merely is there a marked increase in the visual area of the cerebral cortex, but also in the tactile, motor, and kinaesthetic areas, all of which sensibilities had been developed. A whole new range of increased adaptation was opened up by the new correlated powers of hand and eye. Above all, this enhanced curiosity developed an organ of attention, so to speak—an area associated with the co-ordination of the activities of the neopallium or cerebral cortex as a whole, so as to guide the senses and secure the harmonious concentrated action of the muscles in carrying out some particular skilled movement. In this we find the earliest indications of what develops into the prefrontal area of the human brain, with which are associated the faculty of attention and the co-ordination of mental processes.

It is unnecessary to attempt to trace the history or migrations of the primitive *Tarsius*-like forms or the related lemurs proper. The palaeontological evidence suggests the evolution of some of the former into true monkeys of a very primitive Platyrrhine type in North America during Early Eocene days. Evidence of Catarrhine monkeys has been found in the Lower Oligocene of Egypt,[1] and by the Miocene, the Catarrhine Anthropoid Apes are known in Europe. Now the weight of the Platyrrhine marmoset's brain is some four or five times that of the Tarsian brain. This is in part due to the larger size of the animal which exposes it to more dangers, but the development is noticeable along the same main lines. There is greater development and specialisation in the motor area of the cortex, corresponding to increased power of skilled movement. The hands are now used in place of the jaws for taking up food, and there is a marked development of the tactile areas in the brain corresponding to this growing use of the hands for inquiry and experiment upon the outside world. In climbing, also, the hind-limbs tend to become organs of support, while the creature reaches out or feels around with its fore-limbs. In particular, Professor Elliot Smith considers that the acquisition of stereoscopic vision, which had not been developed at the Tarsian stage, was of

[1] Cf. p. 65.

superlative importance, as bringing the organism into new relations to the environment that further stimulated curiosity and inquiry, and so, advance. This added power involved the development in the brain of a complicated area where the conjugate movement of the eyes was more exactly regulated, and the range of such movements extended so as to bring about convergence and more perfect focussing of the eyes upon objects in the field of vision. The mere act of focussing the eyes on an object for such examination involved the beginnings of that power of attention and concentration that is necessary for the development of mind itself. More than ever as the result of various structural modifications and developments, the eye became the principal avenue of sensory impression, and vision the guiding sense. Now for the first time the creature saw in a large degree as man sees, and could appreciate as never before size and form, colour and texture, spatial position and relation. The handling of objects, interest in which was evoked by this apparently new revelation or unveiling of the Environment—the change, however, really being, as in all critical advances, in the beholder—could not fail to result in greater manipulative finger power, and increased plasticity of touch. Professor Elliot Smith draws attention to the fact that no forms lower than apes handle and nurse their babies. Further, there is an appreciable increase in the size of the auditory area. Things had become more meaningful and provocative of interest, which began to be increasingly expressed by sounds uttered by the voice. This sound-symbolism, which eventually developed into speech, produced a complementary development of the auditory region of the cortex. In those forms especially, however, that evolved into the South American monkeys proper, the line of advance through sight was not maintained. A tendency developed in the gloom of the forests to trust rather to hearing, and to development of the tail as a prehensile organ in place of the hands. The greater the degree of specialisation or adaptation to a specific physical environment, the greater has always been the risk of failure to advance.

By whatever route the New World Platyrrhine ancestors of the later Catarrhine or Old World Apes reached their new habitat—for the details of this migration are still a subject of debate—the mere fact that they moved out from the ancestral home, letting other environmental stimuli play upon their freshly-acquired powers, served to keep them plastic and free to respond to still newer stimuli. At the same time—for the story has been the same all along—some of the forms fell away from the higher status now established. The baboons, for example, have clearly retrograded in their definite return to quadrupedal progression. In other Catarrhine forms the Tarsian tendency towards the erect posture, with all the complicated series of structural changes that this involved, was persisted in, and the Anthropoid Apes began to come into existence. The ancestral gibbons probably broke off about this stage, and the still greater development in the size and specialisation of the motor and prefrontal areas of the gibbon brain is correlated not merely with the marked increase in range of skilled movement and agility, but particularly with that greater discriminative and manipulative power in the fingers, which made the fore-limb less and less a mere organ of progression, and increasingly an instrument of prehension and investigation. Further, a marked increase in the parietal or ' association ' area of the cortex, which lies between the sensory, auditory, and visual areas, meant growing ability to store the records of states of consciousness compounded of various sensory impressions—registered experience—which in its turn resulted in greater success in skilled movements of the fore-limbs, and so greater inducement to adopt the upright attitude. The orang, chimpanzee, and gorilla branched off later.

Now there is no reason to suppose that *Homosimius*, as our still theoretical ancestral form is conveniently termed, was other than the result of a continuation of the same series of changes as had successively produced the earlier forms. All of the facts tend to indicate that the differentiation of the humanoid stock was a Tertiary event, possibly contemporaneous in a very general way with the differentiation of the great Anthropoids, though subsequent almost certainly to the separation of the gibbons. Data so definitely linking man with the Anthropoid Apes in a community of origin tend to emphasise the importance of this arboreal phase, as well as stimulate interest as to the circumstances which most probably brought it to a close. The adoption of the semi-erect position allowed greater freedom of movement of the fore-limbs in all directions, and conditioned the loss of the tail. As Wood Jones puts it, 'the human stock sat up before it stood,'[1] just as to-day the child sits up before it stands. Again, in relation to climbing, arboreal life offered ample scope for the development of hand and arm in pulling and holding, and of leg and foot in supporting, balancing, and progressing. In Wood Jones' terse phrase, 'arboreal uprightness preceded terrestrial uprightness.'[2] In relation to springing from one branch to another, arboreal life gave occasion for the judging of distances, the estimating of the strength of branches, and the use of the hand in grasping. Such a combination of activities must, as we have seen, have exerted a great influence on the development of the higher brain centres. One fatal difference between the ancestral Anthropoids and the human ancestral form was that the former became too much adapted to arboreal life, conforming entirely to the immediate environment. The gorilla and other Anthropoids, which separated off in Miocene days, show in each case more specialisation of structure than man. In the case of *Homosimius*, the adaptation was not so extreme—it was a case ' of successful minimal adaptive specialisation '[3]—with the result that the way remained open to the ground, and a new environment.

[1] *Op. cit.* p. 224.     [2] *Op. cit.* p. 6.
[3] F. Wood Jones, *op. cit.* p. 212.

In body and fore-limb alike he retained more of the primitive plasticity : man alone of all living forms has never adopted any limiting protective adaptation either of structure or manner of life. At the same time, it is precarious to single out any one factor in this process of advance and describe it as the cause thereof. What we note at this stage are stimuli from the environment, as the result of some new relation to it, acting upon the brain, which responds in experimental movements particularly of the fore-limbs, directed to establishing some fresh understanding with some part of, or object in, the environment. The knowledge thus acquired leads to fresh experimentation, which in turn means further practice in skilled movements. There is thus a mutual reaction, one upon the other, of erectness, use of the hands, and brain development. All this is seen in the parallel development of the prefrontal and motor areas of the brain, the former being especially concerned with control over the functions of the cortex as a whole. But there is also a further development of what has been already referred to in the case of the gibbon, viz. a corresponding growth of the parietal region of the cortex, with which is associated the registration of the states of consciousness composed of the blended and recorded sensory impressions, or, in other words, low-grade memory of experience. The advance has been in some way fundamentally associated with increasing growth and specialisation of the brain, especially of the prefrontal and temporo-parietal and central areas, which are connected with attention and the control of the psychical activities of the cortex, the correlation of cause and effect, and the memories of past actions, respectively. In terms of a later chapter [1] the Anthropoids, having less ability to anticipate and think, and being compelled to respond more immediately to the environmental stimuli, under the continuous stream of sensory impressions which, so to speak, overflow the channels of their less-developed brains, are not so free as

[1] Chap. xi.

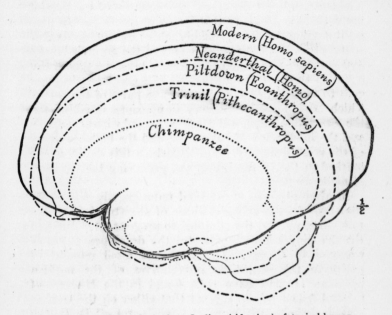

Modern (*Homo sapiens*)
Neanderthal (*Homo*)
Piltdown (*Eoanthropus*)
Trinil (*Pithecanthropus*)
Chimpanzee

½

Fig. 6.—Evolution of the brain.  Outlines (side view) of typical human and pre-human brains, showing the early development of the posterior portions of the brains, and the relatively late development of the anterior portions, the seat of the higher mental faculties.  (From H. F. Osborn's *Men of the Old Stone Age*.)

man.   The content of man's experience is so enriched and
his memory so developed that he can foresee to some
extent the consequences of his actions and deliberate
before he makes response, and if necessary modify that
response in the light of past experience.   According to
Elliot Smith,[1] ' In the course of evolution of the human
brain there is added to this cortex of man's Simian pro-
genitor a mass of tissue, roughly, about five hundred cubic
centimetres, bigger than the whole of the gorilla's brain ;
and as the sensory areas of the human brain are practically
equal to those of the gorilla, all this enormous increase
goes to swell the dimensions of those parts of the cortex
which do not receive sensory impressions directly,' *i.e.*
the association areas, which are concerned with experience
and the influencing of behaviour, and the higher reaches
of the mind generally.   Particularly is this development
marked in the prefrontal region, producing the forehead
of modern man.

In attempting to understand more exactly the causes
that brought the arboreal phase of ancestral human life
to a close, we find the stimulus to progress once again in
the changing Environment and the developed power of
response to change.   The fact that fossil remains of
primitive representatives or relatives of the modern
Simiidan families have been found in the Miocene of
Central Asia tends to suggest that either on the Iranian
plateau or somewhere to the north-east of it, in the
western section of the plateau of Thibet, was *a*, if not *the*,
locus where the descent to the ground—that first fall to
rise—actually took place.   While the opening of the
Tertiary Era in Europe was a period of warm and equable
climate, there is evidence that it became drier and cooler
as the Eocene passed into the Miocene.   Similarly in
Central Asia, of which continent Europe is after all, in a
geographical, zoological, and anthropological respect,
simply the western promontory or extension, and with
which for that matter America and Australia have had

[1] *B. A. Report*, 1912, p. 594.

direct land connections at different periods, a lowering of the temperature and growing aridity accompanied that slow process of continental uplift during the Miocene, which in particular brought the Himalayas into existence at much the same time as the Western Alps. There was growth in the continental areas which must have occasioned profound changes in the character of the areas that had been the haunts of anthropoid forms. Inevitably, forests were largely transformed into steppe regions and grassy plains, as the new mountain ranges shut off moisture-bearing winds from reduced ocean surfaces. As a result of the continued lowering of the temperature and the increasing aridity which became more marked with the advance of the Pliocene, the character of the vegetation further changed ; the fruit trees that supported anthropoid life became scarcer. Thus the arboreal anthropoids were faced with three possibilities—migration, change of life habits, or extinction. The first was the method adopted by the highly-specialised Anthropoid Apes. They tended to move southwards, seeking regions of greater warmth and necessary food supply. Facilitated by the land bridges that were one particular result of the general phase of elevation that lasted through Late Pliocene and Early Pleistocene time, gibbons now ranged throughout a greater South-East Asia, and the orang penetrated as far as Borneo, by way of a larger Malay Peninsula, comprising the present islands of Sumatra and Java as well. The chimpanzee and gorilla gradually moved southwest into Africa. In either case the route offered no insuperable difficulties, and lay through regions where the climate was milder and food more abundant than in the harsher and drier regions to the north, with their reduced forest areas and food supplies, out of which the Anthropoids were being thus driven. Towards the west, the land bridges at the Dardanelles, and across the Mediterranean at Gibraltar and by way of Sicily into Italy, provided additional routes of egress and ingress into Europe, which if not followed at this particular stage by the Apes

owing to climatic conditions, were still of service to man
very soon after.

The second method, that of leaving the trees and
seeking new food supplies, such as roots and shoots and
small mammals, on the ground, by river courses and
lakes, or in thickets, was a desperate and hazardous
adventure for arboreal forms during a period which was
in many respects the zenith of mammalian carnivorous
life. But once the footing became more secure, it meant
entrance into a new Environment, which with its challenging stimuli and beckonings resulted in further mental
advance. *Homosimius* was still more ape than man,
with long arms and short legs, imperfect adaptation to
the upright attitude, with heavy eyebrows, retreating
forehead, and projecting muzzle, but with possibilities
that were henceforth his alone. Comparatively defence-
less, he was gregarious, and the homosimian pack began
to be a force in the world of living things.

In an interesting, though unjustifiably pessimistic,
work entitled *The Origin of Man and of his Superstitions*,
Professor Carveth Read urges the importance of the
adoption of the hunting habit, which becomes markedly
characteristic in Palaeolithic Man, and of the change
from a frugivorous to a flesh-diet as the one operative
cause in the development of the distinctively human line
amongst the various anthropoid groups. Modern man
is certainly omnivorous, and the supplementing of the
vanishing arboreal means of subsistence by the permanent
descent to solid earth and the search there for fruits and
roots and young shoots, must have been further modified
at a very early stage by the inclusion of animal food,
possibly under the stimulus of famine. None of the
Simiidae appear to be strictly vegetarian, with the
exception of the orang, so that this new phase was but
an extension of an already familiar habit. On the other
hand, some of the qualities undoubtedly developed in
connection with the 'pack' life which Professor Read
describes, must at any rate in the earliest stages have at

times concerned man the hunted, almost as much as man the hunter. Gregariousness is a sound means of defence, multiplying as it were the eyes and ears of every individual of the herd. To the part played in social progress by the reduction in the number of offspring and the prolonged and dependent infancy—characters in part directly associated with the phase of arboreal life—attention has often been drawn. The evidence of tender concern for the young is a notable feature from the monkeys upwards, and the prolonged infancy meant that longer association of the parents which developed into the incipient family life of some of the Anthropoids. In certain cases these families combine into larger social or community groups, and the advantages of such a manner of life were more than ever apparent to the terrestrial *Homosimius*. Increasing adventure into the open meant sometimes speedy retreats which confirmed the lower limbs as instruments of progression and support, while the ability to use the hands was probably largely employed in learning the possibilities of sticks and stones as implements, and how to employ them to advantage. Right-handedness is a very old discrimination with which the situation of the heart on the left side may have had something to do. Means of communication by signs and gesture would be more and more superseded by sounds, onomatopoetic in relation to the cries of animals or the sounds of Nature. In the case of every one of these brain-directed actions there was reaction on the brain and resultant development, and as ideas became more and more associated with sounds and actions, the former tended to drive man increasingly into attempts to convey and express them to his fellows ; but new ideas seem to have come and made their way even more slowly than they do to-day.

The steady growth of the brain reacted on the general shape of the face and skull. Already in 1893 Dr. Robert Munro [1] directly connected the retrocession or contrac-

---

[1] *Proc. Royal Soc. Edin.* vol. xxv. p. 93.

tion of the facial bones—especially the jaw-bones—towards the central axis of the spinal column with the anterior development of the cerebral hemispheres, which otherwise would have upset the equipoise of the head on the top of the spinal column. The balancing was also helped by a backward shifting of the cerebrum over the cerebellum. This contraction of the jaw-bones meant a greater crowding of the teeth, with the result that the third molars, which were usually as large and sometimes larger than their neighbours in Palaeolithic jaws, have gradually dwindled until they are almost vestigial in civilised races. Curiously parallel with this process has been the development of the chin. To-day it is possible to get a fairly close approximation of the actual reduction in length in Pleistocene time through measurements on the oldest fossil jaws. ' In the mandibles of very ancient man,' says Sir Arthur Keith, ' the chewing surface exceeds the highest modern development by a considerable amount. In the course of human evolution, the chewing area has become greatly reduced, a reduction which probably followed the growing mastery of the brain.' [1]    There has been a contraction from either end towards the centre of the jaw.

It is undeniable that so far as *Homosimius* learned to co-operate in the chase he had entered an admirable training-school. Here he had everything to learn, having inherited no capacities in this direction, but in learning, as the educable animal, he excelled all contemporary life. Observation of his quarry's haunts and manner of life, the making of weapons and the selection of the material for them, the devising of traps, were all exercises that demanded growing memory of details and aided in forcing him into development of speech and gesture. It is probable also that as sparks were produced in the fashioning of flint implements, man may have come by this way into his knowledge of the use of fire. With this acquisition Alfred Russel Wallace sought to explain the loss of

[1] *The Antiquity of Man*, p. 450.

the anthropoid hairiness, which still persists, however, to a certain degree as a racial characteristic in the Ainus of Yezo. This loss, it is of some importance to recollect, was attributed by Darwin to the action of sexual selection,[1] which has undoubtedly played a great part as a factor in connection with the development of secondary characters in the evolution of man, while the naturalist and traveller, Belt, had correlated the acquirement of the relatively naked skin under the action of natural selection with freedom from parasites. In Wallace's opinion, man ' *may* have lost [his hairy covering] gradually, from the time when he first became Man—the spiritual being, the " living soul " in a corporeal body, in order to render him *more sensitive*. From that moment he was destined to the intellectual advance which we term civilisation. He was to be exposed to a thousand self-created dangers totally unknown to the rest of the animal world. His very earliest advance towards civilisation—the use of fire—became thenceforth a daily and hourly danger to him, to be guarded against only by sudden and acute pain ; and as he advanced onwards and his life became more complex ; as he surrounded himself with dwellings, and made clothing and adopted cookery as a daily practice, he became more and more exposed to loss, to injury, and to death from fire, and thus would be subject to the law of selection by which those less sensitive to fire, and therefore more careless in the use of it, became eliminated.' [2] So specific a human character as the relatively naked skin was probably, however, the resultant of the operation of several causes.

And now with regard to the actual data concerning man. Long before unequivocal proofs of the existence of man, either by way of chipped flints of unmistakably human origin or actual fossil remains, come within our purview, a whole series of objects is offered for examination by serious and enthusiastic workers in this particular

[1] *The Descent of Man*, New Edition, pp. 915-922.
[2] *The World of Life*, p. 378.

F

domain, for which the claim is made that they are artifacts, and that the scant measure of handiwork which
even their sponsors can only demonstrate in them con-
forms exactly to the state of mental development of the
living forms who are supposed to have fashioned them.
It is now several years since attention was first directed
to these Eoliths, as they are called—flints of peculiar shape
found often in great quantities in beds that are undoubtedly of Pliocene origin.   Thus a series of supposed
flint implements was discovered in 1897 by Mr. Lewis
Abbott in the Cromer Forest beds,[1] which are usually
assigned to the very base of the Pleistocene, but it was
more especially the flints taken by Mr. W. G. Clarke in
1905 from under the Norwich Crag formation in East
Anglia, and by Mr. Reid Moir in 1910 from underneath
the Red Crag—both definitely Pliocene deposits—as well
as the remarkable series of objects investigated by M.
Rutot in Belgium of what he has called the Strepyan
industry, that started the vigorous controversy which is
still as yet undecided.   Indeed, as we have already seen,
Rutot includes as early Pleistocene cultures the industries
that he designates as Reutelian, Mafflian, and Mesvinian
respectively, all of which are Eolithic, the first going back
to the very junction of the Pliocene and Pleistocene formations, and being preceded by a St. Prestian culture
definitely Pliocene, so called from objects found originally
by l'Abbé Bourgeois in gravel deposits at Saint Prest
near Chartres (Eure-et-Loire).   The Strepyan culture
which Rutot regards as the direct precursor of the Chellean
culture, and included by him in the Palaeolithic series,
corresponds in time to the lowest of the mid-Pleistocene
deposits, subsequent to the second or Mindelian glacial
period.   Eoliths are broadly reducible to three types represented in fig. 7.   Guesses at their use seldom get beyond

[1] Historically the first eolithic claims were advanced by Mr. Benjamin Harrison on account of discoveries made by him in Kent in 1865,
and by M. l'Abbé Bourgeois in 1867 in connection with the Thenay
flints found by him in Tertiary gravels in the region of Loire-et-Cher.
The acuteness of the controversy is a more recent development.

that of scrapers for skins. The problem of form has recently been complicated by the pretensions advanced on behalf of a much more complex hammer-headed type styled 'rostro-carinate,' from its supposed partial resemblance to a keel, ending in a strong curve like an eagle's beak. For this implement the same purpose is suggested.[1] These forms are all Pliocene, but still older examples, as those from the Miocene found at Le Puy Courny, ' rather less unconvincing' in Macalister's opinion [2] than some

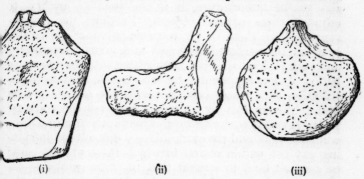

(i)          (ii)          (iii)

FIG. 7.—Types of Kentian eoliths, showing chipping (i) round the edges, (ii) in a hollow between two projections, and (iii) on the two sides of a projection. (From Macalister's *Text-book of European Archaeology.*)

of later date, have been accepted by several expert investigators as the handicraft of some unknown *Homosimius.*

The question of eoliths opens up a very difficult controversy, for they constitute, if artifacts, the sole evidence for Tertiary man. Theoretically there was a Tertiary ancestor ; is there as yet any unequivocal evidence of him, and had he already in the Pliocene evolved from *Homosimius* into *Homo* ? In the light of present know-

[1] For a critical account of ' rostro-carinates ' see Prof. W. J. Sollas, *B. A. Report*, 1913, pp. 788-790, where the evidence afforded by the Selsey flints of this type, examined *in situ*, is stated to be ' uniformly suggestive of the action of natural causes.'

[2] *Op. cit.* p. 162.

ledge, the first question must still be answered in the negative, and to the second the fairest answer is, We do not know as yet with any certainty. In default of an objective standard or test whereby we can with certainty distinguish between man's earliest attempts at tool-making and natural objects, all judgment upon the nature of eoliths must necessarily be subjective, and as long as there are alternative natural explanations of their origin, as *e.g.* the pressure of overlying soil or the effects of changes of temperature, it is the sounder method to adjudge them natural objects. Further, the circumstances that there is no intrinsic advance noticeable between the earliest (Oligocene) and latest (Pleistocene, and even Holocene) eoliths comparable with the enormous period of time represented by this stretch, that their distribution as a whole coincides with the distribution of flint (although this by no means involves the converse statement that wherever flint is found, there also eoliths will be found), and the extraordinary difficulty in imagining any use within reason to which these objects could be put, all tend to suggest that the more probable explanation of the evidence produced to date lies in the working of non-human causes. Even in the case of the Piltdown remains, where eoliths were taken from the same gravel bed, there is no irresistible compulsion in the actual evidence to suppose that they are artifacts. As matters stand to-day, and particularly in face of the possibility of such deliberate judgments as those of Professor Sollas and Mr. S. Hazzledine Warren,[1] it seems barely justifiable to base theories about the existence of Tertiary man, or his precursors, on the strength of the present eolithic evidence. So far as the Quaternary industries classified by Rutot are concerned, they are from deposits

[1] ' As a result of tedious and careful digging with small hand tools I have seen the rostro-carinates, the Foxhall type of flakes with edge trimming, pseudo-borers, pseudo-scrapers, spur implements, single notches, double notches, and many more, all in the actual process of manufacture by the movement-under-pressure of one stone against another.'—(*Man*, vol. xxii. No. 6.

FIG. 8.—Restoration of *Pithecanthropus*, under the direction of Mons. Rutot. (By permission.)

*Page* 85.

where, as the children say in their search for a concealed object, we are becoming ' warm.' But as the external control is still wanting, no definite judgment can be passed upon them either way.

When, finally, we consider the organic fossil remains dating from the period when the manlike Ape was evolving into the apelike Man, there is only one specimen that calls for serious consideration, and of definitely human Lower Pleistocene remains, only two or three. The attempt is sometimes made to depreciate the value of the evidence on the ground of its paucity. When due regard is had to all the conditions militating against the probability of the preservation of human remains from such a remote period, the remarkable circumstance is that any evidence has come to light at all. It is also certain that evidence of incalculable importance has been in human hands during past decades, and been lost or destroyed through the failure of the discoverers to realise the importance of what they had found. It can be confidently stated in the light of what is already unquestionably known that the discoveries of the next hundred years will not merely place the great antiquity of man beyond all doubt, but provide a solution of many of the unsolved problems of to-day regarding the development of the earliest human races.

Undoubtedly the remains which first claim attention are those to which the discoverer gave the name of *Pithecanthropus erectus*. Here the difficulty of determining the geological horizon is great and the conclusions depending thereon exceedingly eventful. The remains, which consist of a skull cap (*calvaria*), a left femur (pathological in part), and two teeth (second upper left and third upper right molars),[1] were discovered by a Dutch army doctor, Eugène Dubois, near Trinil in the Island of Java during the years 1892-1894, in strata (*andesite tufa*) sup-

---

[1] To these may be added a small fragment of a lower jaw undescribed by Dubois, and a third tooth discovered in the same locality by a subsequent expedition under Frau Selenka (1906).

posed by him to be of Pliocene age, but more generally determined as early Pleistocene, on the left bank of the river Bengawan, about 15 metres below the surface. The remains were not all found at the same time, but at considerable intervals, and it is possible, though improbable, that they did not all belong to the same individual, for the skull-cap and thigh-bone were lying about 15 metres apart. Dubois at once challenged interest by his creation of a new family for the bones, and stated that in them we had evidence of a form intermediate between Simiidae and Hominidae, *i.e.* ancestral to both. In support of the previous indications as to the place of origin of the human race, it is important to bear in mind that Java and Borneo at this particular period formed parts of the Asiatic Continent, and that there was therefore the possibility of a wide range of distribution for forms of which we have earlier evidence in the foot-hills of the Himalayas.

Several interesting features arose in connection with the detailed study of the parts. Of these the most striking was the fact that they all show features both simian and human, in varying degrees. In the case of the skull have been noted [1] as simian the massive brutal brow-ridges, and the low, flattened curve of the sagittal arc of the calvaria; as human, its great absolute size and capacity. The latter at 855 c.c. is more than 30 per cent. greater than the corresponding figure for the largest Simiidan skull, and implies an estimated associated brain weight of 750 grms. At the same time, this content of 855 c.c. is well below the modern normal range of 1300 to 1500 c.c. The narrow forehead also adds to the impression of the calvaria being more simian than human. On the other hand, the actual brain specifications, as gathered from the cast made by Dr. Dubois, forbid any such absolute conclusion. Thus the speech area was about twice as great as that of the Simiidae and half as large as in man, but the frontal areas associated with memory,

[1] Cf. *e.g.* W. L. H. Duckworth, *Morphology and Anthropology*, p. 514.

attention, and co-ordination were in a comparatively early stage of development. In the case of the femur, while some authorities have seen a simian feature in the very straightness of the shaft, its absolute length (455 mm., indicating an associated stature of about 5 feet 8 inches with erect attitude) and the slenderness of the shaft, are human. With regard to the teeth, the marked divergence and size of the roots, together with the large dimensions of the crown, are simian characters, but in all other points and proportions they are more human than simian.

Expert opinion was for long divided into three groups : (a) those who considered that the remains were purely simian, while admitting that the ape thus represented was superior to any other member of the Simiidae, extinct or alive ; (b) those who considered that the remains were purely human, but therefore of a Pleistocene man inferior to any known human form ; and (c) those who found in them the remains of a form ancestral to the human and simian groups alike—not wholly human and yet superior to the Simiidae. So Sir Arthur Keith sees in these bones evidence of ' a being human in stature, human in gait, human in all his parts, save his brain. The full development of the brain came last.' [1] Schwalbe considers *Pithecanthropus erectus* as ' the root of a branch which has sprung from the anthropoid ape root and has led up to man.' [2] Careful measurements of the skull, and a comparative study of it with related forms in connection with an attempt to assign their systematic place to the Aborigines of Tasmania, led Professor Berry to give *Pithecanthropus* an intermediate position in the direct line, yet nearer the ape than man. [3] In the present state of our knowledge, and with due regard to the implications of the other views, some *via media* commends itself most. In short, *Pithecanthropus* is in a sense a ' missing link '

[1] *Op. cit.* p. 268.
[2] Chap. vii. in *Darwin and Modern Science*, p. 135.
[3] *Proc. Royal Society, Edinburgh*, vol. xxxiv. pp. 144-189.

in that it represents a form morphologically between the anthropoid apes and man, and may be a modified Pleistocene survivor of a still earlier human ancestral form. Whether it is considered definitely human or still subhuman depends upon where the line is drawn, analogous to that between youth and manhood.   Investigation of the brain cast shows a development of the auditory region which in Professor Elliot Smith's opinion indicates that *Pithecanthropus* was already on the human side of the line.

Such an account of man's origin, it may be felt, differs in character from that in Genesis 1 $^{26\text{-}28}$ and 2 $^{4b\text{-}7}$, which used to be considered authoritative upon this question. These passages are authoritative with the simple authority of truth as accounts of the relationship of man to God, and of his mental, moral and religious capacity, but to be historical records of his origin they make no pretence. The name ' Adam ' is not the proper name of a particular individual : it is the Hebrew word for *man*.   As we proceed with the Biblical history we find situations developed which are incompatible with the idea of one single individual and his family being the only existing human beings.   In Genesis 4 $^{14}$, when Cain is driven away because of his crime, he expects to meet other men who might kill him.   He also ' builded a city ' (4 $^{17}$), which is intelligible on the view that the proper name represents a tribe of which Cain was the head or representative family, perhaps the eponymous ancestor of the Kenites.   More probably, accordingly, in the story of Adam we have the first stage in that selective process which characterises all Hebrew history from Noah, through Abraham, Isaac, Jacob, the southern kingdom in the time of Rehoboam, the Babylonish captivity, and the early Christian community.

We ought further to observe that the simple notion of the formation of the first parents of the race out of clay by a divine or superhuman being is not limited to Scripture where, in particular, the association of man with the ground was almost literal in the Hebrew mind.[1]  A similar account of origins is found in Babylonian, Egyptian, and Greek mythologies, and the same conception is current amongst modern savages.[2]  Even the details as to the formation of the first woman out of a rib of the man are found in Polynesian folklore under conditions that seem to rule out all possibility of the account being a reminiscence of the Biblical story learned at some remoter period.

And, further, amongst savage peoples there are also philosophies akin to the Darwinian, in which the origin of man from, and his actual kinship with, lower forms of life are leading ideas. In fact, this feeling is the essence of totemism, that strange form of superstition that links certain clans with particular species of plants or animals so closely that men of the tribe unconsciously develop characteristics of the totem, and are as concerned about its welfare as about their own.  Reference is made to this point simply as illustrative of a curiously developed sense of kinship with the lower creation, which is sometimes so strong as to eliminate all sense of distinction between man and beast.  In short, amongst savage peoples, we find traditions of origin that are, very roughly, comparable to Special Creation on the one hand and to Evolution on the other, and some instances, *e.g.* the traditions of the Arunta tribe of Central Australia, where the crudest of attempts is made to combine the two points of view.

[1] ' In Heb. " ground " ('ădāmāh) is in form the fem. of " man " ('ădām) ' ; S. R. Driver, *The Book of Genesis*, p. 37.   Cf. also Latin *humus* and *homo*.

[2] Cf. Sir J. G. Fraser, ' Some Primitive Theories of the Origin of Man,' chap. ix. in *Darwin and Modern Science*.

# CHAPTER V

## PALAEOLITHIC MAN

As the result of the labours of countless workers in all parts of the world, Palaeolithic Man no longer confronts us as an individual rarity, not even as a single type physically or culturally. The actual story of each successive discovery reads like a romance.[1] The gradual fitting in of each piece into the complicated puzzle-picture that represents the evolutionary history of man is the work of the present and of future generations. Doubtless there will be much readjustment with the increase of knowledge, while the number of pieces left lying around the edge of the picture so to speak, still unplaced, will be considerable for a long time to come, especially as recently they have been found more rapidly than it has been possible to see where they should go. Nevertheless the story can be given in rough outline, an outline that is impressive as much by what it omits as by what it includes.

Ordinarily the Palaeolithic Period is subdivided into three stages, Early, Middle, and Late, and these in turn are seen to represent groupings in a well-defined succession of progressive cultural stages represented by the terms Strepyan, Chellean, Acheulean, Mousterian, Aurignacian, Solutrean, and Magdalenian, each of which takes its name from some particular site where the culture was

[1] For authoritative accounts see *Les Hommes Fossiles*, by Marcellin Boule ; *Men of the Old Stone Age*, by H. F. Osborn ; *The Antiquity of Man*, by Sir Arthur Keith, and *A Text-book of European Archaeology*, vol. i., by Prof. R. A. S. Macalister ; for an excellent résumé, *A Guide to the Fossil Remains of Man* (British Museum, Natural History), by Dr. A. Smith Woodward.

originally discovered and studied. Distinctively Early Palaeolithic are all Chellean and Acheulean remains, ushered in by the Strepyan or pre-Chellean phase which borders on Eolithic days. Middle Palaeolithic comprises the Mousterian phase, while Late Palaeolithic corresponds to the Aurignacian, Solutrean, and Magdalenian cultures. Thereafter through the Mesolithic transition stages of Azilian and Campignian cultures we pass on into the Neolithic world. We have already considered the attempted correlation of these sequent archaeological phases of Palaeolithic humanity with the geological phases of the Great Ice Age. It is not remarkable if in the light of the knowledge of the similarity of physical conditions, say in the Continental England and Belgium of those days, Rutot should be able to suggest a correlation of his Strepyan implements with objects found in an ancient gravel on the ' 100-foot terrace ' of the Thames.

## A. Early Palaeolithic

Man when he is first known in Europe is already certainly man. The humanising of the ancestral form has been accomplished, although the product still bears many obvious marks of its lower estate. He is no longer *Pithecanthropus* ; he is *Homo*. The period is so remote that we cannot definitely say whether in the case of these earliest human bones we are dealing with Strepyan or Chellean man. Of his handicraft, however, there is undoubted evidence in the pre-Chellean or Strepyan type of implements found originally in Belgian valley deposits, especially at Strépy, a village to the west of Charleroi, and later elsewhere. These crudest and oldest of flint implements almost divulge the story of their manufacture, so unfinished and hesitating and dimly purposeful do they appear to be, as far as technique is concerned. Nevertheless they stand in evident serial relationship to those of the succeeding Early Palaeolithic cultures—thus suggesting that at any rate within this period of time we have

to deal in Europe with a more or less continuous population, whose efforts towards the improvement of their
handicraft resulted through incredibly long periods in the
more assured touch of the Chellean flintsman and the
finer finish of the Acheulean.

So far as actual remains are concerned, unequivocally
human, and probably the oldest human fossil bone yet
discovered, is the lower jaw described as the Mauer mandible.   It was found in October 1907 at a depth of 24·10
metres below the surface, in a sand-pit near the village of
Mauer, some 10 kilometres to the south-east of Heidelberg, and was fully described by Dr. Schoetensack in a
monograph [1] published the following year.   The stratum
in which the mandible came to light is considered to be
Early Pleistocene on the strength of other fossil remains
found in the same deposit, which included particularly
those of the Etruscan rhinoceros (*Rhinoceros etruscus*) and
the straight-tusked elephant (*E. antiquus*).   Rutot considers that the particular stratum corresponds to his
Eolithic Mafflian phase, just subsequent to the second or
Mindelian glacial phase.   The jaw is certainly human,
yet distinctive in the opinion of its first investigator in
that it surpasses all other known human remains in its
combination of primitive characters, so that it really
suggests a generalised type from which all jaws, ancient
and recent, can be readily derived.   The teeth are characteristically human, showing certain features, such as
enlarged pulp cavities, wide crowns, large bodies, and
diminished roots which relate the jaw closely to the
Neanderthal type, which is characteristic of the Mousterian period : on the other hand, the canine teeth are
even less tusk-like than in modern man.   These characters, further, with ' the wide and relatively short dental
arch, all point to a rough vegetable diet necessitating a
grinding rather than a cutting manner of mastication.' [2]
The enormous breadth of the ascending ramus or branch

[1] *Der Unterkiefer des Homo Heidelbergensis* (Leipzig, 1908).
[2] Sir A. Keith, *op. cit.* p. 239.

FIG. 9.—Sand-pit at Mauer, showing site (marked by white cross) of discovery of Heidelberg jaw. *a-b*, newer loess, probably of Third Interglacial; *b-c*, older loess, of close of Second Interglacial; *e-f*, the sands of Mauer; *d-e*, intermediate clay layer. (From H. F. Osborn's *Men of the Old Stone Age*.)

of the mandible—almost twice that of modern man—to which the muscles of mastication are ordinarily attached, indicates a masticatory system of quite unusual strength. Further, the body of the jaw is of unusual thickness, and there is practically no chin, or one that recedes in the same degree as in the apes. In other features the Mauer jaw shows the same peculiarities as Neanderthal man, although in a more marked and primitive degree. There are also indications of a rudimentary power of speech ; ' the large, shallow pit, always conspicuous on the inner face of the bony chin in the ape, is here nearly filled with a deposit of bone which rises into the characteristically human " genial tubercles " for the origin of the small muscles which help to work the tongue.' [1]

The second group of remains, collected at intervals of several years, but notably in 1912, from a gravel pit on the edge of Piltdown Common, Sussex, are those which have been dignified with the name of *Eoanthropus dawsoni*, in recognition of their discoverer, the late Mr. Charles Dawson.[2] The stratum in which they were found lay at a depth of less than four feet—unusually shallow in view of the suggested age of the deposit. As a matter of fact, however, the chronology of the bed is, as in the case of *Pithecanthropus*, a matter in dispute ; estimates based on the accompanying fossil remains oscillate between Pliocene and Lower Pleistocene. It is not questioned that some, though by no means all, of the animal remains found in the same stratum with the human are those of Pliocene forms, as *e.g.* the elephant Stegodon. What causes the uncertainty are the indications that these may have been washed down and out of some Pliocene bed by a greater Ouse than that which now flows, some eighty feet below the level of, but about a mile away from, the Common, and only secondarily deposited where they were found, in a bed that contains undoubtedly many typically Pleistocene fossils. Sir Arthur Keith, basing his opinion as

---

[1] A. Smith Woodward, *op. cit.* p. 26.
[2] Why a new generic name should have been given is not so obvious.

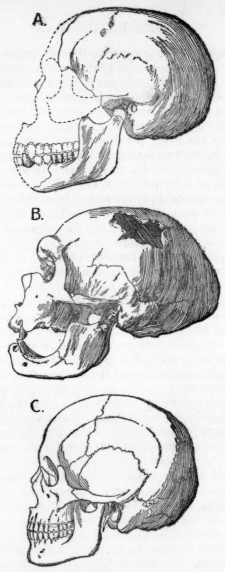

FIG. 10.—Left side view of (A) skull of *Eoanthropus*,
(B) Neanderthal (Mousterian) skull from La-Chapelle-
aux-Saints, and (C) modern human skull ($\frac{1}{4}$).   (From
British Museum Guide to the Fossil Remains of
Man ; by permission.)

an anatomist on the circumstance that ' in the Piltdown mandible the conformation is that of an ape,' [1] inclines very strongly to the Pliocene date. He considers that ' the Heidelberg mandible shows that the human contour of the chin had already appeared at the beginning of the Pleistocene, but a change of this kind has not become manifest in the Piltdown mandible.' [2] This might suggest that the Piltdown remains are older than the Mauer jaw, although this is open to dispute, but in default of absolute fixation of the date of the latter specimen it does not necessarily involve a Pliocene date for the former. Eoliths were found in the same stratum as the human remains, and, in the layer just above, implements that have been tentatively described as Chellean, as also part of an elephant's femur showing undoubted evidence of having been worked upon by the hand of man.

The fragments actually found were those of a skull— a part of the frontal bone, practically the whole of the left, and about two-thirds of the right parietal bones, which form the greater part of the roof and sides of the brain cavity, a considerable fragment of the occipital or posterior bone, almost the whole of the left temporal bone, which forms the side of the skull below the level of the brain cavity, and the two nasal bones. An immediate impression made by the examination of these particular bones is that of their extraordinary thickness, which is on an average about twice as great as that of the corresponding bones of a modern skull. In addition the almost complete right half of the mandible was recovered, showing, however, such remarkable simian features as compared with the skull, that several competent anatomists consider it more accurate to record the discovery of ' a,' rather than ' the,' mandible. It contains two molar teeth which are quite human in character, but shows a characteristic simian chin or rather lack of chin. The right upper canine tooth found later, which most probably belonged to the mandible, is of special interest

[1] *Op. cit.* p. 310.        [2] *Ibid.*

because while pointed and shaped as in anthropoid apes,
' its crown differs a little in shape from the canine of any
known ape, and agrees more closely with the temporary
(or milk-) canine of modern man,' [1] which is exactly what
might be expected in an ancestral form.    At the same
time, the circumstance that the mandible shows anthropoid characters which have never been previously found
in a human mandible, *e.g.* the strengthening ledge of bone
that unites the two halves on the inside, furnished the
reason why from the first occasion on which an account
of this historic find was made—at a meeting of the
Geological Society of London on December 18, 1912—
Professor Waterston maintained [2] that the mandible was
that of an anthropoid ape and did not belong to the skull,
a position which has also found the support of Boule,
Gregory, Osborn, and others.    It involves, however, the
difficult supposition that in closest association were found
the remains of the earliest known man and of the first ape
discovered in Britain.    In the opinion of Sir Arthur Keith,
who accepts the mandible as belonging to the skull, the
' humanisation ' of the Piltdown canine tooth had not
gone so far as in the case of the Mauer jaw.    In fact it
had just begun, whereas in the case of the Heidelberg
fossil it is complete.

The task of attempting to reconstruct the skull from
the available fragments has led to much ingenious experimenting, and the drawing of conclusions, some of
which are necessarily problematic.    At the same time,
there is now a fair measure of agreement that the cubic
content of the brain was about 1300 c.c.    The latest reconstruction by Professors Elliot Smith and Hunter gives
a capacity below 1300 c.c., and confirms Dr. Smith Woodward's opinion.    In this reconstruction ' the occipital
fragment assumes a more vertical position, with the effect
that the skull is brought into closer relation with the skull
of the anthropoids.    As a result the cranium falls into

---

[1] A. Smith Woodward, *op. cit.* p. 24.
[2] Cf. also *Nature*, 1913, vol. xcii. p. 319.

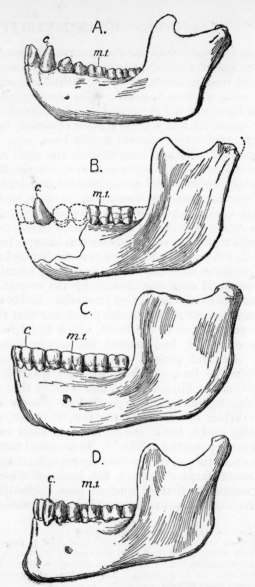

Fig. 11.—Left outer side view of lower jaw of (A) chimpanzee, (B) *Eoanthropus*, (C) Heidelberg man, and (D) modern man ($\frac{1}{2}$). c = canine tooth; m.1 = first molar tooth. (From British Museum Guide to the Fossil Remains of Man; by permission.)

complete harmony with the chimpanzee-like jaw.' [1]  This cubic content is equivalent to that of the smaller human brains of to-day, like that of the Australian aboriginal which rarely exceeds 1250 c.c., while the average for the modern European is 1480 c.c.   If the Piltdown individual was a female, for which there is some evidence, the corresponding male cubic content would have been roughly 100 c.c. more.   Viewed from behind, the skull is not so depressed from above downwards as either the Neanderthal or anthropoid skull (being shaped and balanced as in modern man), and shows other differences, such as the great thickness of the bones and the marked development of a forehead.   Further, it was distinctly brachycephalic.[2] The facial region as restored shows this unexpectedly high frontal development, a broad nasal formation as in certain primitive tribes of to-day, and a projecting muzzle whose sharpness is at once accentuated by the retreating chin and masked by the developed forehead.   In his study of the brain-cast, Sir Arthur Keith points out that the third frontal convolution of the brain, which is related to the faculty of speech, had reached the human standard so far as size and general conformation are concerned. ' Accordingly,' he concludes, ' we have grounds for believing that the Piltdown man had reached that point of brain development where speech had become a possibility.   When one looks at the jaw, however, and the projecting canine teeth, one hesitates to allow him more than a mere potential ability.' [3]   In essential features, so far as can be judged by this literally superficial and somewhat unsatisfactory method, the brain of *Eoanthropus* corresponded to that of modern man, although many primitive conditions are noticeable in the former.   Thus

---

[1] *Nature*, No. 2744, p. 726 (3rd June 1922)

[2] This term (=round or short-headed) is applied to races in which the average width of the skull is 80 per cent. of the length, or more. When the proportion is only 75 per cent. or less, the race is said to be dolichocephalic, *i.e.* long-headed.   The intermediate group is sometimes termed mesocephalic.

[3] *Op. cit.* p. 408.

Fig. 12.—Restoration of *Eoanthropus*, under the direction of Mons. Rutot. (By permission.)

*Page* 98.

in particular there was, in Professor Elliot Smith's words, ' a precocious expansion ' of the superior temporal area of the brain which is concerned with the appreciation of auditory symbolism. On the other hand, compared with the brain of modern man there was a deficiency in other areas—the prefrontal, upper parietals, and inferior temporals, concerned with the higher reaches of the human mind—which are gradually filled out in succeeding types.

Of Chellean or pre-Chellean man there are no other indisputable skeletal remains. Of his handiwork, which takes its name from the kind of flint implement first found in certain ancient deposits at Chelles in the valley of the Marne, some eight miles to the east of Paris, the most typical form is that which is still called by de Mortillet's original designation, the *coup-de-poing*, or hand-axe. This flint implement, which may be considered as a natural development of some of the Strepyan attempts, is generally shaped by chipping so as to be more or less sharp and pointed at the business end, while the other, which is held in the hand, is rounded and blunt. *Coups-de-poing* vary in shape, being oval, triangular, and lozenge-shaped. Normally they are some 3 to 4 inches in length, but specimens are known three times as large. There is no reason to suppose that they were attached to a wooden shaft, or employed as weapons. Their use was probably very general, the tool, like some modern successors, being axe, scraper, borer, knife, and saw, all in one. At the same time specialisation had already begun, since *coups-de-poing* fashioned more particularly to carry out one or other of these functions are also known. In default of flint, other local pebbles were employed. Perforated flints and shells have also been described from Chellean and Acheulean gravels, but whether these were worn as personal ornaments or magic charms it is impossible to say.

The Acheulean phase takes its name from St. Acheul near Amiens, in the valley of the Somme, in the gravel deposits of which, at the ' 100-foot terrace' level, Boucher de Perthes, local customs officer and antiquarian, discovered and recognised as human handiwork in 1846, the characteristic flint implements that now bear that designation. Although belonging to the same general types as Chellean implements, the Acheulean *coups-de-poing* are on the whole smaller in size. There is a certain fastidiousness and artistry in their manufacture, showing itself in greater regularity of fashioning. The Acheulean tool is a more finished implement, with more perfect lines in straightened edge or graceful screwlike curve—a distinct advance upon the Chellean predecessor. The more intensive study by the late Professor Commont of the stratified gravels on the four river terraces of the Somme, which have proved to contain a résumé of the whole history of the Palaeolithic Age, shows that the Early Acheulean type of *coup-de-poing* was oval with the greatest thickness in the middle, rather than at the butt end as in the Chellean type, and that the Late Acheulean type was triangular, long, and narrow. The transition to the Mousterian may even be traced in the introduction of a miniature triangular (*La Micoque*) *coup-de-poing* or scraper, often with secondary chipping along one side only, and in the distinctive Levallois scraper, which has been termed ' the parent of all the Mousterian tools.' [1] This characteristic rectangular flake, smooth on the surface which corresponds to that part of the nodule from which it was detached by a practised blow, and secondarily trimmed by chipping along one edge even before it was finally detached from the nodule, persists in varying modification throughout the Mousterian culture. Macalister states that ' there are comparatively few varieties of tools found in Acheulean deposits ; not so many, indeed, as appear to exist in Chellean strata. The reason probably is that the improvement in the manufacture of the *coup-de-poing* made it more and more the universal tool.' [2] So far as concerns human fossil remains from the Acheulean,

[1] Macalister, *op. cit.* p. 326.    [2] *Op. cit.* p. 239.

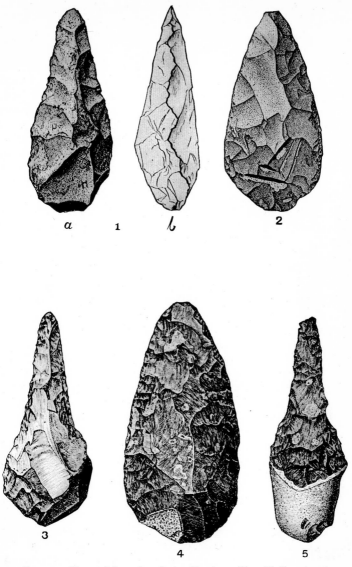

FIG. 13.—Types of Coup-de-poing or Hand-axe ($\frac{1}{3}$).  *Chellean* (1, 2) ;
1 *b* shows sinuous cutting edge of 1 *a*.  *Acheulean* (3-5) ; 4 and 5 preserve at the base portions of the original surface of the nodules.  (After
de Mortillet, from Geikie's *Antiquity of Man in Europe*.)

the only probable examples are the two teeth found at Taubach near Weimar in 1871, and the mandible found at Ehringsdorf in the same district in 1914.

Represented in most of Southern England, particularly in the basins of the Thames, Ouse, and ancient Solent, throughout France and Spain, in Italy and Sicily, and more scantily in the German plain and other parts of Europe, the Early Palaeolithic industries testify to a wide distribution of the population that worked them. Yet it must not be supposed that the configuration of these countries was that with which the modern map makes us familiar. To take but one example. In Chellean time the British Archipelago of to-day represented the more elevated areas of a north-western extension of the Continent. Caves such as Kent's Cavern by the seashore at Torquay were originally high up on the slopes of a well-watered valley, whose luxuriant vegetation attracted the herbivorous forms that were the prey of the cave bears and hyaenas whose bones, together with that of their victims, are found embedded in the cave floor. Thus the physical and organic history of the Southern England and North-Western France of these days was a common history, whose common fluctuations may be read alike on either side of the Channel river. That history is preserved, as we have seen, in the terraces on the banks of the Thames and Somme alike, each of the four terraces marking a stage in the gradual erosion of the beds of these rivers through Strepyan and pre-Chellean time from that greater height at which they stood in the beginning of the Pleistocene. This in the case of the Somme at Amiens was 170 feet, and of the Thames, 90 feet above the present level. Thereafter followed a period of depression of the land, and invasion of the Channel by the sea which invaded the valley of the Somme as far as Abbeville, submerging three of the terraces. In the alluvial deposits on the sides of the valley marking the height of the river's activity, and just below the level of the highest or first of the Chellean terraces, have been found the typical

Acheulean implements. This period of depression was in turn followed by a period of emergence, in keeping pace with which the Somme cut not merely through the Acheulean loams and the underlying terraces of gravel, but deeper into the rocky base of its bed. It is in the alluvia deposited on the lower re-emerging terraces through this age-long process that implements of Mousterian and then of Late Palaeolithic date are found. Thereafter at the close of the Pleistocene came again a period of submergence, resulting in the land level of to-day. Very similar, even to the number of gravel terraces, and the kind of implements found in them, is the correspondence that has been worked out in the history of the ancient banks and flood-levels of the once mile-broad Thames. It is in contemplating the amount of time required for a river to cut down its valley through a hundred feet, as for the whole series of slow oscillations of land surface as outlined above, that we begin to have some understanding of what is meant by geological time. Acheulean days probably commenced anywhere from 75,000 to 100,000 years ago.

With regard to the climate of the Chellean period in Europe, there can be little doubt from the indications of the fauna and flora preserved in the strata characterised by objects of that culture, that it was of a tropical and semi-tropical character. The presence of such forms as the hippopotamus, rhinoceros ($R. mercki$), straight-tusked elephant ($E. antiquus$), together with the great beaver ($Trogontherium cuvieri$), spotted hyaena ($H. crocuta$), and brown bear ($Ursus arctos$) leave little question upon the matter. As we work upwards into the Acheulean strata, the changing fauna and flora indicate a passage to a more temperate and genial climate, but towards the close of the Acheulean there is evidence of a change for the worse, heralding another advance of the ice-sheet, which took place during the Mousterian. The hippopotamus disappears from Europe, probably migrating along the land bridges into Africa ; the mammoth ($E. primigenius$) replaces the straight-tusked elephant (*E. antiquus*), and Merck's rhinoceros disappears before the woolly rhinoceros (*R. tichorinus*).

As we peer back into the mists of antiquity trying to reconstruct the life of man as we first know him, we catch only a few fugitive glimpses. We are aware of a being lower in every respect than any modern savage tribe, and yet widely removed from all these arrested or degenerate types because in him or his congeners lay the potentiality of the best to which man has attained to-day. He is nomadic in bent, wandering from district to district and earning the precarious livelihood of a fisherman and hunter. Probably he migrated into Europe from regions to the east, but he arrived as man. And from the beginning he was a social creature, living in his small temporary communities near the rivers, or inland sheets of water, or on the higher plateaux. The rivers provided him with water and fish, as also with guidance and, it may be, passage, through the forests. It was an open-air life, for his shelters can have been no more than the simplest structures compacted of branches and of skins. There is no evidence of agriculture or the domestication of animals : the art of the potter had not been discovered. Yet just because he was man, he could match his wits against the fierce strength of carnivores or the fleetness of herbivores, and trap where he could not directly engage. And just because he was man, the superlatively educable animal, he could learn and improve his methods and his handicraft.

It has been stated that man may well have entered Europe as an immigrant from the east. There is at any rate as yet no evidence to suggest that the previous phases of his evolution took place in Europe. The only skeletal remains from an earlier stage have been found in Asia. Of the other continents, North and South America and Australia have supplied nothing as yet of intrinsic importance to this earliest period of human development, nor from the theoretical point of view is it probable that they will.[1]   In North America there is considerable evidence to indicate that there was an Ice Age during the Pleistocene with phases of advance and retreat that corresponded to those that have been recognised in Europe.   It is quite certain also that the original North American Indian was the representative and descendant of a Mongolian people that reached that continent from Asia by way of a land connection over the Behring Straits.   As yet there has been no unequivocal discovery of human remains in any American interglacial deposit. That is to say, the peopling of North America has been essentially a post-glacial process even in its earliest phases, so far as we know, and the same is even more true of South America.   Africa, on the other hand, remains a land of alluring prospect in this connection, and it is highly probable that discoveries of the greatest importance, bearing on the origin and antiquity of the human race, will yet be made within this continental area.   It is not without sound reason that several investigators are inclined to look here for future elucidation of these problems. Thus two of the anthropoid apes have their home in west tropical Africa, although probably immigrants, as we have seen, from farther east.   Again, implements similar to those of the various cultural periods from the Chellean onwards have been described from the ancient river deposits, especially of South Africa, while, as we shall see, the suggested connection of the Aurignacians and Magdalenians with Africa, would demand some previous history for their antecedents there.   In physical structure African Bushmen and pygmy races show degrees of specialisation which must involve great racial antiquity.

[1] A tooth discovered in 1922 in a North American Upper Pliocene bed, and described by W. K. Gregory as belonging to an unknown genus whose ' nearest resemblances are with Pithecanthropus and with men rather than with apes,' may be the hindmost upper molar of a primitive bear (Smith Woodward).

## B. Middle Palaeolithic

In contrast with his predecessors, mid-Palaeolithic or Mousterian man stands out with greater distinctness ; the conditions of his life are also somewhat more reproducible. For this there are several reasons. The time distance is not so great, and accordingly the picture is more in focus. Further, the representatives may now be counted in dozens—some sixty in all—even if a complete skeleton is still a rarity. The period, which probably began some fifty thousand years ago and lasted half that spell, derives its name from the discoveries originally made as long ago as 1863 in the Le Moustier cave, near the village of Les Eyzies on the right bank of the Vézère in the Dordogne region of France. For Mousterian man was typically a troglodyte, driven to cave life owing to the increasing cold and damp as a fresh glacial epoch swept on, whose testing inquisition he does not seem to have survived. In any case such a life, more settled indeed, but under social and sanitary conditions which cannot have been as healthy as these of the earlier nomadic life, resulted in degeneration of physical type and handicraft.

While distinctive Mousterian flints have been found at various points in England, such as the brick-earths at Crayford in the Thames valley, at Ipswich and near Mildenhall in Suffolk, associated in the first case with the typical fauna of mammoth (*E. primigenius*), the lion (*Felis leo*), different species of rhinoceros, the musk ox (*Ovibos moschatus*), and the lemming (*Myodes*), all bearing witness to cold conditions, no remains of Mousterian man himself have as yet been found. They are, however, well represented on the Continent. In particular, the skeleton exposed by M. O. Hauser in 1908, some five feet below the floor of another cave on a terrace behind the town of Le Moustier in the Vézère Valley, made it possible, by the comparative completeness of the remains, to establish beyond all doubt the existence of a distinct type now known as Mousterian or Neanderthal man, which almost certainly diverged into a line that ended with itself and did not develop into any modern human race. In this particular instance the body, which had been that of a lad of some sixteen summers, was deliberately buried, having been laid on its right side, with the right hand under the head, which in turn was cushioned on a pillow composed of chippings of flint. Charred remains of the urus or wild ox (*Bos primigenius*) were found beside the skeleton, suggesting a funeral feast, together with typical Mousterian implements. About the same time (1908) in a small cave on the side of the valley of the Sourdoire, another tributary of the Dordogne, near the village of La Chapelle-aux-Saints in the department of Corrèze, a similar Mousterian or Neanderthal skeleton was found three feet below the surface with bones of the woolly rhinoceros (*R. tich.*), reindeer (*Rangifer tarandus*), bison (*Bison priscus*), cave hyaena (*H. spelaea*), and marmot (*Arctomys marmotta*). The body had been laid upon its back in a prepared grave, with the head to the west, protected by an arrangement of flat stones, and with flexed legs and arms. Remains of part of the leg and foot bones of a wild ox—a food supply for ' the great adventure '—with numerous Mousterian flints lay beside the body : evidently for Mousterian man this life was not the end of the story. An individual of perhaps some forty years of age,[1] he exhibited the outstanding Neanderthal features — the beetling apelike supra-orbital ridges, the massive jaws, low retreating forehead and chin, and projecting occipital region — that made Huxley describe the type-skull in 1863 as ' the most pithecoid of human crania yet discovered.'[2] On the other hand, he had a brain that was normal in that all the parts were represented, yet with a cubic capacity of 1625 c.c., at least 175 c.c. above the modern average.

---

[1] Keith, *op. cit.* p. 118.
[2] *Evidence as to Man's Place in Nature*, p. 156.   In Lyell's *Antiquity of Man*, p. 84, Huxley is quoted as calling it ' the most brutal of all known human skulls.'

While he was small (5 feet 4 inches), like all men of the Neanderthal race, his forearm and leg, unlike that of the apes and other ancient and modern races, were relatively short, compared with the upper arm and thigh. Study of the brain-cast suggested to Professors Boule and Anthony a human brain retaining simian traits, yet showing a degree of organisation that corresponded to a mentality far in advance of the ape, if patently below that of modern man. These remains, together with the skeletons of a man, woman, and two children—a family burial—discovered (1909-1911) in a rock shelter at La Ferrassie, also in the Vézère Valley, and the skeleton exposed in 1911 at La Quina in the department of Charente immediately to the north-west of the Dordogne region, tend to show that the whole of this area was inhabited in Mousterian time by Neanderthal man ; for Neanderthal man is essentially Mousterian, and Mousterian man almost without exception is Neanderthal in physical type.

To the same horizon are now referred, in addition to other incomplete remains in France, the famous Gibraltar skull, which as found there in the Forbes Quarry in 1848, although unrecognised till long afterwards, was actually the first Neanderthal skull to be discovered : as also the remains, principally teeth, found in 1910 at Saint-Brélade in the Island of Jersey, which was a part of the Continent in Mousterian times. In Belgium the Naulette mandible—that of a woman, a supposition maintained also in the case of the Piltdown and Gibraltar remains—found in 1866 in a cave floor at a depth of 14 feet below the surface, together with remains of the mammoth (*Elephas primigenius*), woolly rhinoceros (*R. tich.*), cave bear (*Ursus spelaeus*), reindeer (*Rangifer tarandus*), and Mousterian implements, as also the two skeletons found in 1886 at a depth of $12\frac{1}{2}$ feet in a terrace in front of the Spy cave, 8 miles east of Namur, are also confidently placed in this period because of their marked Neanderthal characteristics. In some respects the Spy forms show an advance on the average Mousterian.

The Neanderthal type-skull, found with other bones of the skeleton, at a depth of 5 feet, in a cave on the left side of the valley of the Düssel near Elberfeld in Germany in the year 1857, may have been washed or have fallen into the cave, which seems from Lyell's diagram to have had more than one entrance, for no animal or cultural remains, the tooth of a bear excepted, appear to have been recorded along with it. On the other hand, at this early date, various fossil remains may not have been recognised as such by the labourers who were quarrying there. Several other fragments, particularly the mandibles from Malarnaud and Shipka, and the two teeth found in 1917 in a cave in Malta, would fall to be included in any full account of Mousterian osseous remains. A reference must also be made to the remarkable series of deposits, showing nine different levels marked by human occupation, in a rock shelter at Krapina in Croatia, investigated by Kramberger during six years from 1899 onwards. Remains of at least a dozen individuals were associated with some two thousand fragments of bones of Merck's Rhinoceros,[1] the wild ox or urus (*Bos primigenius*), mammoth, and other forms, all of which had been articles of diet, the bones in some cases having been split to secure the marrow. The fact that many of the human bones have been broken across in a way to which there is nothing comparable in any other Palaeolithic deposit, has been, perhaps without sufficient warrant, interpreted as evidence of cannibal practices. Especially instructive were the skulls of children, showing a greater likeness to modern children than did the adult skeleton to the skeleton of modern man. In the case of Neanderthal man, as in the case of modern apes, the characteristically simian massive eyebrow ridges are adult, and not adolescent, features. Further, some of these Krapina men and women, while definitely Neanderthal, apparently had brachycephalic (round-headed) skulls. Ordinarily the Neanderthal skulls

---

[1] The presence of this form leads some authorities to refer the principal Krapina deposits to the Acheulean phase.

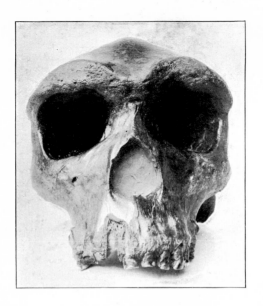

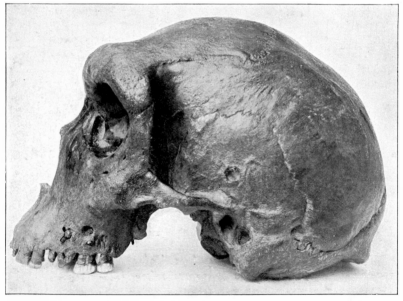

FIG. 15.—Front and left side views of skull of Rhodesian Man, showing large face with prominent brow-ridges; (about ½). (From British Museum Guide to the Fossil Remains of Man; by permission.)

are dolichocephalic, but the Gibraltar specimen is inter-mediate. There was thus a certain range of skeletal variation in Mousterian times such as we continue to have to-day—perhaps also a wider area of distribution than we have as yet discovered.

Especially is this seen to be the case if expert opinion proves to be right in considering the remains found in 1921 at the Broken Hill Mine in Northern Rhodesia to be connected with the Neanderthal type. The bones con-sist of parts of the skeletons of two individuals—a nearly complete skull, tibia (shin-bone), and two ends of a femur (thigh-bone) of one individual, and part of the upper jaw and shaft of the femur of a slightly smaller individual : a sacrum or basal part of the vertebral column may belong to either.[1] The bones have a remarkably fresh appearance but were largely encrusted with tiny crystals of silicate of zinc. The skull is characterised by the uniquely large size of its very simian face, as by the prominent supra-orbital ridges which extend unusually far out at the external lateral angles above gaping quadrangular orbits, so reminiscent in this particular of the Gibraltar skull. Dr. Smith Woodward notes the inflation of the maxillary bones, which are indented in the modern skull, as another apelike characteristic. The size of the face comes especi-ally from its great depth, which is brought about by an unusual lengthening in the maxillary region below the nose-opening. This in turn is supported by an abnorm-ally large palate. The human teeth met in the primitive edge-to-edge bite. The skull, which was poised on an erect skeleton and does not show the occipital protuber-ance and depressed character of a typical Neanderthal skull, is dolichocephalic, with an estimated brain capacity of about 1280 c.c. The brain was primitive, and un-developed in those particular areas already referred to as concerned with attention, the finer sensory discrimina-tions, and the more delicate manipulations. In fact,

[1] A. Smith Woodward, ‘The Problem of the Rhodesian Fossil Man,’ *Science Progress*, vol. xvi. No. 64.

Professor Elliot Smith considers that the cranial casts of *Pithecanthropus, Eoanthropus, Homo rhodesiensis* (which he is on this account more inclined to consider as an off-shoot from *Homo heidelbergensis*) and *Homo Neanderthalensis* show a progressive advance in the gradual expansion and filling out of the prefrontal, upper parietal, and inferior temporal areas of the cortex. This represents a very great range of development in the human brain within the long period covered by the history of man himself, and it is a remarkable demonstration of the inherent truth of the evolutionary account of man, that in the development of the brain of the individual child, the last three areas to come into existence are precisely the three instanced above as having been the latest developments in the history of the race. In other features the skull suggests the modern Australian type ; the limb bones are quite modern. The fact that the brow-ridges are more markedly developed in *Homo rhodesiensis* than in Neanderthal man suggests that the former is a later, although related, form. For in many animal species such skeletal excrescences have proved to be a premonitory symptom of racial extinction.

Neanderthal man, as we have already seen in part, had many distinctive structural features, but in almost every respect he was more primitive than modern man. The low, depressed, thick skull, with its exaggerated facial region, seems almost an outgrowth from the short, powerful neck. Above the broad nasal bones were unusually large, round eye-sockets. While the skull contained a brain whose size (which involves, however, no necessarily corresponding quality of texture) was on the average greater than that of modern man, yet in conformation that brain was suggestively anthropoid : the skull was also, as in the apes, set further forward on the top of the vertebral column than in modern man. Again, it is only in the skull of the chimpanzee and gorilla that we find to-day the corresponding development, which was less prominent in females, of eyebrow ridges and retreating forehead.

These ridges were directly concerned with the muscular strength of the broad massive jaw.  The absence or rudimentary state of the chin is likewise simian, as also various other anatomical details, particularly those in the structure of the mandible, which point to a comparatively low degree of mobility of the tongue.  With sturdy legs, short in proportion to the cumbrous body, he probably progressed with something between a crouch and a slouch.  In fact, as Sir Arthur Keith puts it, ' The great majority of those structural features which mark Neanderthal species off from modern races are essentially of a simian or anthropoid nature. . . . Every bone of the skeleton has its distinctive or specific characters.' [1]  This does not mean, however, that modern man possesses no simian physical characteristics in a greater degree than Neanderthal man. The contrary is the fact, and in the case of the very distinctive Neanderthal type of tooth, it is the extreme degree of specialisation and unlikeness to the simian and modern types alike in respect of the shortness of the roots and development of the pulp cavity, as also the size of the teeth and the width of the palate, that lead Keith, Klaatsch, Boule, and other authorities to speak of Neanderthal man as ' a distinct and extinct species of man,' perhaps, also, vegetarian.  There is at any rate no question that Neanderthal man presents physical differences from modern man greater than the differences between the most divergent of modern human races, and that it is not possible to find any forms in the subsequent periods that link him with any modern types.  To maintain, however, that he was a distinct species in the recognised sense of that term would require a proof of the only (although by no means absolute) test of species, viz. cross-sterility, which is unobtainable.  On the other hand, there is no basis for dogmatic statements of any kind based on a supposed organic unity of the human race.

Mousterian culture, so far as it is represented in implements, we have already seen to be summarised in a de-

---

[1] *The Antiquity of Man*, pp. 144, 157.

velopment of the Levallois scraper.   Along with this goes a decline in the importance of the *coup-de-poing*.   On the whole, however, there is not the general advance in technique and range of invention that might naturally have been expected in so long and well-defined a period as the Mousterian.   This may in part be explained by the repressive harshness of the climate and the gradual decline of the race.   At the same time, this does not mean that Mousterian implements are simply copies of Acheulean types.   There is some evidence of industrial evolution, but it is in the direction of ' an economy of labour,' [1] as if man were living in conditions in which the struggle for existence had become physically intensified, and he had no wish to do more than was absolutely necessary. Thus there is neither the same artistic feeling or workmanship in the finish of the average Mousterian implement : it is also distinguishable from its Acheulean forerunner in being chipped on one side of the flake only. The outer surface shows the impression of the flakes that have been removed in chipping ;   the inner surface is smooth except for the peculiar ' bulb of percussion ' which arises, owing to certain physical qualities of flint, immediately below the point at which the blow separating the implement from the original nodule was directed. Sharply-pointed *coups-de-poing*, perhaps used for splitting bones to get out the marrow, side-scrapers for service in the preparation of skins, with varieties showing a scraping edge now on both sides, now at one end rather than on the side—the latter a late Mousterian development— notched scrapers possibly for smoothing rounded wooden shafts, primitive saws and borers in flake form, and implements so delicately chipped at a definite part as to suggest that they may have been employed in some kind of primitive engraving on wood or bone, are some of the more characteristic types of Mousterian tool.   As the period develops, there is seen to be a growing preponder-

[1] Bourlon, ' L'industrie moustérienne au Moustier,' quoted in Macalister, *op. cit.* p. 316.

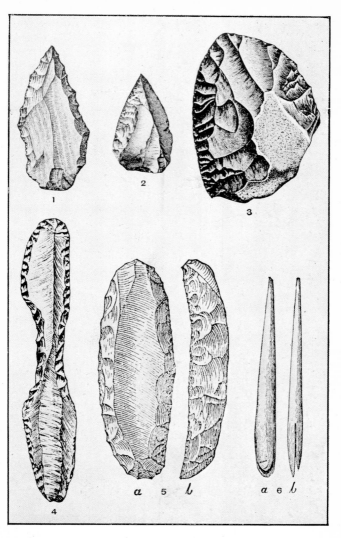

FIG. 16.—Types of Mousterian and Aurignacian Implements. *Mousterian*, 1 and 2, points ; 3, side scraper. *Aurignacian*, 4, notched flake ; 5, double-edged scraper ; 6, bone implement. (After de Mortillet and Breuil, from Geikie's *Antiquity of Man in Europe*.)

ance of cutting, over other kinds of, implements, and the use of bone begins to be general, not at first in a direct way, so to speak, for its own sake, but rather as a means in the manufacture or perfecting of implements of other material. Thus bones of the lower extremities of horses and oxen seem from their general character and the scratches on them to have been used as anvils on which wooden implements were pared down with flints. A scraper with a curved beak anticipates a type of implement that was developed in Aurignacian times and persisted into Mesolithic days.

With an even wider, and, on the whole, richer distribution in Europe than that of Early Palaeolithic culture, Northern France and South Britain excepted, Mousterian man makes the problem of his complete disappearance only the harder to understand. The fauna by which he is surrounded testifies eloquently to the fact that the Mousterian lived through the climax of a glacial phase. The woolly rhinoceros (*R. tichorinus*) and the mammoth (*Elephas primigenius*) with its coat of fur, have supplanted the broad-nosed rhinoceros (*R. mercki*) and the straight-tusked elephant (*E. antiquus*). The reindeer (*Rangifer tarandus*), new to Central Europe, the Saiga antelope (*Saiga tatarica*), the Arctic fox (*Canis lagopus*), the glutton (*Gulo borealis*), and the invasion of Europe as far west as the Thames Valley by small rodents from Siberia and Eastern Europe like the lemmings (*Myodes torquatus* and *obensis*) and different species of voles (*Arvicola*) are evidence of a radical change of fauna which with the accompanying change in flora meant a long, slow process of substitution. All these changing conditions of the physical environment reacted, on the whole, unfavourably on the representatives of humanity in those days.

The attempt to reconstruct the social and mental life of the Mousterian period would seem therefore to have something of the element of tragedy about it. But it is not unrelieved. We are now dealing with a people whom climatic conditions forced into the shelter of caves, in the mouths of which they seem to have lived their residential life. Such small communities may be supposed to have developed a higher social system than that, if any, which characterised the previous nomadic phase. At any rate there is evidence of advance in certain lines. Mousterian man assuredly knew the use of fire ; he buried his dead ; he believed in a hereafter. He is, in short, not merely a reasonable, but clearly a religious, being.

It is outside the purpose of this work to attempt to enter upon the vexed question of the origin of religion,[1] but it is worth while to try and picture to ourselves some of the elements in this particular phase of human history, which probably had a share in developing the religious feeling and belief of which we now find certain definite expressions. Examination of brain-casts of the interior of Mousterian skulls, although a method of approach with very definite limitations, leads, as we have seen, to the suggestion that while the organ is distinctively human, the marked simian traits indicate a degree of organisation and development not yet that of modern man. The cubic content may exceed that of modern man, but the intellectual capacity is more nearly that of a child of five. Yet we have spoken of man as the religious creature, and can form a tolerably intelligible picture of the conditions of Mousterian life under which this higher sensitivity developed, aided by recollection of that stage in our own early experience when we feared to go along certain creaky passages in a gloomy castle, or take a particular pathway in the twilight through a wood that skirted a mysterious-looking pond. Watching, from the mouth of his cave habitation high up on the side of the valley, the play of the elements as lightning shivered the trees below him and the thunder-crash accompanied the torrential rains, Mousterian man must have felt himself in the presence

[1] Cf. R. R. Marett, *The Threshold of Religion*, and Th. Mainage, *Les Réligions de la Préhistoire*.

of Powers that he did not understand, and which, just because he did not understand them, mystified and even terrified him. It was natural for the mind of primitive man to think of everything that showed signs of movement—be it animate or inanimate as we understand these terms to-day—as invested with a power of independent activity, to think of it as informed by a spirit such as he was assured of in himself as he reflected upon his dream life, almost as real to him as his waking life, or pondered on the significance of his shadow. Later, reflection probably on calamities caused him to wonder whether certain courses of action were not perhaps attended by misfortune, whether certain things should or should not be done. He felt increasingly that his life had some kind of relation to these Powers, that he was not alone in the world. Convictions arose—for which in many cases no very clear reason could have been given, beyond a vague association of some supernatural wonder-working power (*mana*) which might be set in motion against him—that certain places should be avoided, certain objects should not be touched, certain things should not be done—in short, that whole restrictive, and, as it happened, disciplinary conception of life, which is involved in *tabu*. They became the convictions of the community, matters of group and later of tribal responsibility, in which infraction of a prohibition involved the group along with the individual. And as these Powers or spirits, growingly personalised and more definitely localised, impressed him as the result of his experience with their capacity to assist him or to harm him, it became a necessity of existence to earn the goodwill of the one, or ward off or placate the hurtful intentions of the other. Hence arose the whole conception of ritual in its endeavours to conciliate, perhaps even to control, these Powers. The setting apart of a share of a feast developed into sacrifice. Once again, the maker of flint implements, knowing himself as such, must at an early stage of reflection have striven to make clear to himself Who in turn made the flint nodules, the rocks, the trees, the myriad forms of animal life around him.

The most objective evidence of the religious beliefs of Mousterian man is connected with the burial of his dead. The facts seem to express a belief in some sort of a future existence that was a continuation of the present. Food was placed beside the traveller—for only slowly did the spirit extricate itself from its tenement of clay—and his flint implements and ornaments, or it may be the most prized ones of those who were his friends, were buried with him ; he would have need of them.[1] The interest becomes evidence of real affection when we consider how, as at La Ferrassie, flat stones had been laid over the head and shoulders as if to protect them, and in the case of the youth buried at Le Moustier, the head had been laid on a pillow of flint chippings. In the case of the interment at La Chapelle-aux-Saints a hearth, from its position in relation to the grave, inevitably suggests burial rites and a funeral feast, in which the dead was believed to take a part. But in other cases, possibly for reasons similar to those on account of which men are loved or disliked to-day, there is evidence which may be interpreted as a desire to put the dead man out of sight as quickly as possible. And this may very easily have passed over into fear of the power of his spirit to return and work evil. Often the Mousterian dead were buried in a trussed sort of fashion, with the knees drawn up tightly under the chin, and it is supposed that the corpse may even have been bound with leathern thongs in that position in an endeavour to hamper the movements of the departed, and prevent him coming back to molest his enemies. There are no positive indications at this stage of a worship of the dead, still less that burial was accorded to all.

What exactly were the conditions under which the conviction of a possible hereafter entered the mind of man we have no means of knowing. In a moving passage Macalister dwells on the rigour of Mousterian life ' passed in gloomy and awe-inspiring caves, which resounded with

---

[1] Not the actual implements themselves, of course, but their ' shadow-souls.'

the flutterings of bats and with the shrieks of owls ' as an element in inevitably turning the thoughts of the Mousterians to the terrors of the Unseen. ' The cave-folk went to sleep as night fell, and awoke on the following day ; but one by one they would fall into a different kind of sleep, from which they could not be aroused. Then the survivors would ask of one another the question of questions, which has passed down ever since from graveside to graveside through the generations—*if a man die, shall he live again ?* As they sat round the fires and discussed this momentous problem, one would tell of a dream that he had had, in which the dead had appeared to him ; another would relate how something, he knew not what, but which surely was not of the common things of nature, had startled him when he was wandering abroad in the gloom of the forest. With the weird dancing shadows cast by the fire on the rocky wall of their cave, with the wild noises of nocturnal nature all around them, small wonder that they found to their question an affirmative answer. Already even the lowly Mousterian Man, degenerate though he may have been, was conscious of something more than merely animal within him : already he had begun to look forward to a life beyond the grave—a life like that to which he was accustomed, for he could conceive of none other, where he would need food and clothing, and the instruments for procuring them. As his comrades passed, each in his turn, into the silent land, he laid beside their bodies such things as he imagined would minister to their necessities in the mysterious otherworld.

' How far that otherworld was conceived of as being governed by beings more than human, we have no means of knowing. But it would seem psychologically scarcely possible for a community to imagine an entirely atheistic otherworld. The " gods " may be men, beasts, insects, monsters, what you will : but we may reasonably look upon Mousterian man as being, within the inevitable limitations of our knowledge, the first seeker after God.' [1]

[1] *Op. cit.* pp. 343, 344.

It is a startling thought that mayhap to the dying Mousterian race came the first glimmerings of immortality. On the objective facts Macalister is right in maintaining that Mousterian man was ' the first seeker after God.' But we must not forget that he was directly connected with previous stages of humanity whose mental capacity, so far as the uncertain methods of judging of it teach us, was not very far below that of the Mousterian. Chellean man was man, and if the cubic capacity of a Mousterian brain was over 1600 c.c., yet that of *Eoanthropus* was about 1400, corresponding, if a female skull, to a male capacity of about 1550 c.c. It is probably the case that in the open-air nomadic life of the Chellean and Acheulean periods, man may have disposed of his dead more unconcernedly, leaving them unburied as he moved on in the morning to a new hunting-ground, or covering them simply with boughs and leaves. The more settled life of the Mousterian community may have induced more thought upon life and the dead from whom they could not get away. But wherever he is, man cannot get away from his thoughts, and the probability seems to be that at whatever stage he first began to reflect—at whatever stage he began first, intermittently doubtless, to wonder at the things he did not understand, and that stage was certainly long pre-Mousterian—he had begun to move towards the conception of a Power or Powers in the world other than himself which stood in some sort of determining relation to him, and of himself as possessed by an invisible form of being which might persist apart from his body. In short, Archaeology does not gainsay the suggestion that from the beginning of rational, *i.e.* of human, life, God ' set eternity ' [1] and some knowledge of Himself, in the heart of man.

[1] Eccles. 3 [11].

# CHAPTER VI

## PALEOLITHIC MAN (*continued*)

### C. Late Palaeolithic

#### (i) *Aurignacian*

WE have stated that the application of distinct names to the different systems of the geological eras, as to the various phases of Palaeolithic culture, is apt to suggest a discontinuity, comparable to that represented by the use of these separate words, which does not exist in reality. To this as to all such statements there are exceptions, one of which meets us at the close of the Mousterian. The Aurignacian cultural strata lie immediately above the former, distinctive in actual human remains and implements, and without the requisite evidence in the way of transitional forms that would imply continuity of development. We saw reason to believe that under the stress of climatic adversity, the insanitary conditions of cave life, and possibly, as has also been suggested, the effects of inbreeding in these small communities, a racial deterioration set in, and that in consequence the debilitated Mousterians were unable to withstand the irruption of a new population who entered Europe with a civilisation of their own. It was perhaps the first example of a situation that has recurred at different periods in history. How far the Aurignacians carried on an actual war of extermination against the Mousterians we do not know. Suffice it to say that the latter with their well-marked characteristics disappeared as a race, and no people can be confidently indicated who can be looked on as their evolutionary descendants.  At the same time, there are suggestions in the blended types discovered at Predmost in Moravia that possibly at a later stage some of the invaders and the last of the Mousterians may have become reconciled.

But who were the Aurignacians, and whence did they come ?  The question may help in its own solution if we proceed to the examination of Aurignacian human remains and handicraft, but it can only be tentatively answered even after consideration of the Late Palaeolithic phase as a whole.  Now, as a matter of fact, it is Aurignacians who were the first Palaeolithic people to be discovered, for to this stage, on the basis of the flint implements and the ornaments and implements in ivory and bone, are referred the very imperfect skeleton found by Dean Buckland in 1822 in the Paviland Cave, South Wales, the Engis skull of 1833, and, most important of all, the corresponding but fuller collection of objects found by Edouard Lartet in 1860 in the floor of a cave on the side of a hill near the village of Aurignac in Haute Garonne. There at a depth of two to three feet he found evidence of the association of man with the cave bear (*Ursus spelaeus*), cave lion (*Felis spelaea*), cave hyaena (*H. spelaea*), mammoth (*Elephas primigenius*), woolly rhinoceros (*R. tich.*), bison (*B. priscus*), and Irish elk (*Cervus giganteus*), together with modern forms, which had all been used by him in different ways for food and ornamentation and tool formation.  In these three localities the same kind of touch was noticeable in the handicraft, fashioning the same ideas—tools of flint, carvings in ivory, necklaces of shells or perforated teeth, implements in ivory and bone or the antlers of reindeer.  Eight years passed, however, before Louis Lartet discovered four adult skeletons in a rock shelter at Cromagnon in the valley of the Vézère (Dordogne), which the associated cultural remains showed to be referable to the now established Aurignacian phase. They were tall individuals (5 feet 10 inches and over), with large skulls whose brain capacity was also considerably above the modern average.[1] This is a remarkable circumstance, even if we know on other grounds that a man's intellectual qualities bear no relation to the size of his hat. We are evidently dealing with a highly developed race, and it is worthy of notice that within the period of time from the Aurignacian to the present day—say twenty-five thousand years—there has been no advance in cranial cubic content. On the other hand, in the Aurignacian period there is, further, evidence of a very wide range of diversity in cranial cubic content and other features that leads Sir Arthur Keith to state that 'at Cromagnon . . . we meet with another race of men.' [2] Of the four adult skeletons, one of them, usually referred to as 'the Old Man of Cromagnon,' is probably better known than any other individual in Archaeology: at any rate, more is known of him. The skull was markedly dolichocephalic, with a cranial capacity which is usually given as 1590 c.c.[3] The cheek-bones were particularly prominent, the orbits rectangular rather than round, though with rounded angles. There were no supra-orbital ridges, and the nose and chin were well developed.

One of the best Aurignacian sites is the Grimaldi series of caves, near Mentone, close to the shore of the Mediterranean, about 200 yards on the eastern side of the Franco-Italian frontier. A small museum has been erected in the immediate vicinity, in which many of the discoveries are systematically exposed. The cave deposits are Aurignacian throughout, and their great interest is that the skeletons of sixteen individuals of widely different ages have been found at the various levels. In the Grotte des Enfants there were 31 feet of deposits, throughout which at different levels as many as nine ancient hearth floors were exposed : of these the two lowest were Early or Middle Palaeolithic. Associated with these

---

[1] 1480 c.c.       [2] *The Antiquity of Man*, p. 54.
[3] Keith's estimate of this (?) Cromagnon brain is 1660 c.c. (*The Antiquity of Man*, p. 55) about 180 c.c. above the modern average, and seems the more likely, if that of 1550 c.c. for a female subject amongst the same group of four is correct.

deposits were ornaments and implements in stone and bone, together with remains of the typical fauna brought to light in the original Aurignacian station—cave lion (*Felis spelaea*), cave bear (*Ursus spelaeus*), and cave hyaena (*H. spelaea*). The woolly rhinoceros (*R. tich.*) and the mammoth (*Elephas primigenius*) had apparently not come so far south, but in the lowest stratum were the remains of even older forms, the broad-nosed rhinoceros (*R. mercki*) and the straight-tusked elephant (*E. antiquus*). It looks as if the caves had been first inhabited towards the onset of a glacial episode.

All the skeletons showed unmistakable evidence of having been definitely buried. Indeed, in the case of an old woman whose remains lay in the second stratum from the top, there was evidence to suggest that the body had been scraped up by hyaenas, carried off, recovered and reburied, thus showing incidentally a notable development of regard for the dead on the part of her contemporaries. The two young children from whom the cave took its name had been interred in the top stratum, laid on their backs with their heads to the west, apparently having been buried in some kind of mantle or apron composed of seashells. At the fourth level from the bottom the skeleton of a very tall man of this Cromagnon race (6 feet 2½ inches) was unearthed, also lying on his back, with a slab of red sandstone under his head, and a flat stone over it for protection, while large stones were grouped around his feet. His body had been decorated and his head crowned with garlands or ornaments composed, at any rate in part, of shells, while a worked piece of a deer's antler lay close by. At the third level from the bottom, over 25 feet beneath the surface, two other skeletons were found, one of a woman and (possibly) her son of about sixteen years, but in their case the skeletons lay drawn up in a contracted posture. In both cases the head was protected by a slab of stone resting on two others ; and the bodies had been decorated with ornaments composed probably of a leathern ground covered with perforated shells. These skeletons showed definite negroid features. While it is possible to make too much of these characters —for it is a very questionable procedure to posit a race on the basis of two individuals—one of which indeed is apparently common to all the known Aurignacian skeletons, it is interesting to note this degree of differentiation within a race so far back in the Palaeolithic. It may have been the result of a mixture of races. The remains from the other Grimaldi caves add very little that is distinctive to our knowledge, other than the fact that the bones of the skeletons were sometimes treated with an ochreous powder which stained them red : possibly the Grimaldi people also painted the living body. There was, further, a certain variety in the design and composition of the tiaras, and head and neck bands with which the dead were decorated, as also of the flint implements occasionally buried with them.

To the same period has been referred the Brünn skeleton[1] found (1891) in the vicinity of typical Aurignacian cultural and faunal remains at a depth of 11½ feet in the town of that name, somewhat puzzling in its combination of Middle and Late Palaeolithic characters, as also the even more aberrant skeleton brought to light by the exploratory work of M. O. Hauser in 1909 on a terrace high up on the side of a valley at Combe Capelle in the Dordogne region. At a depth of over seven feet, beneath strata showing evidence of Solutrean and widely separated phases of Aurignacian culture, the latter remains were found definitely buried, with the thighs drawn up, and with an abundance of flints and perforated shells beside them. Unlike the Cromagnon variety of Aurignacian man, the Combe Capelle skeleton was that of a short man (5 feet 2 inches) with a long skull and narrow face, having a cranial capacity (1440 c.c.) slightly under the modern average. Whether the peculiarities are individual or racial it is impossible to say. The fact that the Cromagnon

[1] So *e.g.* Boule. Other investigators refer it to the subsequent Solutrean.

people had ' dysharmonic ' heads like the Esquimaux of to-day, *i.e.* showing the unusual combination of dolicho-cephaly (long-headedness) with a broad face, has sug-gested to some anatomists that they had their origin in a blend, and that this true dolichocephalic individual—for there was nothing to distinguish him from many Europeans of to-day—may represent a reversion to one of the parent types.[1]

The general aspect of the fauna found in the lowest stratum of the type station at Aurignac was still markedly that of a glacial episode, and there is evidence of a regular invasion of Europe, as we have also seen, by small Arctic rodents at the close of the Mousterian and the beginning of the Aurignacian phase. As the latter progressed through tundra to steppe conditions, these rodents dis-appeared, and the reindeer, mammoth, and woolly rhinoceros went with them. The most distinctive repre-sentative of the Aurignacian fauna in Europe is the horse, testifying to the steppe conditions of physical geography and climate which were the dominant features of that phase.

The Aurignacian industry is sometimes divided into three stages—Lower, Middle, and Upper. The physical distinctiveness of Cromagnon man as compared with his Mousterian predecessor, the mental development implicit in the pictorial craft of this phase, and the absence of any really transitional forms of implement compel archae-ologists to regard various Mousterian types of side-scraper, point, and *coup-de-poing* exposed in some Lower Aurig-nacian stations as actual Mousterian implements found by the invaders in some old Mousterian site occupied by them, and used, perhaps occasionally duplicated, by them. But in addition the Aurignacians had their own tools, amongst which may be mentioned the so-called Châtelperron knife —a flake with one side secondarily chipped on a curve ending in a sharp point, while the opposite side remains sharp and straight, with the butt usually rounded—various

[1] See Macalister, *op. cit.* pp. 359, 360.

kinds of end-scrapers, and engravers with which Aurignacian man fashioned and engraved his most characteristic implements of bone and horn, more rarely, ivory.
Bone in fact is more characteristic of the Late Palaeolithic than stone, although in the Lower Aurignacian the
development has not got past prickers—some of them
looking like the most primitive of bodkins—and other
flat slips of bone whose purpose is more obscure, and to
which the general name of ' polishers ' has been given.
The Middle Aurignacian is distinguished by the development of a thick type of end-scraper, which from its general
resemblance to an inverted boat is spoken of as ' carinate,'
certain peculiar knife-like flakes with a notch on one or
both sides, many types of engraver, and a finer and smaller
variety of the Châtelperron knife known as the Gravette
point. In the Upper Aurignacian this reduction in size
in flint implements is even more marked. This stage was
also marked by the first use of bone needles with eyes, and
the appearance of pendants and the problematical *bâton
de commandement*, whose use was more general in the
succeeding phases.

The mentality of Aurignacian man and his successors
is best seen, however, in connection with their art. The
fact that expression in sculpture, engraving, and painting
is a totally new phenomenon in Europe, encountered for
the first time in the Late Palaeolithic deposits, is one of
the many circumstances that suggest a break between
the Mousterians and Aurignacians, although this means
a continuity of pre-Aurignacian development elsewhere.
The discovery of the evidence of Palaeolithic Art was
made comparatively early—thus the mural paintings in
the cave of Altamira, near Santander, in N.-E. Spain were
discovered in 1879, while an engraved figure had been
recognised as far back as 1834 in the cave of Chaffaud
(Vienne). But at that time, in view of the comparatively
slight knowledge of prehistory, it seemed almost ridiculous
to think of art in connection with the wild herald of the
race, or imagine the primeval savage amidst the half

brutal conditions of his existence with that struggling within him which only came to a full birth in a Holbein or a Rembrandt—struggling so that he must needs find relief in these strange flint pencillings that testify as with the speaking silence of the night to the spirit of the man. But the criticism engendered of these early doubts has only resulted in the more complete establishment and general acceptance of the evidence.

Aurignacian art took various forms, but it is doubtful if the different phases that are sometimes noted in Europe stood in an exactly developmental relation to one another. In any case, such a view would not accord very well with the other indications which point to the arrival in Europe of a fully developed Aurignacian stock. The evidence includes detached sculptures of objects in stone, ivory, reindeer antlers, and horn. So far as they have been preserved, these are all of the human female figure, often with a gross exaggeration of details. In some cases the hair is represented as braided, but it is difficult to draw any conclusions from them as to the physiognomy of Aurignacian woman. All these figures are Late Aurignacian, and of little aesthetic value. The human figure, male and female, is also sculptured in relief, as in the rock shelter at Laussel (Dordogne). The age of these specimens of Aurignacian art is established by the implements associated with them, and the configuration of adjacent beds in the case of fixtures. Then, again, outlines of animals have been engraved or deeply scratched on the walls of caves, as e.g. at Pair-non-Pair (Gironde), Les Combarelles (Dordogne), and elsewhere. In several cases the engravings have been made on the inner walls of the caverns, sometimes in actual recesses : small stone cups have been found in the contemporary deposits which give evidence of having been used as lamps. In some cases the outlines of animals have been superposed over those of others. In one or two instances traces of ochre and black colouring were detected which had been used to help to bring out the lines in the engraving. In the cave drawings of Les Combarelles more than a hundred different animals have been recognised, principally the horse, buffalo, reindeer, mammoth, ibex, bear, etc. ; less rarely patterns and 'tectiform' designs are outlined. Actually the oldest Aurignacian paintings are the stencilled silhouettes of human hands which have been found upon the walls of the Gargas cave near Aventignan (Hautes-Pyrénées), and elsewhere. The fact that the hand thus represented is in the great majority of cases the left, suggests that right-handedness had already become a dominant human character. Many of the silhouetted fingers appear to lack one or more joints, which is accepted as evidence of a practice of mutilation not unknown amongst primitive peoples to-day, an explanation which would carry more conviction if any Aurignacian skeleton had been found lacking such joints. The results do not seem impossible of attainment by simply bending the fingers, and there is structural evidence of greater flexibility in the hand and fingers of Palaeolithic man than in modern man. In addition to these hand-silhouettes, the walls of the Gargas cave are adorned at places with groups of red dots in an irregular and undeciphered arrangement, while on the walls of the caves at Font-de-Gaume, La Mouthe, Les Combarelles, Altamira, and elsewhere, are very remarkable coloured outlines of animals in black or in red. Sometimes these representations are embellished by means of strokes or stippling, painted or engraved : the stippling in particular gives an added effect of relief. Aurignacian art is essentially line work ; it was not till Magdalenian times that we get the whole surface of the figure treated with colour.

The Aurignacian culture was widespread in Europe, extending at any rate from Wales in the west to Czecho-Slovakia in the east, and as far south as the shores of the Mediterranean. In Great Britain, however, there is not the same wealth of Late, as of Middle, or even possibly Lower, Palaeolithic material. In addition to the Paviland Cave, Aurignacian remains have been described with most certainty in connection with deposits in the Robin Hood Cave in the Cresswell Crags (Derbyshire), and Brixham (Devonshire). In Italy, a country where, owing possibly to climatic reasons, Palaeolithic man does not seem to have made so much progress as in the regions farther north, the Aurignacian is the only Late Palaeolithic phase that is represented. While Northern France is poor, Southern France is peculiarly rich in Aurignacian deposits, some of the stations, as *e.g.* Le Ruth near Le Moustier (Dordogne), providing, as the result of long habitation, very complete series of the different phases of Late Palaeolithic life; they are only less abundant in Spain. In Germany also the Aurignacian is well represented, caves like der Sirgenstein in the Achtal being peculiarly rich in sequences and actual remains. In the regions covered to-day by Austria, Hungary and Czecho-Slovakia, there is a number of important Aurignacian sites, notably at Willendorf on the Danube in the neighbourhood of Krems, where eight successive layers of occupation have yielded a very clear picture of the development of Aurignacian handicraft.

## (ii) *Solutrean*

The records of Solutrean history are more scant—remarkably so in the case of a people about whom some very definite assertions have been made. Yet it was only as recently as 1895 that the Abbé Breuil finally established the fact of the existence of two well-marked periods of culture, the Solutrean and Magdalenian, as lying between the Aurignacian and Neolithic times. The Solutrean culture takes its name from the contents of the remarkable deposits near the village of Solutré in the region of the Saone, opened up by Arcelin, de Perry, and others, from 1866 onwards. This open Palaeolithic habitation covered more than two acres on a slope rising from the river to a face of rock, the interglacial weathering of which had resulted in the formation of a layer that

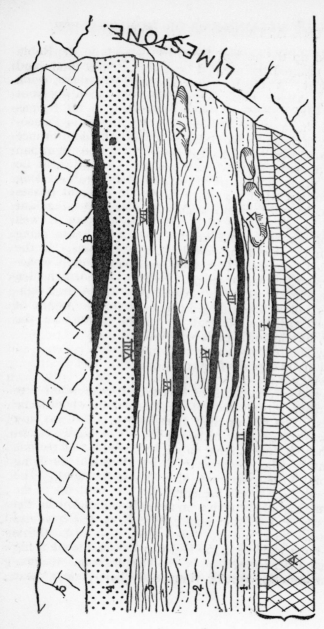

Fig. 17.—Succession of Deposits in Cave of Sirgenstein. (A) Tertiary; (1) Mousterian; (2) Aurignacian; (3) Solutrean; (4) Magdalenian; (5) Bronze and later ages; (B) relic bed (Bronze Age); I-VIII, Palaeolithic hearths; X, X, Limestone blocks. (After Schmidt, from Geikie's *Antiquity of Man in Europe.*)

covered up the ancient levels of occupation. These deposits covered the original land surface to a total depth of 34 feet. At the bottom were found Mousterian implements. Above these were characteristic Aurignacian layers with a peculiar ' equine ' layer from 15 to 20 inches in thickness, some 10 feet below the surface, composed mainly of the broken and charred bones of horses. Arcelin estimated that these Aurignacians had consumed at least one hundred thousand wild horses, captured solely for food : there is no hint yet of the domestication of the horse or indeed of any other animal. Numerous remains of hearths and typical Aurignacian flint implements were found in association with this ' equine ' layer. Other animal remains found at this level were those of the mammoth, cave lion, cave bear, hyaena, hare (*Lagomys pusillus*), marmot (*Arctomys marmotta*), and various species of deer and antelope. Next to the horse, remains of the reindeer were most in evidence, the increase again in this animal betokening a change from the Aurignacian steppe conditions to that of tundra in the Solutrean phase, foreshadowing a later revival of glacial conditions.

The Solutrean stratum proper—likewise covered and sealed up by deposits formed by the continued weathering of the rock face—lay above the ' equine ' layer, with which it showed several points of contrast. Not merely did the Solutreans leave traces of their hearths, but also their graves. The former show that their principal article of diet was the reindeer, although horse flesh was still eaten. The hearth burials seem to imply interment of the dead in huts similar to those in which they had lived, and so point to a conception of a future life analogous in its conditions to the present.

Remains of Solutrean man are only less rare than those of Early Palaeolithic man. Several of the discovered skeletons have not yet been fully described. Certain deep-lying beds near Predmost in Czecho-Slovakia have yielded a rich series of steppe and tundra forms, including the mammoth, woolly rhinoceros, horse, urus, bison, musk ox, Alpine ibex, reindeer, moose, red deer, banded lemming, cave lion, cave hyaena, glutton, and the Arctic fox, as also twenty human skeletons in differing states of preservation. 'The skulls, of which ten were found perfect, displayed the sloping Mousterian forehead and the conspicuous brow-ridges, but in a less marked degree than the full-blooded Mousterian.' [1] Another important fossil is the skeleton already referred to as exposed during some digging operations in the town of Brünn, the capital of Moravia, in 1891, at a depth of 11½ feet. A number of other interesting objects were found with these remains, including a large mammoth tusk and an ivory statuette. The skull, like those of Predmost, shows an interesting combination of Middle and Late Palaeolithic characters. The brow-ridges are still there, but the forehead is higher and less sloping than in Mousterian man. As with some of the Aurignacian skeletons, the bones were in this case stained with ochre. The Brüx skull (Bohemia) discovered in 1871 has been stated by Schwalbe to be also intermediate between Mousterian and modern man : in fact, he finds close resemblances between it and that of the native Australian. On the whole, however, the Solutrean human remains are disappointingly few. We can only say with Macalister that ' the Solutreans of Eastern Europe *seem* to be intermediate between the Mousterians and the Aurignacians in some respects ; and that as for the Solutreans of Western Europe, we know nothing whatever about their racial position,' for the simple reason that as yet no undoubted West European Solutrean skeleton has come to light.[2]

Now, this is the more remarkable, because their tool industry is quite distinctive. In fact, no more beautiful flint flaking was ever done than that by Solutrean hands. Their characteristic ' laurel-leaf ' and ' willow-leaf ' shaped javelin-heads show a most delicate secondary chipping all

---

[1] Macalister, *op. cit.* p. 374.
[2] *Op. cit.* p. 376. It is possible, however, that certain remains from the Grotte du Placard (Charente) are West Solutrean.

over the surfaces of both sides, supposed to have been produced by pressure with a bone flaking-tool rather than by blows. The same artistry was applied to their borers and scrapers, which in general design were similar to those of the preceding phase, although the carinate form is unknown. On the other hand, the Solutreans show no advance—rather the reverse—upon the Aurignacians in bone work, while their pictorial art, apart from the application of sculpture in the round to the representation of animals, also records a decline from the preceding Aurignacian level.

Solutrean stations in addition to those already mentioned are not uncommon in Southern France, as e.g. Laugerie Haute (Dordogne), and Lacave (Lot), but rarer in Spain and Germany. In Great Britain Solutrean remains have been described from the Paviland Cave, as also from Kent's Cavern, Torquay, which has been explored from 1825 onwards, and from the Cresswell Crags. In Hungary and Czecho-Slavakia there are several Solutrean sites, notably the cave of Szeleta, near Miskolcz.

### (iii) Magdalenian

The Magdalenian culture takes its name from the remains found at the prehistoric site of La Madeleine in the ravine of the Lower Vézère. In sheer human interest no phase of Palaeolithic history is more romantically rich. The actual fossil remains are still few—not more numerous than those of the Solutrean—and often incompletely described. A skeleton from Laugerie Basse reminded the investigators of Cromagnon man : it had even been decorated with shells. This reminiscence of the Aurignacian in the Magdalenian is not without significance. The skeleton from Chancelade (Dordogne) forced the same recollection, even in spite of the fact that it was that of a dwarf. He had been buried in a very flexed position. Another skeleton discovered in 1895 in the Grotte des Hôteaux near Roussillon (Ain) at a depth of

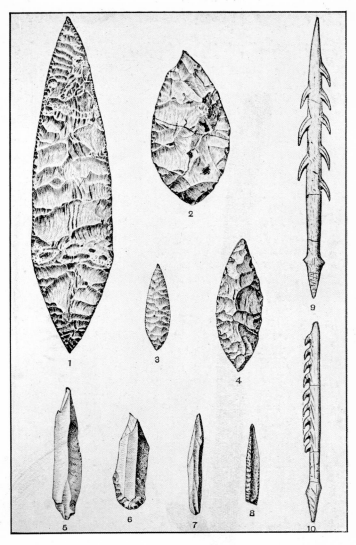

FIG. 18.—Types of Solutrean and Magdalenian Implements of War and Chase. *Solutrean*, 1-4, 'laurel-leaf' points and poniard blades. *Magdalenian*, 5-9 : 5, straight flint graver ; 6, combined scraper and graver ; 7, characteristic flint blade ; 8, pointed tool ; 9 and 10, double and single bone harpoons. (After de Mortillet, from Geikie's *Antiquity of Man in Europe*.)

2·35 metres gave indubitable proof, through the mistaken rearrangement of the bones, of the practice of ' double sepulture,' *i.e.* of a preliminary temporary interment till the flesh had disappeared, followed by a permanent burial of the skeleton. In this case the bones rested on an ochreous bed, and beside them had been placed flint implements of Magdalenian workmanship, various ornaments, and a *bâton de commandement*. The cave further contained the remains of reindeer (*Rangifer tarandus*), Alpine ibex (*Capra ibex*), the red deer (*Cervus elaphus*), the moose (*Alces latifrons*), the brown bear (*Ursus arctos*), the marmot (*Arctomys marmotta*), the wild boar (*Sus scrofa ferus*), the beaver (*Castor fiber*), the common hare (*Lepus timidus*), the cave hyaena (*C. spelaea*), the badger (*Meles taxus*), etc. Several other skeletons give the same general indications.

In flintwork the Magdalenians do not compare with their Solutrean predecessors, for the simple reason that their genius lay in the development of implements in bone and horn and ivory. The average Magdalenian flint implement is a flake, sometimes of a peculiarly long ribbon-like character, detached from the nodule with a single blow, and thereafter adapted as a knife or scraper, or with an added fine point as a borer, with a minimum of secondary chipping. In form they largely resemble those of immediately preceding stages, and the reappearance of the keel-shaped (carinate) scraper and other characteristic Aurignacian forms is not without significance from an ethnological point of view. The distinctively new is to be found in the forms in bone and ivory and horn. Heads of assegais in bone and ivory, barbed harpoon-like forms in reindeer horn whose evolution can be traced through different stages, the problematical *bâtons de commandement*, usually of reindeer horn, often elaborately ornamented, which are as likely to have been (assegai) shaft straighteners as anything else, and ' propulsors ' to aid in the throwing of javelins, are amongst some of the new types of implement. Needles with pierced eyes, made out of polished splinters of bone, seem to have been in general use for sewing hides together as garments and vessels to hold liquid, the holes being first drilled with a flint piercer. There seems to be some evidence of the fashioning of the vaults of human skulls (almost certainly those of enemies) for use as drinking cups. Macalister states that the only object of Magdalenian woodcraft that has come down to us—probably owing to the perishable nature of the medium—is the figure of a beetle found in one of the caves at Arcy-sur-Cure (Yonne).[1] It had a hole drilled through it, and was probably worn as an amulet. There is no evidence of the knowledge of pottery even in the Magdalenian deposits.

In Great Britain, Magdalenian implements have been found notably in Kent's Cavern, Torquay, and Gough's Cavern (Cheddar, Somerset). Several of the classical Magdalenian sites are found in Southern France in addition to the type station, as e.g. Laugerie Basse and Le Mas d'Azil. They are also common in Spain and Germany (der Sirgenstein, Propstfels, near Beuron in Hohenzollern, etc.). In Switzerland there are two sites of superlative importance from the Magdalenian point of view, viz. the Kesslerloch (Schaffhausen) which yielded thousands of flint and other implements, a very wide series of mammalian bones, and some of the best examples of Magdalenian sculpture and engraving, e.g. the famous browsing reindeer. Of only less importance is the neighbouring open-air rock-station of Schweizersbild, which shows signs of habitation, not however continuous, from Aurignacian times to the Bronze Age. The Magdalenian implements numbered over fourteen thousand. Some of the pierced shells, evidently articles of personal adornment, were fossil marine forms from strata which are only known at a considerable distance from the station in question,[2] and whose presence there is accordingly held to indicate con-

---

[1] Op. cit. p. 401.
[2] The reference is to the Tertiary marine deposits at Mayence. Cf. Macalister, op. cit. p. 422.

FIG. 19.—Reindeer and Landscape engraved around a piece of reindeer antler, from Kesslerloch, Switzerland. (After Heim, from H. F. Osborn's *Men of the Old Stone Age.* Slightly more than three-quarters actual size.) *Page 136.*

siderable movement of, or amongst, the Magdalenian people, and probable exchange of commodities. In Czecho-Slovakia and Yugo-Slavia there are several important Magdalenian stations, which also have yielded examples of Magdalenian art. The same holds true of the remarkable series of caves near Ojków in Poland, and of a small group of stations in South Russia. Of these the most interesting were the discoveries made at a depth of twenty metres during excavations over a long period previous to 1903 along the right bank of the Dnieper in making the street of Saint Kyril in Kiev. Several hearths were found of Magdalenian date, and around them split bones of mammoth, a horn of the woolly rhinoceros (*R. tich.*), bones of cave lion and cave bear, flint implements, and an engraved fragment of a mammoth tusk.

Magdalenian art reaches so high a level in some of its phases that only an artist or art critic can do real justice to it. A few outstanding features may, however, be noted. So far as sculpture in the round is concerned, there is no example of the human figure. The subjects are animals—horses, oxen, reindeer—or parts of animals, and the figures are sometimes done with distinctive skill. The same holds of their sculpture in relief ; the subjects so far as known, as *e.g.* in the rock-shelter at Cap-Blanc near Laussel, are animals. In the case of their engravings, whether on walls or on small objects, the great majority of the subjects are again animals—reindeer, horses, bisons, mammoths. Here the drawing is peculiarly true to nature—so true that zoological varieties have been founded upon it. The bold strong lines of the Aurignacian engraver have been replaced by finer and more delicate strokes. So the browsing reindeer from the Kesslerloch, done with fine feeling on a piece of reindeer horn, is often cited as the high-water mark of Palaeolithic engraving. Yet there is very striking failure when it comes to portraying the human figure, which in any case is very rarely done. Many of the attempts are so bizarre as to call for the explanation, based on analogies

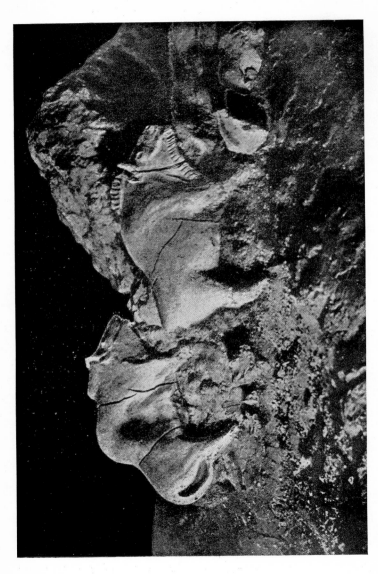

Fɪɢ. 20.—Two bison, male and female, modelled in clay, and discovered in the Cavern of Tuc d'Audoubert (Ariège). The models are each about two feet long, and rest against blocks of rock fallen from the roof. (After Bégouen.)

*Page* 137.

from modern savage ceremonies, that they represent human figures engaged in some kind of religious dance and wearing animal masks. It may have been due to a low sense of human individuality and so of interest in man *quâ* man. More probably it was the result of a direct engrossment with those animals that meant most to him for food and clothing, or as enemies—an interest illumined by magic. Other objects such as plant life, or conventional designs, are also sometimes figured.

Of clay modelling there is one very remarkable example, more interesting in its connotations even than in the actual handiwork. For in the inmost recess of a cave system (Tuc d'Audoubert) in the department of Ariège, to reach which involved not merely the passage of several galleries and halls, but more than one perilous ascent—in particular a climb of twelve metres up a ' chimney ' in the corner of one of these halls to attain the final level—Count Bégouen found two statuettes of bisons modelled in clay, and set up against a block of rock that had once fallen from the roof of the chamber. On the cave floor still remained the impress of the heels of those who had evidently participated in some sort of ceremonial dance in which apparently only the heels were permitted to touch the ground. Some of the passages and the top of the ' chimney ' were adorned with engravings of bisons. Evidently the inner recess was the secret shrine of some cult, supposed to be of Aurignacian age.

Magdalenian painting is a real advance on the corresponding Aurignacian art, in that the whole surface of the figure was filled in with paint, usually red or yellow ochre or the black of manganese oxide. In the last developments of this phase these and other colours and mixtures of them were made use of in the same representation, and even natural irregularities in the rocky slab were sometimes worked into the figures with a view to heightening effects. As in the other methods of delineation, the majority of subjects are animals. Man is seldom represented, and there is nothing of Magdalenian date comparable to the

Gargas Cave hand stencillings. Of the animals or parts of animals depicted on the walls of caves there is an immense variety of species, all of them being forms that come into some kind of a relationship to man, most of them forms that are of service to him. Thus bison, horses, reindeer, cows, goats, deer, the chamois, rhinoceros and mammoth are common subjects, the cave lion and cave bear much less so. In some cases, as in the famous caverns of Font-de-Gaume at Les Eyzies (Dordogne) and Altamira in N.-E. Spain, there are great series of representations of the same animal, e.g. the bison, or the mammoth. The realism is only equalled by the delicacy of execution. Action, however, is seldom represented ; there is no story, and rarely is any interest or contact with human life depicted. It is apparently in the animal itself that the interest lies. Now, this concentration on one particular form cannot be without meaning, and attempts have been made to explain it, as will appear in the sequel. Sometimes, as in the cave of Marsoulas (Haute-Garonne), figures of the dominant form—in this case the bison—are drawn in very awkward places, as on the roof of a narrow passage. Any attempt, on the other hand, to picture a human face is always on a much lower plane of artistic excellence, while certain patterns and devices afford scope for ingenuity in archaeological guess-work, but contribute little in the present state of knowledge to the understanding of Late Palaeolithic life. In one other group of cave and rock-paintings, viz. those found in Eastern and Southern Spain as at Cogul and Alpera, we find the work of another school, or maybe population, probably contemporary with the more typical Magdalenian art—for as Macalister points out,[1] the later Azilian culture seems to inherit from both—yet providing quite a different atmosphere. The interest is now in life, in action, in the representation of a scene, so much so that the portrayal of the actors when they are human—and both men and women are freely depicted—takes a

[1] *Op. cit.* p. 498.

FIG. 21.—Examples of Magdalenian Art from the Cave of Font-de-Gaume. Above, reindeer partly painted, partly incised ; below, bison painted in ochre. (After Capitan and Breuil, from R. Munro's *Palaeolithic Man.*)

stylistic form of little sprites—a sort of reduction of humanity to its lowest common measure—while that of animals is sometimes in similar terms, but more often with admirable miniature truth to life. The chase—in which bows and arrows now play a great part—warfare, and the ritualistic dance are amongst the subjects portrayed. A modicum of information may even be gleaned as to dress, but much in connection not merely with the actual representations but with their history still remains obscure.

At the same time the general impression left by Magdalenian art, as we have it, is that it points beyond itself. It is something more than mere ' Art for Art's sake,' for, whatever else he was, the struggle for existence made primitive man an intensely practical being. This does not mean that the engraver of, say, the Kesslerloch browsing reindeer felt no pride in his performance comparable to the admiration expended upon it by the professionally competent of later generations. But it does mean that he did not produce this *chef-d'œuvre* simply because he wanted to make a representation of a reindeer. Late Palaeolithic man was pre-eminently a hunter, pitiably dependent upon his quarry for food and clothing, and even on its bones and fats for making certain implements and compounding colouring materials. But at any moment the herds of more timid forms might leave his district and the depredations of aggressive carnivores become a real threat. Without stores and no calculable routine of agricultural production, famine must often have beleaguered his encampments. Palaeolithic man deemed these animals more powerful than himself, and possessed of mysterious qualities. He was practically at their mercy at this stage, so great was his dependence on them. This preoccupation with them expressed itself in representations of them. But to his primitive mind the representations were as the very animals themselves,[1] and to that extent in some measure within his power.

[1] Mainage, *op. cit.* pp. 329, 337.

Accordingly, when we consider all the facts about the portraiture of bisons, mammoths, reindeer, and any other form in connection with which there is thus evidence of a concentration of interest, noting also the apparent absence of interest in sun, moon, and stars or even the world of plant life, we begin to suspect that we are in the region of that early accompaniment of religion, viz. magic. When we find bisons depicted with javelins in their sides (Marsoulas grotto), or bleeding from a mortal wound (Niaux cavern), it is difficult to resist the impression that the wish or desire is father to the painting, and that it is hoped that the representations may be fulfilled in actual life. The picture in short is a portrayed prayer, a piece of sympathetic magic. And the prayer might be repeated in one form or another, for over a previous representation, which seems thereby to be considered as finished and done with, having served its purpose of promoting some capture and increase of supplies, is sometimes superposed a second picture, which mayhap inherited, so to speak, the magical power that had been in the previous representation. ' The primitive hunter wishes to make sure of his subsistence. He employs every kind of means. Because he is ingenious he improves his weapons and uses them. Because he is religious, and thinks of the animals as superior beings, he prays, he fasts, he mortifies his members. And because magic seems to him to lead assuredly to results, he practises magic. With harmonising these different tendencies, he has no concern.' [1]

In this way, perhaps, we can understand why such representations are commonly found in the dark innermost recesses of the caverns, reached often only with considerable difficulty, where apparently magical rites were performed, as in the case of the Cult of the Bison at Tuc d'Audoubert. It is apparent that pictographs made upon roofs of passages, under what must have been in some instances very trying physical conditions, and where they could never be seen by natural light, can

[1] Mainage, *op. cit.* p. 348.

hardly have been for purposes of ornamentation simply.
So Marett, in his description of 'a prehistoric sanctuary,'
speaks of the Niaux cavern (Ariège) as 'a mile-long subterranean cathedral with pillars, side-chapels, and con-
fessionals all complete,' where of the seventy or eighty
animal subjects 'nearly all have what look like weapons—
spears of various shapes or a throwing club—attached to

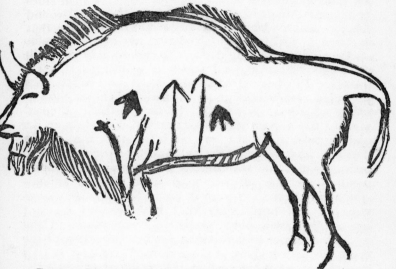

FIG. 22.—Large bison from the Niaux Cavern, with four arrow marks.
(After Capitan and Breuil, from R. Munro's *Palaeolithic Man*.)

their sides or overlying the region of the heart. . . . And
perhaps the best proof of all is that the spirit of awe and
mystery still broods in these dark galleries within a
mountain, that are, to a modern mind, symbolic of nothing
so much as of the dim subliminal recesses of the human
soul.' [1]    In the same sort of atmosphere the stencilled
representations of hands, as on the walls of the Gargas
Cave, have sometimes been explained in accordance with

[1] R. R. Marett, *The Threshold of Religion*, pp. 206, 213, 220.

a widespread modern custom, as the provision of an amulet against the evil eye, or the registration of a vow in direct physical contact with some holy place.[1]

When dealing with the religion of Late Palaeolithic man we are on somewhat surer ground. It has been suggested with very great probability, on the basis of analogous figures in Semitic art, that some of the Aurignacian sculptured figures to which reference has been made may be representations of a goddess of fertility and birth, and there is clear evidence of ritualistic and masked dancing,[2] in connection with cults. The dance, too, is an expression of desire ; in a hunting dance the various actions of the chase are rehearsed, and power is gained to slay the quarry. To what extent an associated form of fetichism prevailed alongside of more ultimate beliefs we have no means at present of judging. So far as belief in the survival of the human spirit is concerned it is clear, in the case of most of the Aurignacian interments, that we are dealing with intentional burial. As before, ornaments and pendants of value are interred with the remains—ornaments sometimes of perforated teeth of wild animals which may have been worn in life as amulets—as well as weapons and implements that had been of service : apparently they would be needed in the hereafter. There is often evidence of care taken for the protection of the body by placing slabs of stone around and over it. Of special interest is the custom of staining or painting the bones with red ochre, after the first temporary burial. Sometimes the same end was sought by covering the bottom of the grave with this colouring substance so that the actual interment was, so to speak, in a bed of ochre. There was purpose and belief in it all. Red is the colour of the warm living flesh and blood, and the bones, so painted, would preserve something of their vital relation-

---

[1] A totemistic explanation of these Palaeolithic cave paintings, although not without some possible support, seems to be ruled out by the wide range of animal life depicted in most caves and by the wide area over which several of them are found.

[2] Cf. Mainage, *op. cit.* pp. 313-314.

ship and function. In his own way the Aurignacian could have said, ' I believe in the resurrection of the body, and the life everlasting.'

There still remains the problem of the origin of the Aurignacians. But like all problems in origins it is far from clear. We have seen some reason to believe in an evolution through Chellean and Acheulean to Mousterian man, the earliest representatives having probably entered Europe as emigrants from the Iranian plateau in Central Asia. Whether this long continued process of diffusion was through Asia Minor by way of the land bridge at the Dardanelles, or by the other great route that swept northwards and round the Caspian and Black Seas, we do not know. But assuredly just as at an earlier stage the chimpanzee and gorilla had found their way from Central Asia into Africa through Arabia and the Egypt of to-day, so at a later period did representatives of the original human stock follow the same route, and an evolution took place there in the Negrito line, modern representatives of whom are seen in the pygmies and Bushmen, and in the later Negroid waves which often submerged the Negritoes. Now we have observed that the Aurignacian culture is particularly well represented in Spain, Southern France and Italy : these people evidently entered Europe from the south, not necessarily on one occasion, and with them were individuals showing somewhat markedly negroid characteristics.[1] There is also a remarkable correspondence between Aurignacian art and that of the Bushmen, and those who consider that the Gargas hands are mutilated find another parallel in the Bushman custom of finger lopping. Physically, however, there can be no direct relationship, even if it is probable that the Bushman migrated southward from Central Africa. But we may with a certain amount of reason suppose the Aurignacians to have been an offshoot from that original human wave that entered Africa, and which for a time had its

[1] Cf. p. 123.

centre somewhere in the north-west region of that continent. Under pressure from the succeeding waves that ultimately developed into the more Negroid lines, or from other causes, one section of them may have taken a northward direction and crossed into Europe by the land bridges at Gibraltar and Sicily.[1] Macalister, who thinks of ' the cradle of the Aurignacian people, as such,' being ' somewhere between the head waters of the Nile and of the Congo,'[2] without further inquiry into their origin, suggests two other directions of dispersal. One section ' passed down the Nile, to found the civilisation of Egypt'; the other ' traversed the mountain-passes of Abyssinia and crossed the Strait of Bab-el-Mandeb, to become the parent of the various Semitic civilisations which radiated from Arabia.' A retracing of the ancestral route such as is thus implied does not appear altogether probable.

The Aurignacians, then, entered Europe from Africa, bringing with them a distinctive and in many ways a superior civilisation to the Mousterian which they found. This tall, well-developed, big-brained Cromagnon race gradually replaced the Mousterians, who either died out or were exterminated. The next stages are more difficult to follow. There appears, however, in the eastern part of Central Europe the Solutrean race, who seem to hold a position, both physically and culturally, midway between the Mousterian and Aurignacian. Their flint chipping is the perfection of Palaeolithic craftsmanship, their most characteristic handiwork (the ' laurel-leaf ' javelin head) being recognised at the same time as a development of the best Acheulean *coups-de-poing*, while on the other hand they showed no advance or particular skill in art such as the Aurignacians had. It has been suggested [3] that this balance of qualities was the result

[1] There may therefore be something more than mere resemblance between the crimped braiding of the hair of Aurignacian women and the characteristic style of ancient Egyptian perruque.

[2] *Op. cit.* p. 577.

[3] *E.g.* by Macalister, *op. cit.* p. 385. The same general position is adopted by Prof. Mainage, *Les Réligions de la Préhistoire*, pp. 412-416.

of an actual blend between Aurignacians and Mousterians in this region in the later period of the Aurignacian occupation, and that the resultant Solutrean race moved westwards, driving out the Aurignacians before them. The latter retreated south into Italy, where there are no Solutrean remains, and later when the Solutrean episode had passed, returned as a modified people—the Magdalenians—with developments in culture and artistry that yet manifestly preserve their continuity with the past. Events such as these, however, were not the matter of a day, and not merely in connection with the changes in the climate, but the earlier less stimulating stay in the south, may have been correlated the physical differences, in no way profound, which distinguished the Magdalenian from the Aurignacian race. But once again with the oncoming of a glacial episode, a race deteriorated so as in the end to vanish completely.

A certain amount of probability is further given to this hypothesis by the existence of a so-called Capsian culture in North Africa, a region further that shows no trace of either Solutrean or Magdalenian deposits. It is conceivable that the Capsian may have been a sort of étape colony left by the Aurignacian wave in its advance into Europe. Thus the Lower Capsian shows the characteristic implements of the Lower Aurignacian, as e.g. the Châtelperron knife. The Upper Capsian shows the bone needles and scrapers of the Upper Aurignacian, but it is noticeable that the Aurignacian flints of the Lower Capsian ' degenerate into flints of geometrical form,' [1] which dwindle further and directly into the Tardenoisian ' pygmy ' flints [2] of the Mesolithic—there is no Solutrean or Magdalenian stage. Now the remarkable fact is that these stages are not found in Spain, with the exception of a limited region in the north. A Capsian culture follows directly upon the Aurignacian in Spain, and is limited to that country in Europe, and it is undoubtedly with this Capsian culture that the peculiar parietal art

[1] Macalister, op. cit. p. 538.    [2] Cf. p. 150.

K

of Cogul and Alpera must be associated. The Capsians also probably introduced the bow into Europe, and while they seem to have successfully held the greater part of the Iberian Peninsula against the Magdalenians, yet it is the cultures of these two populations that unite in the Mesolithic Azilian.

Already, then, at the close of the Palaeolithic we are aware of considerable variation in human stocks, of great migrations, and of barter on a scale that must have meant considerable coming and going in the inhabited areas. The problem of origins meets us continually, sometimes with still baffling results, but we feel ourselves already in the midst of race movements that were almost world-wide. An attractive train of speculation has sought for reasons to link the various races of Palaeolithic man with modern peoples.[1] The resemblances between the Mousterian and the native Australian are perhaps best explained by the fact that just as the orang in Borneo and Sumatra and the gibbon in the Malay Archipelago are descendants of the simian ancestral forms that spread to the south-east from the original Central Asiatic home, so the Australian aboriginals are also descendants of that first wave of human life, part of which dispersed westward into Europe and part of which went to the southwest. The European Aurignacians are believed by some to be represented in the Basque people of Perigueux. This may be true in the sense that these people may have a more direct connection with some isolated Aurignacian community than the average post-Magdalenian inhabitant of Europe. The more natural supposition, perhaps, is that one which links the Aurignacian after-history with the Magdalenians, and sees in the latter a people who in the end succumbed to, or were absorbed by, the ever incoming peoples from the east, rather than as pushed by the latter slowly north with their reindeer to be rediscovered in the Esquimaux of to-day.

[1] Cf. especially Prof. W. J. Sollas, *Ancient Hunters and their Modern Representatives.*

# CHAPTER VII

### MESOLITHIC AND NEOLITHIC MAN

As recently as the year 1887, for those who constituted the interested audience, the curtain fell at the close of the first, the Palaeolithic Act, in the Drama of Human History, and when it rose again upon Neolithic scenes, it was in the presence of an entirely new cast, with new habits and new manners of living, moving amidst a fauna and flora and under climatic conditions that were much more familiar than those of Pleistocene days—in fact essentially modern. The Arctic mammalia and their southern contemporaries had been removed by the scene shifters, and the last Palaeolithic man had for ever left the stage. The latter, as he was last seen in the form of the dolichocephalic, artistic reindeer-hunter of Aquitaine, was a very distinctive human being—for all time Magdalenian art will be, of its kind, at once an acme and a criterion—but his successor was no less remarkable in his own way. Brachycephalic or dolichocephalic, Neolithic man was a shepherd and a tiller of the soil, who polished his stone implements and had begun to live in settled communities. He erected places of sojourn for the living and for the dead—there are no Palaeolithic structures. He could make hand-moulded pottery, and he had some knowledge of the art of weaving.

Now this unquestionable break disturbed the sense of continuity in the audience, who felt certain that there ought to be an Entr'acte, and that could they but get behind the curtain, *i.e.* find the right but till then undiscovered cave, gravel deposit or valley drift, they would see the actual transformation scene. The undoubted gap that occurred was, as Professor Geikie used to remark, but a gap in our knowledge—much as the recorded distributions of insects sometimes correspond more to the distribution of the entomologist than of the insects. In this faith they were to be justified : transition deposits containing human relics were eventually found. In 1887 Edouard Piette began the systematic investigation of a cavern-like subterranean river-channel near the village of Le Mas d'Azil on a spur of the Pyrenees (Ariège), and found a series of strata embedding remains of cultures that marked the transition from Palaeolithic to Neolithic times. The lowest of them was 23 feet above the present bed of the river (Arise). The actual intermediate culture is now known as Azilian, and it lay, in this case in two strata (which can be further differentiated) about 20 inches in thickness, over strata of a total depth of 17 feet, including two long periods of Magdalenian occupation. Above it were three deposits of a total thickness of 6½ feet which contained remains of cultures from the Neolithic to Roman days. Two thick alluvial beds of yellow silt lying immediately above each of the Magdalenian deposits testified to long periods of flood or submergence during which the gallery must have been uninhabitable. Remains of the reindeer characterised the Magdalenian layers—in a vanishing degree in the upper one—but were absent from the Azilian, where its place was taken by the stag.

Azilian life as revealed by the remains in the type station was genuinely Mesolithic—intermediate between Palaeolithic and Neolithic conditions. The fauna was in facies definitely later than the true Palaeolithic, while there were indications of a damper climate than now exists in that region. The numerous remains of plants and fruit stones suggested that some steps in agriculture might have been taken. There was, however, no pottery, and nothing to indicate the domestication of any animal. The Azilians worked their flints in very similar fashion to the Magdalenians, but had not discovered the art of polishing stone. They made the same sorts of carved and barbed harpoons—characteristically flat in section—and arrow heads, but from the bone and antlers of the stag, and with less skill. The dainty Magdalenian needles are no longer in evidence : in fact, in all their bone industry there was deterioration in design and craftsmanship. A new element in culture is the Azilian adornment of rounded pebbles with peculiar hieroglyphics in red ochre. These have been carefully studied, and compared with the marks painted on the walls in the Capsian Spanish caves (Alpera and Cogul). The result very forcibly suggests that both are still further stylistic representations of human figures reduced to their lowest terms. ' Perhaps,' adds Macalister, ' we shall not greatly err if we suppose that these pebbles were what may be called " soul-houses," abodes for the spirits of deceased members of the community, and as such associated with a cult of the dead.' [1] The remarkable fact is that the wonderful Magdalenian art has entirely disappeared, or degenerated into the rude outlines on the pebbles.

We do not, however, know very much about Azilian psychology as expressed in burials, for few strictly Azilian skeletons have been found. There is the same staining of the bones with red ochre as before, which implies an initial temporary burial or the application of some method by which the flesh was separated from the bones. In the Greater Ofnet, one of two caves near Nördlingen (Würtemberg), which showed more or less continuous occupation from the base of the Late Palaeolithic, a couple of pits had been sunk through the Magdalenian stratum. They were lined with a coating of red ochre, and into one of them twenty-seven skulls had been closely packed, with the aid of fine earth similarly coloured. All the skulls were arranged to face the west, and showed that the heads had been severed from the bodies and buried in that state.

[1] *Op. cit.* p. 531. This suggestion, making these pebbles comparable to the native Australian churinga or bull-roarer, is criticised by Mainage, *op. cit.* pp. 196-198.

Similarly six skulls had been deposited in the second pit. Flints and ornaments—thousands of perforated shells and deer-teeth strung as tiaras and necklaces—were buried with the skulls, which represented an instance of the peculiar practice of head-burial or cephalotaphy, to use Macalister's term, which had already come into existence in Magdalenian times. The skulls were both of the dolichocephalic and brachycephalic types, with some intermediate forms comparable to those found in the oldest Neolithic lake-dwellings of Central Europe.

Evidence of this Azilian stage has been found at other stations, particularly in Northern Spain and Southern France, in Germany, possibly in the Schweizersbild rock-shelter near Schaffhausen, and apparently in the British Isles. Sometimes associated with Azilian remains are the so-called Tardenoisian [1] ' pygmy ' flints, usually under an inch in length, of varying yet often geometric form, which may have been fashioned for harpoon teeth and other purposes, and which we have already seen to be an evolution of the Capsian flint industry. [2] On the basis of these ' pygmy ' flints and the absence of pottery, it would seem best to correlate at this point the Maglemose peat-moss deposits in the island of Seeland in Northern Europe. These correspond to the period when the Baltic was closed at both ends, forming the so-called freshwater Ancylus Lake. [3] Occupation evidently began when the site was a large lake, and continued throughout the drying-up process that transformed it into a peat-bog. Many considerations indicate that the population lived on a large raft, or series of rafts, close to the shore. The implements were all made of stone, bone, or horn, some of them rather unusual and explained as netting-needles for making fishing-nets. A slightly later deposit at

[1] From the type station at Fère-en-Tardenois (Aisne).   [2] Cf. p. 145.
[3] The name, as that of the preceding Yoldia Sea stage, when the Baltic had an outlet to the North Sea, and the Littorina Sea stage, subsequent to the Ancylus Lake, when the Baltic was opened again by land depression to the south-west, is derived from the principal mollusc in the deposits of these different bodies of water.

Viby near Aarhus yielded the first evidence of the use of the boomerang in Europe, as also the end of a wooden bow.

Showing affinities with the Tardenoisian culture also are the shell-heaps in connection with certain early settlements discovered at Mugem in the valley of the river Tagus in Portugal. In the course of the excavations some six hundred skeletons were brought to light. If the burials had apparently been less individual than in previous cases, yet they were not altogether without regard for the future welfare of the deceased, as evidenced by the presence of numerous flints. The deposits, in containing no polished stone implements or pottery or traces of domesticated animals, as also in the presence of ' pygmy ' flints, are undoubtedly Mesolithic. While the majority of the skulls were dolichocephalic, there was clear evidence as at Ofnet not merely of a brachycephalic strain, but of a mixture between the two. Now Palaeolithic man was distinctively dolichocephalic, while Neolithic man shows definite strains of both types, as also blends. It is noteworthy, then, that in this intermediate or Mesolithic period we find the first evidence on a large scale of brachycephaly in Europe ; the Piltdown, and a few of the Krapina skulls were the sole previous examples noted. Central Asia is the recent home of brachycephaly, and it is to this region that we look again as the womb from which issued these successive birth-waves of human life that spread eastward and westward alike. Confirmation of the presence now of this short-headed race in Europe is found in the caves at Furfooz on the Lesse in Belgium. This westward movement from Central Asia was a long slow diffusive movement of ' peaceful penetration,' in which the nomadic herdsman, reaching out to find fresh pastures, followed a line which in the end brought him into Central Europe. There he apparently at first proved superior to the declining dolichocephalic population, with whom he mixed, teaching them what he knew about the domestication of animals and pastoral life generally. With the passage of time, and consequent on this infusion of new blood, the dolichocephalic population reasserted itself, and while that of Europe to-day is very mixed, the purely brachycephalic people are mainly represented in certain mountainous areas whither they were driven from the plains.

We are now at the middle of the Mesolithic period, that critically formative episode in the life of the Europe of to-day, for while the Azilian phase is more Palaeolithic than Neolithic, the succeeding Campignian is on the whole more Neolithic than Palaeolithic. It takes its name from a hut-site at Le Campigny, a hill near the town of Blangy-sur-Bresle (Seine-Inférieure). Amongst flint implements of already familiar types are flake knives like those of the Magdalenian, scrapers, saws, engravers, and borers. But there are also two new distinctive types—a sort of pick-like bar of flint about 8-15 centimetres long, with blunt points at either end, and a chisel-like implement, made out of a nodule of flint, sometimes referred to as the ' kitchen-midden axe ' from the frequency with which it is found in the ' kitchen-middens ' or shell-heaps of Denmark. There is no suggestion as yet of the art of polishing stone, but pottery was now in use, and the presence of mill-stones seems to prove that agriculture was now practised. The fauna and flora were essentially modern.

Campignian sites have been described at various points in France and Germany, in Italy, England and Ireland. According to Macalister, Campignian is the oldest culture that appears in Ireland,[1] as, similarly, Azilian in Scotland : but throughout we must allow sometimes for considerable overlapping of phases. Particularly characteristic, although of varying age, are the Danish shell-heaps, enormous piles at different points on the coast, sometimes as much as 800-1000 feet in length, 140-200 feet in breadth, and 10 feet in height, and consisting for the most part of oyster, scallop, and other shells, the broken bones of various mammals (especially deer and wild boar),

[1] *Op. cit.* p. 554.

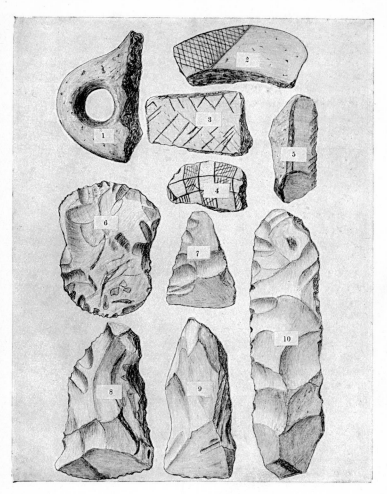

FIG. 23.—Examples of Campignian Pottery (1-4) and Flint Implements (5-10): 5, a saw; 6, a double scraper; 7-9, chisel or Danish 'kitchen-midden axe'; 10, a pick. (From R. Munro's *Palaeolithic Man.*)

birds and deep-sea fish, together with rudely chipped unpolished flint implements, combs, daggers, awls, and needles of bone, and shreds of coarse pottery, but no cultivated plants except wheat. The characteristic pick and chisel-axe date these refuse-heaps with tolerable accuracy. Certain circular depressions on the surface are supposed to indicate the site of the huts or shelters in which this rather needy population lived all the year round, although apparently in a climate that was somewhat warmer on the whole in that particular locality than it is to-day. No graves or human remains have been found, but there was evidence of the domestication of a small species of dog. Detailed examination of the depressed shoreline and the character of the molluscs on the shell-heaps prove that they correspond to that phase of the history of the Baltic known as the Littorina Sea, when it had an even more open connection with the North Sea and was more salt than at the present time. The Campignian culture has also been recognised at sites in Norway and Sweden, having been carried across the land bridge that ran northward from Jutland during the Ancylus period. In fact, it almost looks as if this Southern Baltic region may have been the principal centre of distribution of the Campignian culture, which was then ' taken up and carried ' farther west and south ' by the invading Asiatic.' [1] The culture itself, however, is linked, through the harpoons and 'pygmy' flints, not merely with the Azilian, but also through well-known rock engravings in Norway and Sweden with Magdalenian art itself. Of Campignian man, so few skeletal remains are known that it is not yet possible to make any reliable statements with regard to his physical characters. This whole transition period gives the impression of a clash of cultures and silent conflict of peoples as the steady flow from the east seeped in amongst the scattered communities of Europe, each of which had been living its own kind of life, and so reacted in very different ways in presence of the new stimulus.

[1] Macalister, *op. cit.* p. 569.

The relationship of the Mesolithic and Neolithic stages with the later phases of the Ice Age may be approximately represented as follows :

LATE PLEISTOCENE AND POST-PLEISTOCENE

| GEOLOGICAL PHASES. | | ARCHAEOLOGICAL PHASES. | | | |
|---|---|---|---|---|---|
| Western and Middle Europe. | Northern Europe. | Western and Middle Europe. | Northern Europe. | Asia and Africa. | Date B.C. Europe. |
| — | Beech | Iron | — | — | 1500 |
| — | Oak | Bronze | — | Bronze | 1900-2500 |
| — | Oak | — | — | Copper Pre-dynastic Egyptians | — |
| — | Fir | Neolithic | — | — | 8000 |
| IV. Daun (glacial) | Littorina Oak Phase (Baltic with wider outlet than present) | Campignian | Shell-heaps | Sumerian | 9000 |
| III. Gschnitz (glacial) | Ancylus Pine Phase (Baltic a fresh-water lake) | Azilian-Tar-denoisian | Magle-mose | Anau founded. Neolithic settlements in Crete | 12,000 |
| Loess for-mation | — | Late Mag-dalenian | — | Susa founded | — |
| Steppe | Yoldia Phase | — | — | — | — |
| Tundra | Swedish-Finnish moraines | Middle Mag-dalenian | — | — | — |
| II. Bühl (glacial) | — | Early Mag-dalenian and Capsian invasion | — | — | 20,000 |
| Tundra | — | Solutrean | — | — | — |
| Steppe | — | Aurignacian | — | — | — |
| I. Aachen (glacial) | — | — | — | — | — |

FIG. 24.—Restoration of Neolithic Man, under the direction of Mons. Rutot.
(By permission.)

*Page* 155.

The term Neolithic, then, is applied to remains of man
and his handicraft that are specially distinguished in the
case of the latter by the fact that on the whole they are
smooth and polished and very finely worked as compared with those of his Palaeolithic predecessors.   In the
history of man as a whole, the Neolithic Age closed about
2000 B.C., when bronze became known in Western Europe,
but certain tribes may be considered to be still on the
cultural level of Neolithic times, although they are not
Neolithic people.   The life of Neolithic times differed in
certain broad respects from that of the Palaeolithic Age.
Man, now that he was no longer persistently nomadic,
could accumulate ; the sense of property is very old, as
we can see from its marked development in children. He
began to domesticate animals, and agriculture, the
development of which was certainly a slow process, was
also introduced into Western Europe from farther east.
Pottery is also a distinctive feature of Neolithic times.

The examination of Neolithic skeletons shows that man
was still evolving physically, though very slowly.  Dolichocephalic, with a cranial capacity equivalent to that of
modern man and sometimes exceeding it, Neolithic man
in England differed in some interesting respects from
his successors.   His teeth met edge-on when closed, and
wore one another down : they were also more regularly
arranged, while the palate was not so contracted as in
modern man—changes that are all probably consequent
upon change in diet.   Neolithic man throughout Europe,
and indeed on the African side of the Mediterranean,
shows these same general characteristics, although negroid
features have been noticed in addition in Neolithic skulls
from Egypt and elsewhere.   A very good example of
Neolithic man of the earlier period is the so-called Tilbury
man,[1] whose remains were found in 1883 at a depth of
35 feet beneath the present surface, or 3 feet below the
actual land surface of his day.   These remains may per-

[1] See accounts in Keith's *Ancient Types of Man* (1911), and *The
Antiquity of Man*, pp. 25-30.

haps be taken as typical of the English Neolithic people,—
somewhat under medium stature, but ' with well-shaped
heads of rather more than average size.' [1]  The evidence
indicating that subsidence in the lower reaches of the
valleys of the Thames and Medway [2] has been in progress
at a rate of 4 feet in a thousand years, would, if the rate
has been uniform, make the Tilbury man a contemporary
of the Pre-dynastic Egyptians between seven and eight
thousand years ago.  In calculating the duration of the
Neolithic period there are many factors to be taken into
consideration.  There is in particular the evidence,
through continuity of deposits, that England and the
Channel Islands were part of the Continent of Europe so
recently as the beginning of the Post-Pleistocene.  There
was therefore a wide range of territory over which Neolithic man could wander from his eastern source.  Time
has to be allowed for the formation of the English Channel
by subsidence and erosion.  Greater assurance can be
placed in the conclusion that indicates the close of the
Neolithic Age as about 2000 B.C. than on any date fixed
as its opening.  It probably lasted between seven and nine
thousand years, which if the inside figure is taken, would
indicate the commencement as roughly about 9000 B.C.

In reconstructing the Europe of Neolithic time we have
to take note of considerable physico-geographical changes
that synchronised with the close of the Pleistocene.  It
is most natural to correlate the period of maximum glaciation with periods of land elevation, although there may
have been local variations, and subsidences have been
going on in England while elevation was in progress in
Scotland.  But, on the whole, there is evidence in Britain
of a period of depression, probably in part induced by the
sheer weight of the ice-sheet, which as it gradually retreated, may have left this country entirely separated
from the Continent, and transformed into an archipelago,

---

[1] Keith, *The Antiquity of Man*, pp. 9 and 43.
[2] This subsidence affected the whole southern part of England : on
the other hand, a movement of elevation was in progress in Scotland.

whose coast-lines now show in some places at a height
of 1300 feet above the present level. A corresponding
depression over a large area of North-Western Europe
for a prolonged period may well have had a disrupting
and dispersing, if not a seriously eliminating, effect upon
the Magdalenians. Of the extent of this depression
it is impossible to give any exact account. If the
separation of Great Britain from the Continent was
complete, thus breaking a land connection that had
been preserved in varying degree from the Riss-Würmian
interglacial phase onwards, then it appears that it was
while this immense area was once more being slowly
elevated that the Neolithic human waves began to
enter Europe from the east. It is, however, possible
that Neolithic man reached Britain by a land connection that still persisted. Certain it is, however, that
he lived through the last readjustment and subsidence
that once again made an English Channel. It is when
we come to estimate the time required to produce the
change to the scenery and contours with which we are
familiar to-day, that we realise the necessity to posit
a considerable period which for the Neolithic alone may
well have been 9000 years.

Of the various features that have already been mentioned as characteristic of the Neolithic Age, undoubtedly
that one which led to the great advance in civilisation
was the discovery, however made, of the possibility
of domesticating certain animals. There is no shred
of evidence that this idea had ever entered the mind of
Palaeolithic man. He had to go out after every form of
animal life that he desired, whether for food or clothing.
Hence his characteristically nomadic hunter's life, continually compelled to seek fresh hunting-grounds. It is
almost certain that the first animal to be domesticated—
man's oldest friend and ally—was some kind of jackal-
like dog. Its value as a watcher and in the chase would
quickly be appreciated. With its help the possibility of
securing and keeping food-animals was increased. At

first small (*Canis familiaris palustris*), towards the close of the period, and in association with the evident increase in flocks of sheep, a larger form appears, of a more wolfish aspect. This domestication of food-animals meant a great saving of time for man, which he could thus put to other purposes : to some extent also it meant the removal of the dread of want. It further implied that man could settle for slightly longer periods in localities, and such settlement meant the opportunity to accumulate property. On the steppes of Central Asia man for the first time captured and began to tame the wild horses, cattle, goats, and sheep amidst which he lived.

Neolithic deposits which are typically represented by remains of land habitations, lake-dwellings, sepulchral and religious structures, and implements of polished stone, are often disappointing, in that being more superficial than those of Palaeolithic times, they have been less protected on the one hand, and on the other more easily recognised and disturbed, whether by men seeking for buried treasure or by burrowing animals. As a result their chronological value has been sometimes destroyed, and their actual value greatly diminished through ruthless robbery. Neolithic cave remains are not uncommon, but the marked development in civilisation and growth of population made caves as a general rule too confined and unsuitable as occupational sites. The most common type of land habitation was a circular pit-dwelling, some 6 feet in diameter, excavated to a varying depth of from 3 to 6 feet, with a conical, wattled superstructure plastered with clay. The hearth was in the centre. As the period progressed there was development in the type of dwelling-place, with differentiation and elaboration sometimes in the case of the central structure, which is regarded accordingly as having been the residence of the head of the community. At Grosgartach near Heilbronn in the Neckar Valley, a Late Neolithic village was carefully explored by Schliz. In this instance the two-roomed house of the chief was rectangular—5·80 metres by 5·35

Fig. 25.—Reconstructed Lake-Dwellings. (From J. M. Tyler's *New Stone Age in N. Europe.*)

metres—with an outer wall of posts supporting between them a wattling of twigs, plastered with clay. The sleeping-room was on the level of the ground, while the kitchen, which was the larger of the two, was sunk to the depth of one metre, and entered by an inclined plane. Something like a primitive farm building was also exposed in the vicinity, with stalls and a granary floor. As a matter of fact, however, there was very considerable variety in the types of structure and mode of life in the Neolithic settlements in different parts of Europe throughout that period. On the whole, the settlements north of the Alps and round the Baltic were neither so large or well developed as those in Italy or the Balkan Peninsula. The northern communities were more of the nature of pioneer settlements with no great wealth to defend, such as induced the habit in the south of fortifying villages, before the close of the Neolithic Age. But in any case it was a matter of finding the spots where, with greatest ease, clearings could be made in the primeval forest, or seeking the more open steppe regions, which are still recognisable in the Germany and Czecho-Slovakia of to-day.

More characteristic in their way were the lake-dwellings of Neolithic times. Remains of these are found especially in Switzerland, and on the Italian lakes : they are in evidence on the New Guinea coastlands to-day. Communities that settled on a lakeshore obviously possessed advantages that tribes wandering in the woodlands or on the steppes could not enjoy. The resources of both water and land were at their disposal, and by means of navigation they could add to the interest of their existence through barter or piracy. Safety could be sought in their hollowed boats, but was more certainly secured for themselves and their belongings by living off the shore in huts upon platforms supported on piles driven into the mud or sand of the shelving beach. The labour expended in the erection of these lakeshore habitations must have been enormous, particularly when we consider that a stone axe and fire were the principal tools at the disposal of the builders. Thus it has been calculated that at Robenhausen, on the south side of Lake Pfäffikon in Switzerland, more than 100,000 piles had been used. They were in three sets at as many different levels, pointing to three successive occupations of the site. The sharpened piles were apparently driven in by heavy stone mallets, and further supported in some instances by accumulations of stones dropped in between them. The houses erected on the platforms were generally rectangular, and of distinctly larger size than those found inland, although of similar construction. These Swiss lake stations are peculiarly rich in antiquities. The hearths, composed of three or four stone slabs, were not always safe, and on many occasions the whole station seems to have been destroyed by fire. The lacustrine mud below proved a sound preservative receptacle for all manner of objects.

Thus of animals, remains of more than seventy species have been discovered, of which perhaps six were domesticated. Bones of the stag and ox are most common. *Bos brachyceros* seems to have been an imported and domesticated form : the wild ox or urus (*Bos primigenius*), whose bones and long spreading horns are also found, was not in process of domestication till towards the close of the Neolithic Age. The same is true of the horse. Both for cattle and for horses, the Bronze Age was the era of domestication. Other domesticated and imported forms were the so-called 'turbary' pig (*Sus scrofa palustris*) —to be distinguished from the native wild boar (*Sus scrofa ferus*), whose remains as a product of the chase also occur—together with the goat and 'turbary' sheep. The latter (*Ovis aries palustris*) is apparently the result of the crossing of three other distinct forms. 'The balance of probabilities,' says Professor J. M. Tyler,[1] ' seems to incline toward the view that the turbary sheep came into Europe from western and central Asia with other " turbary " forms, that it had been long domesticated, and

---

[1] *The New Stone Age in Northern Europe*, p. 79.

either here or on its westward migration may have more
or less crossed with the descendants of other varieties.'

The mere presence of these forms, which were kept in
stalls on the platform through the winter, proves that
the Neolithic lake-dwellers practised agriculture, to provide them with food.    Wheat and barley in particular
were cultivated.    Of both of these forms there were
several varieties, and also two kinds of millet.    Oats do
not appear before the Bronze Age.    The remains also
of many different kinds of fruits were found.    Neolithic
man in these localities occasionally flavoured his wheaten
bread with cultivated caraway seeds.

Amongst Neolithic industries, in addition to the fundamental pursuits of tillage and stock-raising, basket-
making held a high place, and they also knew how to
spin, weave, and dye flax, making cloth and thread and
rope from it.    The use of wool quickly followed.    Most
characteristic of all are the stone axes and pottery, and
as their development can be distinctly traced, they
give great assistance in fixing the comparative dates of
deposits.

Although the Neolithic Age takes its name from the
distinctive polished stone implements of that period, it
is important to bear in mind that not all Neolithic stone
implements were polished, although the majority undoubtedly were.    Palaeolithic man chipped and flaked
his flints by blows, and later, more delicately, by pressure :
he never seems to have ground or polished his implements,
and in any case flint is a difficult substance to polish.
In the Magdalenian period, bone implements were
smoothed and polished, and probably the first attempts
in stone were made in regions—whether in Asia or Europe
we do not know—where flint was scarce.    Flint, however,
was still the principal raw material for the manufacture
of tool-heads : consequently it was eagerly sought after
and prized.    Neolithic flint mines and tool factories are
a feature of the Neolithic records, as at Grand Pressigny
near Tours (France), Spiennes in Belgium  and Cissbury

in England. The Neolithic workers not merely used different kinds of pebbles, but had learned to discern minerals harder than flint, such as nephrite or jade and saussurite, making small chisel-like blades which they set in a socket of horn ; the latter was in turn fixed in a wooden handle. Of the implements or celts with flint or stone heads there is a great variety in shape and manufacture. They ranged in length from one or two up to as many as twelve inches. The handles were usually of wood or the antlers of deer. Some were in the form of primitive hoes or mattocks ; others, more adze-like, with a sharp transverse edge, were used for hollowing out boats. Salt, gold in small quantities, copper, amber, and the various hard minerals used in the manufacture of stone axes became also commodities of barter and exchange over increasingly wide areas, as the use of cattle as beasts of burden, and greater skill in the construction of boats, enabled Neolithic man to come and go in the development of Neolithic trade.

If there is no evidence as yet of the domestication of the horse in Europe, and no wheeled cart is known before the Bronze Age, still the trails of Neolithic man led by the less heavily wooded uplands, or by the sides of the rivers, or along the shores of the lakes, from one known point to another. Several of the greatest civilisations of the world are associated with a river valley, and it was not otherwise in Neolithic times, as the Danube could evidence. If Magdalenian man was something of a fisherman, Neolithic man was even more so. The occupants of the Danish shell-heaps went out far enough to catch cod, and emigrants from Asia Minor constructed boats that took them to Crete. Before the end of this Age there were trade routes between the countries around the Baltic, while the shores of the Black Sea and the rivers falling into it were also the scenes of expeditions for trade or plunder. There is further evidence of close communication between the Mediterranean lands and Egypt and Asia Minor ; indeed, the territorial limits of Neolithic commerce have still to be discovered. Certainly the trade in amber followed a well-marked route by way of the Vistula and Dniester between the Baltic and the Mediterranean. Perhaps the mutual desire to exchange amber for copper between the north and south, led, as has been suggested, to the more rapid passing of the Neolithic Age in Northern Europe. For with these commodities must have gone much exchange of ideas and customs, and most of what was new in those days came into the south of Europe from the east. But there is also evidence that the northerners did not merely receive, but critically examined, and in many cases improved upon that which was introduced to them, by admixture with what was local, whether in the business of stock raising, or the expression of ideas in implements and works of art. Amongst the latter group, pottery holds an out-standing place. Indeed, as Professor J. M. Tyler remarks, ' pottery is to the archaeologist what characteristic fossils are to the palaeontologist.' [1] It is fairly indestructible, and by its texture, form, and decoration provides an admirable indication of date and relationship. As we have seen, pottery is not known before Mesolithic days. Shells and gourds, skulls, skins, and vessels of bark and wood were probably all used as receptacles for fluids before the potter's art was discovered. His wheel is not known before the Bronze Age, although beautiful and well-made work has been described by Pumpelly from the oldest deposits at Susa. The more artistic pieces have been often found in graves.

By far the most important witnesses to Neolithic man and the spirit that was in him are the megalithic struc-tures that he erected in such numbers throughout the world. Varying greatly both in size and form, they are yet ' reducible to two fundamental types, the *polylith* or *cell* and the *monolith* or *block*.' [2] To the former class are referable the so-called cromlechs or dolmens (stone chambers), cairns, tumuli or barrows ; under the second

[1] *Op. cit.* p. 153.    [2] A. H. Keane, *Ethnology*, p. 123.

group are included the menhirs, alignments or avenues, and stone circles. Both groups are associated with burial and religious rites, probably connected, in some cases, with ancestor-worship. The simplest type of cell or dolmen was a rectangular sepulchral chamber made by setting up four or more megaliths on edge with little or no foundation excavated, and covering them with a still larger horizontal slab. Usually the stone at one end, facing the east, was somewhat smaller, leaving an aperture between it and the roof, through which access was gained to the chamber. The megaliths in these simpler structures, such as are found so commonly in Sweden and Denmark to-day, are ordinarily from 5 to 7 feet in length, 2 to 3½ feet wide, and 3 to 5 feet high. Within this chamber were deposited the bodies of the dead—it might be more than one—or urns containing their ashes when cremation was in vogue, with or without gifts. The cell was then covered with a heap of earth, thus producing the cairn or tumulus, particularly when the chamber or system of chambers was of any size or length. In some cases, particularly in the original Egyptian graves, the tumulus was further supported by a containing wall, or walls, of stones (mastaba). In some of the simple types there was a doorway composed of two upright stones and a lintel. In Denmark and elsewhere, occasionally these tumuli are approached by a covered culvert-like entrance, formed out of blocks of stone, the whole structure thus bearing a striking resemblance to primitive dwellings. Under the action of prolonged weathering the super-structure has often disappeared, when the original cell and remains of the mastaba (if present) are left exposed as 'stone circles.' They probably indicate a settled community.

Not merely the polyliths, the individual stones of which sometimes weighed scores of tons and had been transported great distances, but the actual superstructures, must have been a work of enormous labour under the conditions of the Neolithic Age. Thus a cairn like

'Crouching burial,' Adlerborg, near Worms.

Menhir, Carnac, Brittany.

Fig. 26.—Dolmen, Haga, Island of Borust. (From J. M. Tyler's *New Stone Age in N. Europe.*)

Silbury Hill, near Marlborough, covering five acres, and with a height which must once have exceeded the present weathered vertical height of 130 feet, could not be raised over every hereditary chief, and so the idea of the ' family vault ' arose. Further, the entrance to so imposing a burial-place might not always have been easily recognisable ; accordingly it was marked by a menhir or monolith (block), or perhaps by two of them. Those menhirs stand to-day at places in isolation—possibly old boundary marks—or beside dolmens, when they were probably associated with some religious, burial, or nature-worship cult, or yet again in circles, or parallel or converging alignments. Some of these isolated menhirs are of immense size : of the 739 registered in Brittany, the largest, that at Locmariaquer (Morbihan), now fallen and broken, was 67½ feet high and weighed 347 tons. Carnac, in the same department, is representative of several adjacent formations. Here the alignments consist of ten or eleven lines of menhirs, of which 1991 remain, extending·to a distance of more than one mile. In some instances they lead to cromlechs, and it is difficult to suppose that others which to-day seem to lead to nothing, were originally of this purposeless nature. Comparison with the conditions in the case of the circular arrangement at Stonehenge suggests that these structures were primarily places of worship and assembly, divorced in some instances at any rate from the chambered tumulus, and that still later, places of burial were selected near them. These climactic developments of megalithic industry belong to the Bronze Age, and were primarily connected with religion and worship. In the Deccan and other parts of India, such menhirs ' are still erected either as votive offerings or as monuments to the dead,' [1] quite apart from any connection with actual places of burial.

We have seen in the case of Palaeolithic man, that while there is evidence of affection for the dead, there is also evidence of fear, and that it is not improbable that efforts

[1] Keane, *op. cit.* p. 130.

were made to hamper the activity of the spirit which was supposed to reside within, or in the vicinity of, the body, particularly, we may assume, if the individual had not commended himself in life to those with whom he lived. On the other hand, local leaders must have arisen in communities—older men, who by their wisdom, or service of their fellows, had gained their respect, if not their admiration, and whose return would have been welcomed. In some such atmosphere we may suppose ancestry worship, or the cult of the hero, to have arisen. There is at any rate no doubt in the Neolithic mind that there is a spirit world, and that a spirit dwells in the human frame. Remarkable witness to this belief is found in the evidence of the practice of trepanning. Our wonder is increased when we are told that this major operation of exacting delicacy under the best of modern conditions was performed with a certain amount of surgical skill. Apparently the mode of operation consisted in scraping the skull gradually with a sharp flint flake until an oval perforation was made. At any rate, the operation is still performed in this way by the natives of New Ireland, one of the islands to the east of New Guinea, for reasons that have not been adequately investigated, with the aid of an obsidian flake and vegetable bandages.[1] That the Neolithic surgeon had proved successful on many occasions in his operation—about the diagnosis we can only guess—is proved by the circumstance that the margins of the incisions had healed over. It is, however, difficult to be certain as to the purpose of the mysterious performance. It may be that even at this early date such diseases as lunacy and epilepsy were attributed to the presence of evil spirits in the affected subject, and that in this procedure we see a Neolithic effort at redemption. The skull was opened to free the individual from the evil spirit to which he was in bondage. If this were the case, it would be a very clear indication of Neolithic belief in a spiritual world. It has also

[1] Keith, *The Antiquity of Man*, p. 20.

been suggested that as the operation was most frequently performed on the young, it may have partaken of a ceremonial character, forming part of a rite of initiation into some sacred caste : this, however, seems less probable.

Late in the Neolithic Age, when the character of the megalithic structures seems to be more definitely associated with worship, the practice of cremation crept in, and gradually spread till, in the Bronze Age, it became the rule, and inhumation the exception.   It is still uncertain whether burial was general in Neolithic times, so corresponding, perhaps, to a belief in the immortality of all men.   The evidence suggests that in some regions it was selective,—a distinction accorded only to the great ones of the tribe and their families.

The religion of Neolithic times is very largely a development of the vague conceptions of Palaeolithic man. It is still a recognition and worship of Powers, apparently unrestricted in their numbers, and as yet only occasionally conceived in anthropomorphic guise.   The Olympian hierarchy was a much later development.   Nevertheless the idea of spirit has already become more definite and real, particularly in relation to man himself.   Further, the individual member of a Neolithic settled community, pastoral and agricultural as it was, based on a scant and superficial acquaintance with the routine of Nature, and often entirely at a loss to understand why crops had failed or herds had not yielded their increase, was moved to connect the failure of the Powers or Spirits that informed these processes with some infraction of *tabu*, or failure or shortcoming in himself.   There was no other explanation ;  they could not all be malevolently intentioned towards himself.   And so ' there arises an individual feeling of pollution and of the need of expiation which will blaze out in the oldest Greek tragedies as almost a veritable sense of sin.' [1]   In an atmosphere such as this developed the pre-Homeric mysteries with their rites of purification, and renovation of implements and materials.

[1] Tyler, *op. cit.* p. 214.

This simple and yet profound religion of Neolithic man very easily survived the temporary development of the brilliant, aesthetic, superficial Olympian phase.   The latter had little hold on Reality ; it had lost all mysticism, and was largely an exaggerated and sublimated reproduction of the lives of a hierarchy of earthly chieftains.   The Neolithic religion, coarse and superstitious as it doubtless was in many of its phases, yet was based on a profound conviction of the reality of a spiritual world which had direct relationship with the world of everyday life, and upon the understanding of, and right relationship with which depended the whole of life.   It recognised the possibility of the forbidden thing ; it realised the need for purification ; it was ringed round with mystery.

The development of agriculture and of stock-raising could not fail to exert its reflex influence on Neolithic religion.   As the conception of the invisible Powers became more anthropomorphic, the old cult of a goddess of fertility spread throughout the Neolithic world—Isis of the Egyptians, Artemis of the Ephesians, Astarte of the Phoenicians, Demeter of the Greeks.   Often associated with this primary cult of goddesses are traces of a dominant matriarchy or mother right—succession reckoned through the female line, rights of inheritance by the daughter, in short a state of society in which woman really held the commanding position.   It is not difficult to see how this came to be ; for while primitive man was engaged on his hunting and fishing expeditions, and even during the succeeding stage when he was developing the beginnings of pastoral life, the women and children remained in and around the home.   And it is most probable that women took the first steps in agriculture, as they looked for the fruits and roots and seeds that were amongst the early fare of man.   Possibly noticing how seeds that had been thrown out in the vicinity of the settlement or by some revisited watering-place, or laid as a food offering in the upturned soil of some place of burial, had sprung up, they prosecuted, by making holes in the ground with digging sticks, and later with hoes, their first slow and laborious studies in tillage. Cattle ploughing, which came in much later, is man's work. Certainly, also, women discovered and developed all the arts of the home—spinning and weaving and pottery, and probably their sick children forced them to be the first herbalists and physicians.

We have stated that like Palaeolithic man, his Neolithic successor was an immigrant so far as Europe is concerned. If the tall Sikh-like Aurignacian race possibly came by way of Africa, it seems probable that the short-headed 'Alpine' race of Furfooz and Grenelle came by the Central European route. The nursery and forcing-house of these cultures we have laid, following Tyler, in the Iranian plateau, somewhere to the westward or north-westward of the great plateau of Thibet. To a wave like that of the Hamitic-Semitic peoples moving slowly westward, Arabia would not have presented the same difficulties as to-day, being, as was also the Sahara, a well-watered temperate region during the moist climate of the glacial episodes farther to the north and north-west : so Arabia held the Semites, and the Hamites spread along the southern shores of the Mediterranean. At a slightly later stage we may think of another migration from the eastern centre moving up the valley of the Euphrates and along the rich and attractive region of Asia Minor, and crossing over first into Greece and Crete, and later to Italy. These formed the 'Mediterranean' race. Still later, as we shall see, a third route was followed that led from the northern edge of the Iranian plateau, and swinging to the north of the Caspian and Black Seas through Southern Siberia and the Russian plain, entered the valley of the Danube and so reached Central and Northern Europe. These changes of route were in great part determined by the changing physical conditions in Arabia as the climate became warmer and drier.

If we ask for the reason of these migrations, the answer will probably be found in terms of environmental change. As the result of the long-continued and thorough investi-

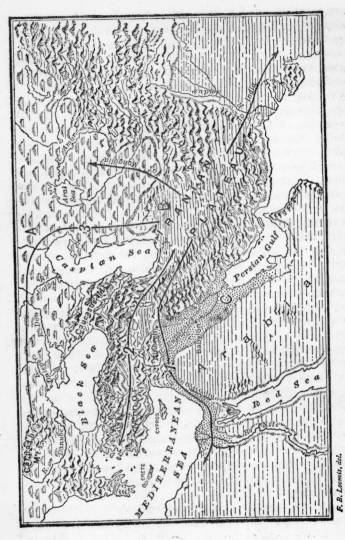

F. B. Loomis, del.

FIG. 27.—Migrations of Peoples. 1, Southernmost route to the Mediterranean and Africa. 2, Middle route through Asia Minor. 3, Northern route around Caspian Sea to Carpathians. A, Grass-lands and steppe. B, Iranian Plateau (central portion). C, Valley of Mesopotamia. (From J. M. Tyler's *New Stone Age in N. Europe.*) Page 169.

gations conducted by Raphael Pumpelly and his co-workers in Turkestan, it is possible to picture to ourselves the progressive desiccation in Central Asia throughout long climatic cycles in the Later Pleistocene, which, while it permitted of local civilisations flourishing in the favourable extremes, on the other hand compelled radial migrations during the arid extremes, which thus brought to Europe the Aryan peoples, culture and language. Evidence of present-day desiccation can be seen throughout the whole Aralo-Caspian depression, formerly a great inland sea. Pumpelly attempts to show [1] that 'Central Asia was, from one of the epochs of the glacial period onward, isolated from Africa and Europe, and that, excepting the elements of the lowest generalised form of human culture, all its cultural requirements were necessarily evolved and differentiated within the region of isolation. Before the supposedly Central-Asian Sumerian fused with the Semites on the Euphrates they had been trained in a struggle with nature which had culminated in the ability to conceive and execute great undertakings, as shown in the work of controlling the great river. Their field of thought was doubtless confined largely to economic effort and organisation. Into the fusion, the contemplative nomadic shepherd Semites brought a new range of speculative thought, and out of the union arose the highly developed Babylonian civilisation. And to the extent that this entered into the origins of pre-classic Aegean and Mycenean cultures, so far did it carry the contribution of the fundaments of civilisation from the Central-Asia oases to the Mediterranean.' Pumpelly further considers that ' the earlier reactions of the oasis cultures on the outside world were, therefore, both as regards migrations and ideas, essentially constructive in character. The later and greater migrations were of a different character. The growth of great nomadic populations, to whose outward movement these were due, could not have begun until after the development of the

[1] *Explorations in Turkestan*, p. xxxii.

vations by de Morgan at Susa, 130 miles due north of the head of the Persian Gulf. Here continuity is preserved through a depth of about 40 metres of mound deposits, the original natural surface—that of the earliest settlement—being about 6 metres below the present-day surface. These earliest deposits, Neolithic in every respect, have been estimated by de Morgan and Montelius to be 18,000 years old. Roughly this would correspond to the Magdalenian in Europe. The distinctive pottery links the site in a general way with Anau and other stations, and suggests that at a very early date Western Asia was a region characterised by a considerable number of settled communities.

It is easy to make mistaken generalisations, particularly where the data are meagre, but such evidence as there is seems to mark out the Neolithic Age as distinctively an Age of Peace. Life in such crowded communities as the Swiss lake-dwellings must have been endurable only on some system of co-operation and forbearance. The conditions do not suggest any very serious economic difficulties. Between their domesticated animals, the waters of the lake, the fruits of tillage, and the forest chase, these lake-dwellers cannot often have been in want. They had great possibilities of communication with other settlements on the lake shore, and were not so remote from other centres of population. There is no local evidence of hostile invasions under pressure of a desire for food or conquest : indeed, weapons other than those of the chase form a very small proportion of Neolithic remains. The general impression of Neolithic life everywhere is very much that of the lake-dwellings in summer—activity, but peace.

Further, there can be little doubt that in this period of pastoral and agricultural settlements, which seem to give little evidence of any highly developed political organisation, the connecting link of the community was religion. Neolithic man believed in a spiritual world, believed also that he could assist the beneficent Powers and work together with them for his own material good. It was a period when, undisturbed, he was able to put his childlike questions to Nature, make simple experiments, and strive to find the relations between things. It was an age of sheer physical robustness, and yet of a strange and deep tenderness—witness the Anau mothers who buried their dead children, and their children only, under the earthen floors of their houses, refusing to let them be banished from the home; or the Neolithic Irish mothers, who sometimes buried a dog along with their children, as indeed some North American Indian tribes do to this day, so that the child should have a guide in the unfamiliar realm of spirits who would always know the way home. Towards the close of the Neolithic Age, however, when the peoples of Northern Germany began to crowd back and in upon those of Central Europe, there begins to be evidence of fortified villages, particularly when there was something to defend, be it a salt mine or a flint factory. Doubtless the minglings and readjustments and reactions did not take place without some disturbances, but out of them came the beginnings of a new Age.

The Neolithic Age, thus briefly described and summarised, is a period of which more detailed examination would reveal a developmental process at work in all its aspects and elements : at the same time there is much overlapping, and different regions are at different stages. This development can, however, be clearly discerned, for example, in the records of the Swiss lake-dwellings. Thus an initial stage is noticeable in which the axe-heads were on the whole small, the workmanship upon horn and bone implements rude, the pottery coarse and without decoration, and sources of supplies for the greater part sought in the chase. The middle of the Neolithic is marked by a growth in size of implements and a finer finish in their workmanship, and efficiency in construction. The pottery is better made and shows traces of ornament. Remains of domesticated and of wild animals occur in about equal proportions. The Late Neolithic is characterised by beautifully finished ' hammer-axes ' somewhat like a light stonemason's hammer, often with one cutting and one blunt end, and with the handle driven through the head. A development of horn and bone implements continues, pottery is still more artistic, and remains of domesticated animals are greatly in excess of those that were taken in the chase. The sheep now occurs in greater numbers than the goat. But the gradual introduction of copper made less demand on minerals like nephrite whether for ornaments, weapons, or other implements.

Thus gradually the Neolithic Age in Europe passed about 2000 B.C. into what is sometimes separately designated as the Copper Age,—a phase which had already commenced in Western Asia some three thousand years previously. This metal probably ' entered south-eastern Europe by way of Troy, or northward from Greece through the Balkan Peninsula to the Danube valley.' [1] It proved attractive for ornaments—armlets and bracelets—and for smaller piercing and cutting implements. But the edge of a copper axe did not hold, and the designation of an Age is hardly justified, at any rate in Europe, for a substance which was most commonly used for articles that were on the whole more in the nature of luxuries. Some unknown genius once noticed that when the ore contained certain impurities the alloy was harder. Still there must have been considerable experimenting before the virtues of a mixture of ninety per cent. of copper and ten per cent. of tin were discovered. But from that discovery, wherever made, unheralded and unlaureated, the Bronze Age dates. To this there succeeded the Iron Age. Thereafter we reach the Historic Era, the age of written records, of literature, of the fine arts and modern culture generally. It is connected by quite definite traditions with the previous Age. So Hesiod tells of times when ' their armour was of bronze, and their houses of bronze,

Tyler, *op. cit.* p. 140.

and of bronze were their implements : there was no black iron.' [1]

A final word may be added with regard to that latest astonishing development of Asiatic Neolithic life and culture which swept westward, carried by the Indo-European or Aryan people, and expressed in part through the medium of a language which underwent development into various Indian and Iranian (Persian) branches on the one hand, and on the other into Greek, Latin, Slav, and other tongues in Europe. It came in amongst other languages, and eventually conquered. These migrations apparently began about 2000 B.C. Tyler [2] quotes E. Meyer as stating that the ' horse-taming ' Achaeans had already arrived in the Southern Balkans from Hungary—originally from farther east by the third or northern route [3]—by that date, and that they reached Greece about 1300 or 1200 B.C. They came in successive waves, followed by Dorians and then by Thracians. Their social organisation was based on the clan system, each with its leader. They were an inflow of rough, boisterous, full-blooded barbarians, who, although certainly less numerous, rather upset for the time being the prosperous and staid old Pelasgic agricultural and pastoral population. Their virility and energy made them dominant, and for the first time in history we are really aware of individual leadership and personality beginning to emerge from the tribal group. National feeling did not exist amongst the Neolithic (Grecian) Pelasgi, and so there was no real resistance to the invaders. These peasant people had lived simple prosperous lives, acting together, and desiring very much to be left alone. These Indo-Europeans—Achaeans and ancient Celts, from whom in the latter case it is not impossible that the Germans received both language and customs—probably came, although few questions are more disputable, from a

---

[1] *Works and Days*, lines 150-151 (Trans. H. G. Evelyn-White, Loeb Classics).
[2] *Op. cit.* p. 253.                    [3] Cf. p. 169.

M

region in what is to-day southern or south-eastern Russia toward the Caspian. Probably they also moved out, as in so many other instances, under the influence of climatic changes.

Until towards the close of the Neolithic, tribal considerations were pre-eminent ; the individual had hardly begun to exist. Education, religion, responsibility were tribal, with promulgations and decisions largely in the hands of a body of elders of the tribe, a sort of Council of Seniors. Land also was mainly common property : religious ritual was a service of the community as a whole. The gods and goddesses were local, very numerous, no one supreme, though some, as *e.g.* the goddess of fertility, were much more important than others. Some were gradually losing their importance, and becoming a part of folklore rather than of full-blooded life. But with the leaders of the Bronze Age, the ' Age of Heroes,' there began to be the possibility of nations—aggregates, that is to say, on a larger scale than the tribe. It was an age of hierarchies on Olympus and on the earth, but only for a season : the fundamental basal recognitions of Neolithic life came into their own again, purified and intensified. Likewise, as almost always, both Celt and Achaean were ultimately absorbed by the people whom they had overcome.

# CHAPTER VIII

## THE PLACE AND FUNCTION OF NATIONALITY

FEW conceptions have come into renewed prominence within the last decade of which the elusiveness in definition is greater than that of Nationality. Dictionary references to qualities, or ' that complex of qualities in a group of persons which combine them in a nation,' still leave unsolved the vital issue—What is a nation ? In some respects it is easier to say what a nation is not. Thus, to begin with, a nation is not necessarily a race. It may include one or more races, and conversely any given race may find its members divided into more than one nation, and even combined in national unity with members of another race. In nation and race we are dealing with two actualities, one of which is in a sense more ultimate than the other, for while a race is conceivable that is not yet a nation, no nation is conceivable that is not composed of a constituent race or races. Nationality, that is to say, is a later development than race. It is a state of mind, a consciousness, an acquiescence, a conviction. It is something, moreover, that the individual can change, which is not the case with race ; a man cannot change his parents or his ancestors. At the same time there are many indications tending to show that, ultimate as it may appear to be, race plays no part comparable with that of ideas or culture as a determining factor in the world's progress. Further, and more important, it is very doubtful whether racial purity exists anywhere in the world to-day. For example, a recent important discussion [1] made it clear that, whatever

[1] The Origin of the Scottish People, *B. A. Report*, 1922, p. 439.

the constituent elements, the Scottish people were in no
ethnographic sense a pure race.   According to Sir Arthur
Keith, it is ' certain ' that the inhabitants of the High-
lands and western parts of Scotland and of the inland
parts of Scandinavia are traceable to the same racial
(Nordic) stock—descendants of a Mesolithic stock in
South-West Europe.   At the time of this dispersal,
which followed the emergence of Scotland and Scandinavia from the ice, ' the North Sea was an estuary
or bay, open to the north, with a western shore leading
up to Scotland ; an eastern leading to Scandinavia.' [1]
Much later, in the second millennium B.C., Scotland also
felt the influence of the Celtic round-headed invasion
that had filtered into Europe from the east during the
preceding millennia.   Again, in the fifth century A.D.,
Dalriad Scots, of the same physical type as those who
had originally settled in Scotland, entered that country
from Ireland, while the East Coast was always open to
immigrants from across the North Sea.   Professor Bryce
considers that a third distinct element, representative
of the Mediterranean Megalithic race, is recognisable
in the Scottish pre-Roman population, and it is matter
of common observation that there is greater mental and
physical community between the Lowland Scot and the
men of Northumbria, than between the former and the
Highland Scot. Scotland, whose people have very
marked mental and moral characteristics, is far from
being a racial unit,[2] and an interesting inquiry might
throw much light on the way in which the Lowlanders
usurped for themselves and their tongue the designation
' Scottish,' which previously belonged to the Highlanders
and Gaelic-speaking elements.

Again, whatever degree of racial purity exists to-day,
it appears to be the case that with the inevitable shrinkage

[1] *Op. cit.* p. 439.

[2] ' Even into the fifteenth century Galloway was governed by laws
of its own, and till the beginning of the eighteenth century it clung to
the Celtic language, which it had inherited from before the days of
St. Columba.'—(P. Hume Brown, *Surveys of Scottish History*, p. 21.)

in the world's circumference as the result of modern methods of transport, intermingling of races is going on to a degree before which all artificial barriers are breaking down. Professor Conklin draws attention to the fact that in the United States ' one-quarter of all persons of African descent contain more or less white blood ; there are about eight million full-blooded negroes and two million mulattoes, and during the past twenty years the latter have increased at twice the rate of the former.' [1] The same thing occurs in every country where different races live together ; even the Jews, who from all time have prided themselves upon the purity of their descent, are becoming increasingly a mixed population, while the term ' Anglo-Indian ' now officially replaces the older word ' Eurasian ' in connection with the process of hybridisation, which is said to be increasing rather than decreasing in India to-day. As is well known from examples in lower forms of life, it by no means follows that such hybrid races are necessarily always inferior to the supposed pure stocks. Probably a great part of the reason for believing the contrary is the fact that people pay more for pedigreed freaks, say in the case of dogs, than they are willing to do for what they choose to call mongrels. Yet none of these unnatural forms, from dachshund to Pekingese, would survive apart from man's special care of them, being singularly ill-equipped for life on the canine plane of things. As a matter of fact, however, few races of living beings are more mongrel than that of mankind to-day. It is doubtful if any race is pure, and indeed there is little to suggest the superiority of a pure human race over a mixed one, even if we could be sure of having the former. In a remarkable book on *The Biology of War*,[2] Professor Nicolai of Berlin ventured at one point to expose some of the pretensions of his pan-Germanist fellow-countrymen so far as they were based on the supposed racial purity of the German

---

[1] *Heredity and Environment in the Development of Men*, p. 417.
[2] Published during the War, 1916 : English trans. 1919.

' the plain common-sense view ' in the speaker's opinion; as such, as he remarked, it is a comparatively recent development in Europe. Indeed, the word *nation* has actually changed its etymological meaning with this development in the actual objective reality. Originally the word *nation* signified a race (*i.e.* tribe) and was applied to any people—especially those who were distant or barbarous—who lived in a country. In the course of history the word came to be applied to any organised group of people, and now to its more precise but even yet vaguely grasped meaning, for it is not always easy to say just what size of a group has a right to call itself a nation or has attained nationhood, or to indicate the principles that should be recognised in the formation of an independent self-governing unit.

Ancient history,[1] then, shows nothing comparable to this modern conception of a nation. It knew of city states, and, later, aggregates of Empires like that of Persia. The forty-six ' nations ' that marched with Xerxes against the Greeks were for the most part little more than wild tribes with very varying degrees of military equipment and social laws. The period covered by the Roman Empire meant definite retardation of national isolation. The dominant ideals of the Middle Ages—the Feudal System and Chivalry—had nothing national in them, as we understand that word. They represented a horizontal stratification of humanity in certain military and religious aggregates of these times. The Holy Roman Empire, in theory a continuance of the Roman Empire, but influenced by the unity of the Church, was deliberately opposed to national or vertical subdivision. In protest against this falsely conceived supra-nationalism of the Roman Empire, true nationalism first crystallised out in France and England, in the later part of the Middle Ages. In Scotland, also, impulses

---

[1] For many of the facts in the immediately following paragraphs the writer would acknowledge his indebtedness to Sir Richard Lodge.

towards nationhood developed, which were largely the result of the War of Independence.

The period of the Reformation, on the other hand, was potent in national development. Initially directed against abuses in a non-national Church, this religious movement could not fail to be influenced by the special political circumstances of the time. The Papal residence in Avignon (1309-1378), followed by the Great Schism (1378-1416), were very influential in combining opposition to the Papacy and its abuses with national sentiment. Luther's imperative demands for reform synchronised with—perhaps were a partial expression of—a general desire for a break-up of the political unity that had for centuries accompanied the superficial religious unity of Europe. Accordingly, with the exception of France, nationality developed more quickly in the Protestant countries of Europe. Roman Catholic France became indeed as completely a national State as England, yet it is interesting to realise by how very little France missed becoming a Protestant State, for the connection of Protestantism with nationality was very strong even there. Sir Richard Lodge has expressed the opinion that if the French Protestant leaders had been abler and more prudent statesmen, France would have become a leading Protestant State. Unfortunately the Huguenots identified themselves with the interests of the classes and towns, and the maintenance of the feudal system, and the Massacre of St. Bartholomew was the result of a fear that they constituted a danger to the political unity and security of France.

In Germany, where the Reformation was only partially successful, it militated against national unity, but it certainly aided in the unification of the separate States, and in furnishing them with a strength and cohesion which they had not previously known. In Holland, Sweden, and Denmark, Protestantism reinforced national feeling. In other European countries there was no real development in a national direction until after the French

Revolution. Thus Spain was for long merely a bundle of foreign provincial states—more of a geographical expression than a nation. But later, when France in the strength of her developed nationhood had thrown back the foreign invaders, and become in turn the aggressor, she thereby excited in Spain and the other countries which she overran that very spirit of nationality in virtue of which she had gained her initial easy triumphs. From that moment the defeat of France was certain. ' Napoleon who, trusting to his armies, despised moral forces in politics, was overthrown by their rising.' [1]

The remarkable thing, however, is that at the Congress of Vienna (1815) which followed on the defeat of Napoleon, Nationality, the rock on which his ambitions foundered, did not triumph. A fatal return was made to that non-national conception of Europe which had been the cause of prolonged disturbance in the past, and the result was that the nineteenth century was a period of gradually increasing, and more and more explosive, hostility to this non-national settlement. In fact during the nineteenth century nationality came to be the most active and basic force in Europe. At first it was held in check and its successes were spasmodic. It was identified in its early stages with the growth of Liberalism, and in Great Britain no one fell more completely under the appeal of the ideal than Mr. Gladstone. Supporting his motion in the House of Commons in 1859 for the uniting of Moldavia and Wallachia as a Roumanian nation, he said, ' Surely the best resistance to be offered to Russia is by the strength and freedom of those countries that will have to resist her. You want to place a living barrier between Russia and Turkey. *There is no barrier like the breast of freemen.*' [2] Nationality was, in short, taking the form of a demand for the abolition of the artificial divisions and unions created by Vienna, *e.g.* the unions of Holland

---

[1] Lord Acton, Essay on ' Nationality ' in *The History of Freedom, and other Essays*, p. 285.
[2] Morley's *Life of Gladstone*, vol. ii. pp. 3 and 4 (italics as in original).

and Belgium, of Sweden and Norway. But especially was attention directed to the demand for unity by the two great peoples who had hitherto failed to attain national unity, viz. Germany and Italy.

The third quarter of the 19th century will always stand out as a period in which Nationality gained three notable triumphs which finally made it the outstanding and invincible political force of that age. 'At the present day,' said Lord Acton, writing in 1862, 'the theory of nationality is not only the most powerful auxiliary of revolution, but its actual substance in the movements of the last three years. . . . A great democracy must either sacrifice self-government to unity, or preserve it by federation.' [1]  In Italy, so long associated with the ideals of the Roman Catholic Church, a memorable movement arose for freedom from the foreigner and unity amongst the component States themselves. There was manifest sympathy throughout Europe with Italy in the attempt to throw off the Austrian yoke, but the general impression was that the union would be of a federal type. Yet Mazzini boldly proclaimed the principle of Nationality, and nationality won. Where nationality exists, he had said, there is an inherent right to independence. The same result was secured in the unification of Germany, although by different means and principles : here Feudalism had hitherto supplied the binding element in society that the Roman Catholic Church had provided in Italy. But Feudalism was a federal link rather than a unifying bond, and in all the early national States the destruction of Feudalism was an essential part of their growth. Once again, across the seas, a struggle was being waged on the North American Continent which, although superficially and sentimentally associated with the economic and humanitarian question of the abolition of slavery, was really primarily concerned with the fundamental issue of the right of any of the component States to secede and form a self-governing unit by themselves.

[1] *Op. cit.* p. 276.

In each of these three instances the guiding principle
was national unity at all hazards—the assertion of the
right to unite and to maintain a union based on ethnographical, cultural, and aspirational demands.

Within the period covered by the first quarter of the
present century and culminating in the Great War, it
has seemed to several highly competent observers as if
Nationality had latterly developed on quite other lines,
and assumed more and more the guise of the right to
separate or divide or break off from some other unit to
which the smaller group had either been compulsorily
attached, or in which it had become absorbed by some
accident of history. If we consider the situation as it
developed in the latter part of 1914, we find three States
united against the Allies, of which two were quite unaffected by the principle of nationality—Austria-Hungary
and Turkey. The case of the former represented an
empire held by dynastic rights acquired by marriage,
the whole conception of which, far from being national,
was rather deliberately anti-national : concessions to
Hungary on this score had been exacted rather than
granted. The Ottoman Empire had been built up on
the negation of nationality ; there had even been an
attempt at the extermination of nationality in at any
rate one instance, but gradually Turkey had been compelled to grant independence to other of its constituent
ethnographical elements. In the case of Germany,
where nationality had been strikingly vindicated as a
principle amongst the strictly Teutonic element, the
incorporation of Slesvig-Holstein, of Posen, and of
Alsace-Lorraine had brought the dominant element into
conflict with that very principle which had made the
German Empire. So it came about that at an early
stage the Allies declared that they were fighting, *inter
alia*, in the interests of the principle of Nationality :—
' Once again the Allies declare that no peace is possible
so long as they have not secured reparation of violated
rights and liberties, recognition of the principle of nation-

alities, and of the free existence of small States.' [1]  When
in the early months of 1918 the situation in Poland and
Czecho-Slovakia made it clear that in countries where the
spirit of nationality was nascent, there was a peculiar
will to resist Germanism and Bolshevism alike, examination of the non-Slav Border regions of Russia disclosed a
corresponding state of affairs to which there was no
parallel in Slav Russia proper.  The non-Slav Border
States wished to be themselves, and this growing national
self-consciousness made them opposed at once to any
foreign domination or internal disorder.  This movement
towards national self-expression has persisted in various
quarters long after the signing of the Versailles Peace
Treaty of 1919, which was drawn up so largely in terms
of triumphant Nationality.

At this point, however, the question may quite legiti-
mately be raised as to whether, after all, the ' sore places '
of Europe have been healed, or are likely to be healed,
by this thorough-going application of the principle of
Nationality.  This must depend ultimately upon the
conception of nationality that underlies the relationships
between the elements involved.  What, then, is a nation,
and what entitles any particular group or combination
of population to call itself a nation ?  Now, as objective
matter of fact, there are coherent groups of population,
rarely, if ever, racially homogeneous, but usually connected with a definite territorial area, which have through
long association developed and maintained, often under
repressive conditions, a degree of social life more complex
than that of the ordinary tribal community, as also a
continuity of tradition, and a depth of common thought
and feeling, more or less distinctive.  All this has in
some instances reached a visible degree of organisation—
that complex of institutions which is called a State.  In
face of all such situations, ' one hardly knows,' with John
Stuart Mill,[2] ' what any division of the human race

---

[1] *Allies' Reply to German Peace Note*, December 30, 1916.
[2] *Considerations on Representative Government*, p. 296.

should be free to do, if not to determine with which of the various collective bodies of human beings they choose to associate themselves.' And, adds Lord Acton, ' it is by this act that a nation constitutes itself.' [1] Now, while the characteristic feature of the 20th century is the formation of national States on the basis of liberty and the right to express what they believe to be distinctive in their cultural life, the characteristic feature of the 18th and 19th centuries in Europe, not yet wholly outgrown, was to form national States on a dynastic basis. A State is a community of people united into one body politic, recognising a central authority; such a State is recognised by itself and other States as independent and sovereign. It is the Nation regarded from a particular and objective, but mechanical and secondary, aspect—as a concrete personality from the point of view of International Law. That which entitles any particular group to call itself a nation is simply its possession of some creative and constructive common feeling, strong enough and persistent enough to organise its claim and impress other nations with the justice of recognising it. To indicate at what stage or size or dignity nationality begins is as hard ' as to say how many grains are needed to form a heap.' [2] But the two terms are not necessarily interchangeable. Thus Scotland is, as we have seen, a Nation but no longer a State, Austria-Hungary was a State but not a Nation, while Holland is a Nation-State. The League of Nations is really a League of States.

The idea that is suggested by the British Commonwealth as the best type of the more inclusive group is that of a group of self-governing States with a Central Government for a minimum of purposes—*e.g.* defence and treaty-making. What is demanded by each unit or member of the group is the right to develop itself in its own way, which must be admitted so long as that is not injurious to the other members. Now where that development

---

[1] *Op. cit.* p. 287.
A. E. Zimmern, *Nationality and Government*, p. 55.

and assertion concern language, literature, traditions, *i.e.* to say, spiritual characters, they are unlikely to be injurious to the other members. It is when ideas of economic monopoly or political supremacy or territorial aggrandisement enter in that the trouble begins. When one nation, believing in the inherent superiority of its national type or ideal, attempts to impose these by force upon other nations, resistance is naturally developed.

It is not generally realised how relatively small is the part played by reason in the lives and activities of mankind even to-day. The integrating factors in all animal societies are instincts, and in man—the bondman in process of winning freedom [1]—instinct is still more universal and powerful than reason. The common opinion to the contrary is, as Professor E. G. Conklin indicates,[2] due to our inveterate habit of acting instinctively and *then* trying to explain to ourselves and others the reason for the act. The dawn of the Age of Reason is indicated by the gradual appreciation by man that he has a growing power to control his instincts and emotions by his intelligence, and that he is most distinctively man when he does so. To insist that racial, national, or class antagonisms are inevitable and ineradicable because they are instinctive, and that therefore war will be a constant element in human society, is to make an assertion in defiance of one of the most significant facts about man, viz. that he is *par excellence* the educable animal, who learns by experience ; it is also to ignore the growing realisation that war is treason to civilisation itself.

It seems, then, very probable that Nationalism, Internationalism, and what may be termed Supra-nationalism are three stages in the political and social evolution of mankind. It was a perverted sense of nationalism that in large part led to the Great War, and it is only a developed sense of supra-nationalism that will in the future make war unthinkable. That is to say, nationalism rightly conceived, can never be an end in itself ; it is only

Cf. chap. xi.　　　　[2] *The Direction of Human Evolution*, p. 90.

a means to an end. True nationalism is a great and a glorious thing, and shows itself in the development of such a State as will develop its distinctive individuality not merely for itself, thus providing a real corrective to all characterless and anaemic cosmopolitanism, but also with a view to that individuality becoming a contribution to the life of the world as a whole. In this way, however, it will gradually take a secondary, which is ultimately its true, place from this wider point of view. For the interests of humanity and civilisation are greater than those of any one nation ; that was in part the meaning of the War. Or, to put the matter in another way : nationalism is a phase through which every such population group or mass must and will pass in the winning of that self-consciousness and recognition by other groups or masses, without which it could not voluntarily enter into relations with these other masses for the greater good of the whole—relations which may involve to a certain degree the surrender of rights. Every nation has to go through certain phases of development comparable in a general way to those of the individual. The germ from which the British Commonwealth developed was undoubtedly the Union of Scotland and England in 1707—two countries differing greatly in habits, laws, and religion, and the subjects of ancient animosities, and conflicting sentiment. Yet it is not too much to say that before Scotland could get to the point of realising the value of such a step, which, it may be added, was highly unpopular at the time in certain circles, it was necessary that she should go through the phase of independence, and attainment of national self-consciousness. Then, only, as an equal was she able voluntarily to enter a limiting union for the sake of greater common ends.

The trend of the world movement in politics on the whole is in recognition of this fact. With the growing security of the idea of national freedom there will be a corresponding tendency to group more and more in large Confederations : thus we may eventually look forward, for example, to a Russian Confederation. On the whole, and in spite of recent events, nations as discrete, self-governing States are gradually being reduced in numbers with the progress of history. Languages are disappearing and the luxury of maintaining and speaking a restricted tongue will become more and more costly. The distinctive national dresses tend to pass into museums ; more and more we eat the same foods and burn the same fuel. The Atlantic has been proved to be only sixteen hours across by aeroplane : increasingly the nations become mixed up together in the bundle of life. The days of physical isolation are gone, though those of moral isolation may persist yet awhile. It may fairly be urged that the United States of America supplies us in a measure with a working-model of the supra-national State, for there is a very real sense in which the United States is a spiritual conception. The population of that country is composed of English, Dutch, French, Germans, Italians, Poles, Irish, Greeks, and others who carried over the seas every physical and mental trait of nationality, as ordinarily recognised under these various types, but agreed to sink them all, so to speak, and put them in a secondary position as they subscribed to those spiritual conceptions of liberty, in virtue of which they became citizens of the United States of America. In this way we may reach the conception of the United States of Europe, and thus of the World—in short, of a Union of Nations which, if and when dominated by certain ideals, will realise that condition of things foreseen by men of faith and vision throughout the ages, and variously described by them as the Perfect Society, the Age of Perpetual Peace, or the Kingdom of God upon earth. It will mean a condition of world affairs in which the phase ' Live and let live,' secured by the Great War, will gradually be replaced by that of ' Live and help live,' an era of rational co-operation in place of insane competition. Not that it is possible or even desirable to attempt to abolish competition : to do so could only be achieved at the cost of the elimination of life itself. For the whole progress of life has resulted from competition and successful response to environmental stimulus. Yet competition can be debrutalised, controlled, and transferred increasingly to the things of the spirit.

The intermediate stage of Internationalism, on which mankind is just entering, will have its full share of the difficulties of every transition period. Objectively it is best represented by the League of Nations, which, by providing for the meeting of representatives of the nations not merely on those occasions when they find themselves brought together by causes of difference, and by the remedial power placed in their hands under a specific clause in the Versailles Peace Treaty itself, will on the one hand obviate a repetition of one of the outstanding blunders of the Congress of Vienna, and on the other introduces a new phenomenon on the political horizon. At the same time it is insufficiently recognised that the nations represented round its table are not all on the same political or moral level, and that the process of education which it must primarily represent will be very slow. The natural self-assertiveness of young nationhood, the peculiar difficulty for it in submitting to the limitations involved in membership of the League before it has hardly had its fling of independence, the possible unscrupulous attempts of maturer nations to corrupt young nationhood, or pander to it to secure local advantages, the temptation for the more advanced nations to compromise on moral issues for the sake of peace and harmony, will for long be disturbing elements whose gradual recognition will, however, ultimately mean their transcendence. Yet the man who is tempted to despair of the future would do well to look back and see the road by which the human race has come—look unto the rock whence it was hewn, and to the hole of the pit whence it was digged.

But all this means that the nations will require to take a much more intelligent interest henceforth in each other's development and welfare, for if one member suffers, the whole body suffers. Indeed, it behoves every nation to watch for indications of retrogressive and uncivilising tendencies on the part of other peoples, expose them mercilessly as soon as they threaten, and so rally the rest of the world by economic boycott or otherwise to extirpate the atavism. A spiritual conquest, or that by virtue of the ideal, such as the United States has been making of its immigrants—although apparently not to the degree in which it was fondly imagined that this was being done prior to the War—is the only one that will eventually justify itself in the world. All the nations have to learn, and can only learn as the result of suffering and experience : they have all to be tested, and will continue to make blunders. Now these failures did not affect other nations so deeply in the days when they were not brought so closely together or interpenetrated one another's life as they do to-day. Probably the outside world was not very much affected, if it even knew, of the occasions when the Scots assassinated their kings, and all through the 19th century Spain had notoriously bad government, but the world went on pretty much the same. It may be hoped, however, that in the future this indifference will grow less and less, and that the pressure of civilisation in the form of the public opinion of a League of Nations will exercise a healthy influence on all retrogressive and incompetent Governments.

We may believe, then—we ought to believe—that every people has some cultural contribution which it can make to civilisation, some, of course, in far greater degree than others : for no one surely will maintain that there is any single nation or even group of nations which knows more about human knowledge or any branch or aspect of it than all the other nations put together. A nation may do one thing well : it may even do one thing best. Thus it is a commonplace that Greece gave the world political philosophy, Rome gave it a system of law, and Palestine gave it a religion. But there is no any rate in any deeper connotation of the word. In the forms of life below him, the vital emphasis apparently is laid upon the species ; it is in the interests of its survival that the constituent individuals appear to lead their lives, and, as sometimes happens amongst lower forms, perish after reproduction of their kind. In the higher phases of organic evolution, not only is there a general reduction in the number of offspring, but the life of the individual is maintained long after the period of reproduction is past. It looks as if in the case of the end term of the process, the individual was coming to have a peculiar meaning and significance.

Yet nothing is more difficult than to indicate with any precision wherein Individuality consists, or to state what is an Individual. From the point of view of etymology the word suggests the idea of inherent wholeness, corresponding to the root idea of the word ' atom,'—that which cannot be cut, or divided : where there is possibility of activity as especially in the case of the organic, the word suggests complementarily the idea of that which is incapable of dividing or fragmenting, of disruption or dissolution. On the physical plane it is apparently impossible to find the Individual as thus defined. With its energetic interpretation of matter, modern physics has abstracted such a character as essential being from the material world. The atom is no longer true to its name ; the electron is a statistical unit whose mass may vary with its velocity. In its practical account of the origin of atom and electron alike, in terms of energy, modern physics furnishes us with discrete particles of such regularity of size and uniformity of value that any one may take the place of any other, and in any mass of them, one portion has identical intrinsic properties with any other portion. To the divisibility of matter, so far as we know, there is no theoretical limit. Again, what is true of one type of crystal is true of all that type ; the same principle holds throughout the whole inorganic kingdom. Wherever we are dealing with the homogeneous, *In*dividuality is not there.   In atmosphere, hydrosphere, lithosphere, and barysphere, individuality in terms of the above definition is unknown.

When we pass, next, to the biosphere, it would seem at first as if the principle in question no longer held, for the organism is characterised by certain distinctive features to which there is no very close parallel in the inorganic world.   Chief amongst these, in this particular connection, is the fact that the organism of whatever species is a discrete body of more or less definite limit of size, which in its apartness and relative persistence is prophetic of a more enduring future.   There is something here that is relatively vastly in advance of either cloud or sandstorm, in respect of active maintenance of form. The crystal, like the organism, has a more or less definite form, but it is elastic, so to speak, and can expand or shrink almost indefinitely under certain conditions. ' In the process of organic growth the relation between mass and form no longer holds in all the exactness with which it applies to the growth of the crystal.' [1]   In the case of the latter there is always a strict relation between mass and geometrical dimensions, whereas the organism tends to change in form as it increases in size.   The characters of an organism depend not only upon what it is but upon what it has been.   Growth in the organism implies a cumulative variability in form which may eventuate in some departure from the typical form, but, at the same time, in size and form alike, the organism shows a concentration and a degree of assertive permanence that are suggestive of a developing end, the progressive achievement of some high purpose.   This concentration and active self-maintenance, expressed in the lessening independence of the constituent units, and by the progressive surrender of the power of regeneration, may be very clearly traced throughout the animal kingdom.   The concentrated united achievement of the first organism presented a unity of action that had hitherto been un-

[1] Prof. James Johnstone, *The Philosophy of Biology*, p. 172.

the general state of biological opinion, and the additional fact that almost all higher organisms commence their existence as the result of the union of two germ cells, the cell is here taken as the unit of life.[1]   But that should not be allowed to obscure the fact that even the simplest types of cell are comparatively highly organised elements, containing intracellular units of a lower order such as chromidia, chloroplasts, etc., which show many of the characteristics of living things, as, for example, growth and division inside their particular environment of a living cell.   The suggestion has already been made [2] that life in its earliest form was probably molecular, and it may well have taken the whole of the Archaeozoic Era to elaborate the cell.   The significance of the essential dividuality of the simplest forms of life is not impaired even when it is realised that the characterisation of the cell as the unit of life is merely a convention.

The transition from the unicellular to the multicellular stage is perhaps represented by colonial Protozoan and Protophytal forms such as *Volvox globator*.   How cells thus began to learn the value of co-operation, differentiation, and division of labour we do not know, although it is not difficult to imagine conditions in the environment of these primitive forms in which grouped cells would have chances of survival that would not have been the lot of single cells.   Further, the probability of this colonial Protozoan stage as the passage to the multicellular form is borne out by the fact that the continued segmentation of the fertilised egg-cell in higher forms, for example the sea urchin, results in the arrangement of the embryonic cells in a form corresponding more or less exactly to a *Volvox* colony.   This stage, resembling a

[1] The circumstance that mature germ cells, though having at that stage only half of the number of chromosomes characteristic of the species and so being morphologically equivalent to only half a cell, are yet considered to be cells, testifies to the present unsatisfactory state of cell doctrine in this and other respects.
[2] P. 16.

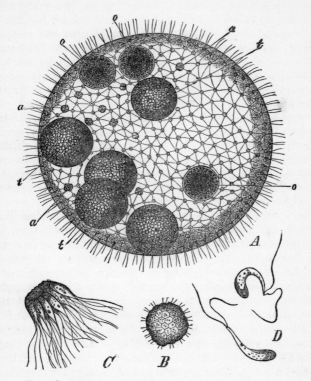

Fig. 28.—*Volvox aureus.* *A*, mature colony containing daughter colonies (*t*) and ova (*o*); *B*, group of 32 developing spermatozoa seen end on; *C*, the same seen sideways; *D*, mature spermatozoa × 824. (From Weismann's *Evolution Theory*.)

*Page* 202.

bramble[1] pattern golf ball in appearance, is technically known as the blastula—a more or less spherical hollow embryo, whose wall consists of a single layer of cells. Here, however, there is no basis as yet for individuality as defined above. There is no constancy in the number of cells composing the *Volvox globator*, and where in some cases, such as *Pandorina*, the number of cells is usually definite, the fact that the whole colony is capable of breaking up into its individual cells, which have the power in turn of dividing till they also reproduce the typical number of cells of the colony, brings us back very much to the condition of things in the Protozoa, so far as the argument for individuality goes : the dividuality, that is to say, has not appreciably lessened. In the case of the branching colonial forms such as the *Vorticellidae*, we get a hint of that differentiation and division of labour which prove so effective later.

The next stage in the advance of life is a definitely multicellular form, which may be represented by the little freshwater *Hydra*, the simplest member of the Coelenterate group. It may be thought of as arising from the preceding stage by the infolding of the blastula upon itself—as if one pressed the upper half of a punctured rubber ball down and in upon the lower half— thus making a sac whose walls are two layers of cells in thickness, with a mouth at the anterior end leading into a primitive digestive cavity. Arrange a tuft of tentacles round the edge of the mouth, and there results the idea of *Hydra*, or a sea anemone. This particular stage, the corresponding form of which—minus the tentacles— is known as a gastrula in the development of higher forms, already shows very marked differentiation of the constituent cells of the two layers, the outer being mainly protective in function and the inner concerned with nutrition. The outer layer is known as the ectoderm in the adult Coelenterate form, and as epiblast in the

---

[1] The earlier solid stage is technically called a *morula*, from the Latin word for a mulberry.

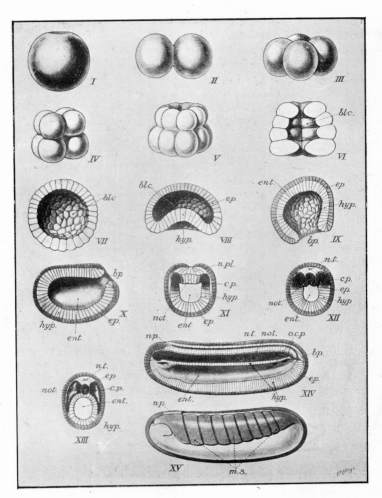

Fig. 29.—Early Development of Primitive Vertebrate Form, Amphioxus.
(Adapted from Ziegler's Models, after Hatschek.)

*I*, the fertilised egg; *II*, two blastomeres or embryonic cells formed by the first cleavage; *III*, stage with four blastomeres; *IV*, morula stage with eight blastomeres; *V*, stage with sixteen blastomeres, *VI*, stage with thirty-two blastomeres, cut in half vertically; *VII*, blastula or blastosphere stage, cut in half; *VIII*, early stage of gastrulation, cut in half; *IX*, *X*, later stages of gastrula in longitudinal section; *XI*, *XII*, *XIII*, transverse sections of older embryos; *XIV*, *XV*, longitudinal section and dissection of same. (From A. Dendy's *Outlines of Evolutionary Biology*.)

gastrular embryonic stage of higher types, while the inner layer is known as endoderm and hypoblast respectively. The correspondence of form is best explained in terms of the Recapitulation Theory, viz. the interpretation that higher forms in their individual history pass through stages representative of stages in the ancestral history.

Life at this level is evidently more organised and integrated than in the case of a mere colony of cells, yet the insertion of a penny into a sea anemone has sufficed to make the creature divide into two, and Loeb's experiments show that a chopped-up Hydra can regrow itself from pieces of very varying size. There is here as yet no individuality in the sense defined. Indeed, where the power of regeneration is developed to any great extent, as is the case throughout the Invertebrate Kingdom and in the Vertebrate Kingdom at any rate as far up as the Amphibia, the conception of individuality cannot be maintained. No phenomenon serves to emphasise the essential plasticity and fluidity of living things so well, perhaps, as just this capacity for regeneration, where it exists. It is noticeable in a marked degree, as might be expected, amongst the Protozoa, in virtue of their dividuality. It is also a feature of forms like *Hydra*, various flat worms, and the Ascidian *Clavellina*, where division and mutilation in varying degree may be practised upon them, with the result that the sundered part or fragmented portions will develop into the type again. In a definitely vertebrate group like the Amphibians, regeneration of a limb or of a sense organ may be repeated in some instances almost indefinitely after mutilation, although the conditions are further narrowed. In the case of the human subject, we realise that the severance of a limb very definitely affects not merely the whole, but even more seriously the part : in fact, the nail is probably the most complex part that man can regrow. There may not be individuality, but certainly there is no regenerative dividuality, in the sense that the term is applicable to humbler forms. That is to say, as we rise in the scale of life, the capacity for regeneration dwindles.   Yet where it exists in any degree, *individuality* as defined above is in that measure compromised.

The next great advance once more follows the line of

FIG. 30.—Branch of a typical Coelenterate colonial form, *Obelia* ; *o*, mouth of expanded nutritive member ; *M*, medusa-buds of the sexual generation forming on reproductive member ; *Th*, horny cup enclosing contracted nutritive member. (From Sedgwick's *Textbook of Zoology*.)

colony formation, just as it did amongst the Protozoa. Consider, for example, amongst the Coelenterata such a group as the Siphonophora, a subdivision of the Hydrozoa.   They are freely floating colonies, in many

of which differentiation and division of labour amongst
the various elements have been carried to such a degree
that their original equality and independence have been
lost, and they might even be considered from the extreme
point of view as mere organs of a higher integrated form,
the colony as a whole. Thus, as seen in the case of
*Nectalia* or *Physophora*, a large number of elements or
zooids are attached to a common stem. One of these,
at the upper end, is modified to form a float. Along the
length of the stalk are two rows of elements modified to
form swimming bells, whose function is solely locomotor.
The bottom of the stem is expanded, and bears a
number of other elements, some of which, with mouths
and stomachs and tentacles armed with stinging (?)
threads for the capture of prey, are assimilative in function, others form protective shields, while yet others are
limited to the formation of germ cells. It is here that the
biologist begins to have great difficulty in applying the
term ' individual,' as ordinarily employed, because there
is uncertainty as to what, in that sense of the definition,
it ought to be applied. Shall it be used of the colony as
a whole, or of one of the elements or zooids, the vegetative
member or the liberated reproductive unit ? From our
restricted point of view, the colony shows itself capable of
demarcation in various ways, while on the other hand no
one of the different elements suggests a sense in which the
term *in*dividual is ultimately true of it. They are not
wholes with a complete life of their own, nor yet are they
free from division. The problem, however, has changed
in form somewhat. We have now to consider degrees
of dividuality, for in some cases the various units, diverse
in their functions, remain organically connected together,
while others are set free to reproduce the whole. Now
community of structure in whatever degree—and the
degree is very marked in these hydroid colonies—negatives
the conception of individuality. There has not yet arrived
that which can persist, unchanged and *in*dividual. Indeed, the great majority of the parts never have a free

and independent existence, and those parts which are liberated do not retain the distinctive character of the part, but develop to reproduce afresh the whole.

FIG. 31.—Dividuality in *Microstoma lineare* (after Graff). A chain produced by fission; *o*, *o'*, mouth openings. (From Sedgwick's *Text-book of Zoology*.)

When we pass to the great phylum of Worms, which undoubtedly came from Coelenterate ancestors, we find that in many groups there is a metameric arrangement of the body in segments, each of which contains its own section of each of the principal functional systems—nervous, vascular, excretory, etc. The animal is a sort of linear colony, and, for example, in the case of the Planarian *Microstoma lineare*, a chain of elements is formed by repeated transverse division which eventually break away as separate daughter Microstomata. Of the phylum as a whole it may be fairly maintained that the *in*dividual is not there. In the case of the Annelidan earthworm, however, which is as typically a segmented form as any other member of the phylum, there is a marked lessening of dividuality, and a degree of differentiation and integration which no longer permits of the budding off of so highly organised and developed a part as a daughter segment. Essential organs such as the reproductive have become restricted to particular segments, and the dividuality is actively associated with these and other parts. At the same time, also, the earthworm has very considerable powers of regeneration, and if cut in two, either half can under certain conditions grow into a complete whole.

The same character of metameric segmentation is also

seen throughout the next large phylum of the Arthropoda or animals with jointed limbs, which have in all probability descended from Annelidan ancestors.   The common crayfish is made up of twenty segments, each with a pair of limbs or appendages and with some of the systems, for example the nervous, also to a certain extent distributed serially.   In the case of the myriapods and centipedes the same characters are seen in an even more extreme degree.   On the other hand, in some classes of this phylum, such as the insects and spiders, the integration and division of labour show a distinct advance upon the earthworm, the segments being now grouped so as to perform their functions more advantageously.   Dividuality further lessens, limited by the hard external carapace, but is still sufficiently in evidence in the reproductive and other systems to justify the statement that the individual in the sense of the definition is not here.

When we pass to the highest phylum of the animal kingdom, that of the Vertebrata, the situation is little changed, for here fundamentally from a morphological point of view, we are also dealing with metamerically segmented forms ' derived in all probability from some metamerically segmented, worm-like ancestral form.' [1] Of these segmented structures, the clearest indications are in the vertebral column and the segmentally arranged cranial and spinal nerves.   Integration is more and more developed, but in every instance there are still distinct traces of physical dividuality in the shedding of cells from various systems of the body.

The essential dividuality of life, resulting in its physical flow throughout the generations, is, however, most clearly seen in considering the phenomenon of Reproduction. This in every form, man included, involves the throwing off of certain definite cells which unite in pairs, and from the resulting fusion, by a succession of cell-divisions, the

[1] Prof. Arthur Dendy, ' The Biological Conception of Individuality, *Journal*, Quekett Microscopical Club, vol. xii. p. 472, from which paper several illustrations have been taken.

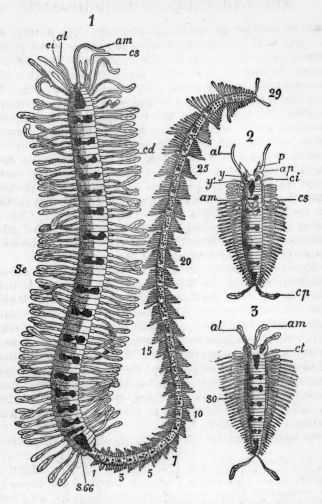

FIG. 32.—Dividuality in the Polychaete worm *Myrianida*.
1, Sexless budding form (Se) with a chain of 29 budded sexual
forms; 2, male form produced by budding; 3, female form
produced by budding. (From Sedgwick's *Textbook of Zoology*.)

Page 209.

unit of another generation is formed. The process may be repeated, and even in the intervals between such repetition, not merely are these reproductive cells still being thrown off, but also cells of epidermal and other character are just as continually and regularly being shed. For there is a constant renewal of such cells as remain, as gives force to the old dictum that the human body is renewed every seven years. Yet all the data connected with reproduction go quite positively to show that no sound theory of Individuality can be based upon them.[1] In fact, that particular form of reproduction that results from fertilisation had originally no direct and necessary relation with the continued life of the organism. When we regard the physical stream of human life simply and solely as such, we find that there are calculable possibilities of that particular combination of germ cells which formed the initial stage in the arena where each of our individualities was developed. ' According to competent authorities,' says Professor Jennings, ' one of the two pre-existing combinations from which my combination was derived possessed somewhat more than 17,000 germ cells, while the other produced the very considerable number of 339 billions of germ cells. So far as conditioned by the characteristics of these germ cells, any one of the 300 billions might have united with any one of the 17,000 ; any combination was *a priori* as probable as any other, and the chance that my particular combination should have been formed was therefore but one in five millions of billions ! '[2] And if we include the generations further back, not merely do the chances rise to prac-

---

[1] Cf. Julian S. Huxley, *The Individual in the Animal Kingdom*, p. 70.

[2] H. S. Jennings, ' Heredity and Personality,' *Science N. S.* vol. xxxiv. No. 887, p. 907. He adds in a footnote : ' If we choose to take into the computation out of the 17,000 ovules only the 400 that actually mature, the chance for any particular combination is one in 120 thousand billions. After reaching the thousand billions, cancellation of a factor of a few hundreds or thousands ceases to produce an impressive difference. The figures here given for the numbers of germ cells are from the *American Textbook of Physiology*, 1901, vol. ii. pp. 444 and 454.'

tically infinity to one against that particular combination which evolved into Jennings (although the same is true equally of every other personality), but we even come in face of the same apparently appalling wastage of potential bases of individuality that characterises lower forms of life. Now, as a matter of fact, there is strictly no *chance* in any of these combinations, but looking at the matter objectively, we get a vivid impression of the real state of affairs, viz. no *in*dividuality on the physical side of things —simply a physical stream, providing as the result of certain relations and activities of its parts, opportunities for the development of individuals, which if they are really *in*dividuals can only be so in some spiritual regard. Or we may change the figure and think of the physical aspects of human life throughout the ages as an enormous web of connected strands, and each individual as a knot tied in some particular grouping of these strands. And if the sense of wastage becomes oppressive, it can in that degree only heighten the sense of value or worth of the actual individuals that do come into being.

Accordingly it may be affirmed that throughout the animal kingdom as a whole there is no physical basis for a conception of *in*dividuality,[1] and it will be found that if an attempt is made to employ the term in the case of members of the different groups, it will not be possible from the morphological point of view to discover a definite criterion that will be of general applicability. Whatever ideas may be attached to the word on the purely physical side will require to undergo considerable change at different stages in any review of the animal kingdom from the Protozoa upwards. In colonial forms of life, even in the case of the simplest Hydroid colony, it is impossible as a rule to state where one element ends and another begins, and the peculiar phenomenon of the alternation

[1] The statement holds true as described, in spite of the interesting and significant fact that in the case of the human organism the cells of the central nervous system cease dividing after a definite stage, although their metabolism still continues.

of generations—asexual and sexual—complicates the situation still further. The same circumstance meets us in the higher plants, where in the case of an ordinary tree—the asexual generation—we can get as many elements out of it as we like, by taking buds or cuttings ; the *in*dividual in the sense of our definition is not there. Further, the extraordinarily composite and mixed results that can be attained by the process of grafting both in animals and plants,[1] show that with such a range of dividuality, natural and artificial alike, no sound basis for individuality can be found on the purely physical side : if the *in*dividual exists, it looks as if it can only be a spiritual creation or development.

To such a statement of the situation with regard to individuality, perhaps the strongest objection will be urged from evolution itself. It will be claimed that the study of the progressive advance of life, beginning with unicellular forms, discloses a growing and ever higher type of community, in which the independence of the whole is gained by the surrender of the independence of the units composing it. The real individual is an aggregate, and at each stage in the advance of life, there has been development of a more complex and harmonious type of aggregate. It will be shown that with each marked advance has gone a tendency on the one hand to ever greater integration and complexity of relationship, and on the other hand towards increasing differentiation and division of labour amongst the units of the colony, so that a more harmonious co-operation results from the increasing complexity and with it a higher degree of independence. Particularly well can this be developed in the case of the cells of the human body, and the not unnatural extension of the view-point is to pass on to human society or the State and treat it in the same way. Thus Julian Huxley,

---

[1] ' We can even join the hind part of one tadpole to the front part of another, and the product may grow into a complete frog, derived from the halves of two distinct species.'—Prof. Arthur Dendy, *in loco*, p. 474.

following the lead of Herbert Spencer, does not hesitate to say of the various groupings of which any man may be a member—family or club, exchange or nation—' that they *are* individuals, that here once more the tendency towards the formation of *closed systems* has manifested itself, though again in very varying degrees, so that some of the systems show but a glimmer of individuality, others begin to let it shine more strongly through.' [1] If such a continued sequence of idea is legitimate, it becomes clear that the value of the individual is lessened. He is nothing in himself : he only finds his *raison d'être* in relation to the community ; he achieves his end with his incorporation in the State. Now there is no doubt that such organisations of increasing degrees of integration and complexity are built up with the progress of life. The question is whether the highest thus developed—the human social organism or the State—constitutes the chief end of the process, or whether that end is primarily concerned with the individuals composing the organisation.

The question seems to receive a partial answer at any rate in the fact that any comparison between human society or the State and an organism is fundamentally misleading. It may appear superficially that the State or human society is composed of individuals as the organism is built up of cells, but the members of a state have no community of origin and so no organic unity such as the cells composing a single organism show. While the cells of the body are all structurally connected with one another, the whole trend of our argument goes to show that the elements composing society or the State are human beings developing *in*dividuality in the literal sense of that word, and so distinct from one another. One result is that no comparison is possible between the perfect social functioning of the cells of the normal organism and the activities of the individuals composing a State. The interests of the individuals are not alike : they are even antagonistic, as when the latter are considered as grouped in dif-

[1] *Op. cit.* p. 143.

ferent so-called 'classes.' Again, we have referred to the number of activities and functions carried on by the different organs and mechanisms of the human body, and in particular to their remarkable co-ordination. To such co-ordination and integration of activities there is little that is comparable in the modern State. Finally, there is nothing in the State or social organism literally corresponding to the brain of the organism, to which can be referred the social consciousness with its various mental and emotional states. If the analogy is used, it must be used the whole way through, which means that it breaks down. Although the highest type of society will undoubtedly be that in which the harmony of toil, mutual aid and co-operation in achievement are at a maximum, and whose complexity does indeed spell increased efficiency, yet the units composing it are ends in themselves, they are the final term in the series that commenced with the ancestral cell, for they alone are individuals. The society may pass away; it may be modified; it may disrupt. Nations or States as such have no immortality. Perhaps the consciousness of this is in part the reason why they struggle so piteously for mastery in the present. Further, we can already see beyond both these conceptions. All their distinctive features are directly associated with purely terrestrial conditions. The vital issue then rests with the individual life, in some kind of relationship. The *in*dividual may perhaps survive—in relationship with God, and this be *the* end and purpose of human life.

# CHAPTER X

## THE METHOD OF EVOLUTION

IF the method of Evolution involves the co-operation of factors whose number and degree of importance are still largely undetermined, and so must therefore continue to be the subject of investigation, certain features of the process stand out in sufficiently bold relief to compel general recognition of them. The theory of Evolution gives us the picture of a physical stream of life flowing down the ages, yet with no even regularity of flow. There are the rapids and the pool-like tracts : or, if we change the figure, the stream ' pulses ' as it flows.[1] If we look at the record of life, fixed and spread out before us in its immeasurably slow length, we realise that there have been crises, expression points, ' times of quickening,' moments of creative evolution. One outstanding fact is that in the more obvious cases these are found to be coincident with environmental change—physico-geographical change mainly, in the pre-human stages. The degree of this relationship will probably be found to be increasingly close and exact, and more and more generally pervasive. Sufficient is established already to put the known coincidences outside any laws of chance. Change in the environmental conditions is the cause of biological change, just as surely as a movement of uplift would increase the rate of flow and the erosive power of rivers. It becomes increasingly probable that physico-geographical change affects land life most subtly through the indirect aspect of climate, the character of which, as well as, indeed, of the ocean currents, is directly affected,

[1] Cf. Prof. R. S. Lull, *Organic Evolution*, p. 687.

let us say, by the whole series of movements (formation
of mountain ranges, etc.) resulting from that warping
of the earth's crust due to shrinkage, as also by the
complex rhythms in solar energy. 'For example,' to
quote from Professor R. S. Lull,[1] 'the most generally
accepted single cause of the last or Pleistocene glacial
period is the great continental elevation which formed the
*Cascadian* revolution, but, so far as our knowledge goes,
that would not account for the successive advances
and retreats of the ice mantle, with the attendant climatic
variation, and some other factor such as the rhythms of
solar energy must be involved as of supplemental influence.'

Of the early crises in connection with the history of life,
we know little or nothing, because it was not possible that
any records could be preserved. All that we find are very
occasional traces of fossil algae, burrows of certain worms,
and the hard parts of some Protozoa (Radiolarians). Yet
study of present-day hot-spring basins and shallow, warm,
freshwater lagoons with their somewhat distinctive life,[2]
enables the competent investigator to reconstruct in
imagination on a certain measure of solid fact still earlier
phases, when in comparable environmental conditions,
then characteristic of large areas of the earth's surface,
' molecular aggregations would, from exposure for millions
of years to varying and often rapidly-changing environal
conditions of liquid tension and temperature, of gaseous
discharges, of liquid chemical stimulation and other
modifications, undergo very distinct and diverse modification as to shape, size, consistence, and relation to surrounding media.'[3] The comparative structural simplicity
and highly developed power of resistance and adaptability to environmental extremes of temperature, desicca-

---

[1] *The Evolution of the Earth and its Inhabitants*, p. 109.
[2] The reference in this connection is principally to Bacteria, and
other non-nucleate forms like the simple Cyanophyceae or blue-green
Algae.
[3] Prof. J. M. Macfarlane, *The Causes and Course of Organic Evolution*, p. 50.

tion, and other forms of stimuli, are suggestive of great antiquity in these particular and allied forms of life. Amongst forms such as these, as Macfarlane reminds us, ' definite and invariable response to environal stimuli first became a permanent phenomenon and hereditary condition of each species.' [1]  It is increasingly probable that the vast deposits of chert, graphite, iron ore, and carbonate of lime found in the Archaean rocks had an organic origin, having been precipitated under the action of pre-cellular organic molecular aggregates. Macfarlane associates with the finer, richer protoplasm of these primitive non-nucleate forms a higher degree of labile potentiality than that which characterises nucleated protoplasm ' when actively vegetating.' [2]  But their power of reconstituting their molecules, *i.e.* of active self-maintenance, and throwing off waste substances, is an advance on anything found in the inorganic realm. It is, however, an energetic, and not a material distinction.

As soon as the lime-secreting habit in plants and animals was developed, there was the possibility of rock records, for structural hard parts were now in existence. What were the particular environmental circumstances that led to this habit, we do not know, and it is possible that a chitinous skeleton may have preceded the limy type in some forms. It is difficult, however, to speak with any confidence about these Proterozoic days. Probably with the exception of the Arthropods (*i.e.* Crustaceans, Insects, and Arachnids) all the great invertebrate groups were already in existence by Cambrian days. At the same time, it is within the period limited by the Upper Cambrian that there must have occurred at least five notable advances, or ' great steps in organic evolution,' as Professor J. Arthur Thomson calls them.[3]  These include cellular organisation, differentiation of the simplest plants and animals, the making of the body, sex di-

---

[1] *Op. cit.* p. 53.    [2] *Op. cit.* p. 57.
[3] *The System of Animate Nature*, vol. ii. p. 383 ff.

morphism, and those progressive differentiations and integrations in structure and function, such as the replacement of the radial symmetry of the starfish by the bilateral and segmented symmetry of the higher types of worm, or the difference in ' respiration ' as it exists for a sea anemone and a crab.

On the other hand, the origin of the five classes of vertebrates comes well within the range of possible discovery. The origin of vertebrates [1] may indeed be thought of as a sixth ' great step,' introducing, as they did, a new type of nervous system, and proving themselves the conquerors of two new media in the dry land and the air. Vertebrates are as a whole distinguished from invertebrates by the fact that they are motor types, which make definite headway, and so contrast with the sluggish, drifting, or sedentary invertebrates, of which some Arthropods (*e.g.* Crustaceans) and cephalopod Molluscs (squids) are the most aggressive of the marine types ; yet even the swift movement of the latter is of the nature of a retreat brought about by a sharp ejection of water. As a matter of fact, in respect of the environment, the invertebrate is as a rule the denizen of comparatively still waters,—marine, or sluggish terrestrial,— where the ebb and flow do not ordinarily carry it outside that particular environment. The vertebrate type, on the other hand, may be considered, originally, as a response to flowing terrestrial waters, where swimming power and ability to make headway were necessary to avoid ' eviction from the realm ' ; hence in part the increasing probability of ' the assumption that the vertebrates are the outcome of terrestrial waters.' [2] It is, of course, the case that certain primitive marine vertebrates (*e.g.* *Amphioxus*, Tunicates, and *Balanoglossus*) are known, a fact which might be held, and is indeed still widely held, to argue a marine ancestry for vertebrates,

[1] For a good account of the principal theories on this still unsolved problem, see Prof. R. S. Lull, *Organic Evolution*, chap. xxviii.
[2] Prof. R. S. Lull, *The Evolution of the Earth*, p. 114.

but it is more consistent with other data to consider these forms, the majority of which are degenerate and found for the most part in littoral regions, as having been unable to maintain themselves in their fluviatile habitat, and, so to speak, swept out to sea.

In determining what it was that caused the change from static to dynamic waters, geology helps us with its account of a great movement of elevation towards the close of the Proterozoic and Early Cambrian days, which ' changed the face of Nature in many regions and quickened the static terrestrial waters to rapid and wide-spread movement over all the uplifted lands.' [1] For the invertebrate it was a case of clinging more tightly to the bottom, being swept seawards, or developing ability to stem the flowing water. It is after this period that we find remains of the earliest vertebrates—armoured *fresh-water* fishes.

But there are very distinct limitations to an aquatic environment, different as it is to an amoeba and a highly developed fish. Organic progress must have reached a definite limit comparatively soon if there had not been the possibility of emergence to the dry land and the air. This was indeed a moment of crisis, an expression point in evolution, even if the process covered by it may have taken myriads of centuries. How the transition was made is again a speculative matter. The tidal zone at once suggests itself, with its alternating dry and aquatic phases, but the forms that pass that frontier with regularity, mainly in search of food, are few (land crabs, and some fish, like the Walkingfish, *Periophthalmus*), while the respiratory adaptations developed in these creatures are merely modifications or extensions of the ordinary gill. Now the lung of the typical vertebrate is the homologue of the air bladder of the fish. Those fish in which the air bladder functions normally as a hydro-static organ—the Elasmobranchs (Sharks and Rays) do

[1] Prof. R. S. Lull, *The Evolution of the Earth*, p. 118, from whose work many of the immediately succeeding facts are taken.

not have it at all [1]—have obviously developed in a distinctively piscine direction, and we should rather expect the transition forms to be more akin to the types that still make use of the air bladder in its primitive capacity of a breathing organ.    The need for this would not, however, develop so intensely in the ocean, but would theoretically be connected rather with such fish as had found their homes in terrestrial waters beyond the limits of the tidal zone, where owing to climatic conditions, the volume of water was periodically reduced to such a state of stagnation as made its aeration insufficient for normal life. Now it is precisely in certain Australian rivers, which are often thus reduced by drought to the condition of stagnant pools, full of decomposing vegetable matter, or in the marshy margins of the Senegal and Amazon, that the representatives of the *Dipnoid* (Double-breather) group of fishes live (*e.g. Neoceradotus, Protopterus, Lepidosiren*) ; in these fish the air bladder functions as a lung.    Another group of piscine air breathers, the Crossopterygii, which includes the tropical African form *Polypterus*, has indeed certain structural features that suggest the kinship of this group with the form which was probably ancestral both to the modern Dipnoids, and terrestrial vertebrates. Once more the geological record helps us by furnishing the evidence of far-reaching terrestrial movements during the Silurian period which resulted in widespread aridity during the late Silurian, and throughout Devonian times. This meant the reduction of rivers, and particularly of the great inland sheets of water, with resulting concentration of their fauna.    In the Old Red Sandstone (Lower Devonian) one remarkable feature is the enormous numbers of fossils found in very restricted areas.    Such congested conditions would provide a great stimulus to air breathing and any activity that would take life ashore out of these packed and foetid swamps.    Aridity, *i.e.* a distinctively climatic condition, would put a premium

---

[1] Unless represented by a small caecal pouch of the pharynx in two or three sharks.

where these now mainly amphibious forms sported about, seem to have been drained as the result of earth movements, thus producing change in food and other conditions to which they were unable to adapt themselves sufficiently to secure survival.

The mammals, which had meanwhile appeared in the Upper Triassic rocks, have been reported as archaic on this horizon from regions as far apart as North Carolina, Germany, and South Africa. They were of no great size, though warm-blooded and very active, and were eventually driven into brain building in order to be able to compete with the immensely larger reptiles. Their evolution, however, made no very rapid progress until after the disappearance of the great saurians, and even then the first expansion of mammalian life appears to have been unusually static as regards three very essential structures—feet, teeth, and brain. There was, however, a certain degree of specialisation. Thus some were herbivorous, and somewhat light-limbed and speedy—the so-called Condylarths, like *Phenacodus*. Others were slow-moving and ponderous, ' relying upon weapons rather than upon fleetness for defence ' ; [1] such were the Amblypods, including the swamp-loving *Coryphodon* and the highly specialised Dinocerata. A third group comprised the carnivorous Creodonts, which, to judge by brain capacity, were slow-witted compared with their modern successors. Few of these archaic mammals survived the Eocene, their place being taken by other forms, invaders of Europe and North America, that came either from some circumpolar land or from the northern part of what is Asia to-day. About the earlier evolution of these invading forms we know nothing. But that they, the predecessors of all the modern mammalian orders, supplanted the archaic Eocene mammalia everywhere, admits of no doubt. Most marked was the predominance of grazing forms, for change in climatic conditions due to continental uplift in Miocene times produced a marked increase in

[1] Prof. R S. Lull, *op. cit.* p. 134.

aridity, and this in turn meant the development of the coarser grasses at the expense of shrubby and herbaceous plants. This development of steppe areas resulted in a great increase of all grazing Ungulates—horses, camels, deer, and their kind—and a corresponding reduction in the browsing forms. With this last Miocene revolution we have already co-ordinated some early stages in the evolution of man.[1]

While it is no necessary part of the general argument of this work to attempt an estimate of the different factors in Evolution,[2] their number and comparative importance, it must be abundantly clear that amongst these the Environment plays a leading, and in a sense directive, rôle. ' Speaking for himself,' writes Professor J. M. Macfarlane in the substantial textbook already referred to, ' the writer would say that this one factor, " environment," greatly outweighs all of the others in importance, and that possibly it is capable of further and wide extension to a degree that even the Neo-Lamarckian does not go.' [3] He refers in particular, under the caption of ' the law of pro-environment,' to the capacity that every organism has of ' correlated resultant response . . . to the summated correlation of stimulatory action, that leads to a temporarily *satisfied* state.' [4] He believes that he has established as the result of much experimentation in plant physiology, that ' certain molecular changes [are] wrought by the stimulating agent on the living substance, and later it may be on certain substances accessory to it, as can be observed during movement in leaves of *Drosera, Dionaea,* or *Mimosa,* amongst many others. These molecular changes inevitably cause a definite course or pathway of movement to be pursued, which is determined during that measurable period of time that we now call the latent period or period of

---

[1] Cf. *antea*, pp. 76, 77
[2] Cf. *The Spiritual Interpretation of Nature*, chaps. v.-xi.
[3] *The Causes and Course of Organic Evolution*, p. 174.
[4] *Op. cit.* p. 193.

excitation. At the close of that period—amounting, it may be, in some plants or plant tissues to [a] quarter second, in others to several minutes, but in most animals of much shorter duration—the organism has plotted a definite line of response or a pathway, even though as yet it may be motionless, that is as exact for the future result as if the response action had already taken place. Or in other words a definite mode or line of response has been determined on, that will cause the organism to reach out or occupy a definite environal relation.'[1] So also from his very different field of work of exploration in Asia, Pumpelly insists : ' What I wish particularly to emphasise is the conception that in the intervention of the glacial period and its reaction on the inner-continental conditions, we must see the initial—the motiving—factors in the evolution of the intellectual and social life of man.'[2] The more this direct action of the Environment is realised, the more it becomes clear that evolution does not take place as the result of the intrinsic forces of the organism independent of the extrinsic forces of the Environment, and the more incredible it becomes that the latter have operated through the aeons of time on organisms without producing characters that become relatively fixed. Throughout there has been interaction,[3] the general result of which has been harmony, although progress has always depended upon that harmony being something very different from complete adaptation to the physical proximate aspects of the Environment of the moment.

One other feature, vital to our line of thought, emerges upon close examination of the racial history of life. It is that of the establishment of dominating structural

[1] *Op. cit.* p. 194.     [2] *Op. cit.* p. 66.
[3] Cf. H. F. Osborn; ' We cannot avoid expressing as our present opinion that these causes [of germ evolution] are internal—external rather than purely internal—in other words, that some kind of relation exists between the actions, reactions, and interactions of the germ, of the organism, and of the environment.'—(*The Origin and Evolution of Life*, p. 283.)

characters of successively progressive value in the well-marked aeons of life, and of a progressive change of criterion in the survival-determining factor. When first we become aware of life it is unicellular in type and strictly limited in the range of its commerce with the environment. A drop of water is the *Amoeba's* universe ; the business and criterion of its existence is assimilation. If it assimilates well, it divides, and continuing to assimilate and divide, maintains itself. Assimilation still holds a very large place in the life of the next highest group, the Coelenterata, whose sac-shaped bodies are principally stomach, but the natural dividuality has lessened, and reproduction is now mainly sexual. On the other hand, the largely sedentary character of the group has left them without any greatly developed muscular system beyond what is needed to carry on digestion. The muscular system is, however, a characteristic feature of the next stage of animal life, from the worms up to the mammals. The muscular body of the worm, so eminently adapted to locomotion, gave it an advantage over preceding types in the securing of food supplies, and in connection with the activities associated with its reproductive system, than which none, with the possible exception of the mollusc, is more complicated. and highly developed. But a developed muscular system implies development of the nervous system that controls it. Increased powers of locomotion call for an added alertness and exploratory power in relation to that Environment which is the arena of movement, and so we find in this group, as in the higher molluscs and insects, a marked development of sense organs and of the nervous system generally. There is an increasing range of commerce with, and at the same time, independence of, the environment, so that while the amoeba and the fish may inhabit the same environment, that environment is a very different thing to the two creatures. This reign of muscular power still continued through the reptilian phase that developed at some point out of the amphibian, and only began to wane when inability to succeed in that line drove birds into the air and some of the early mammals into increased agility and more definite brain-building to escape with their lives where they could not compete in physical strength. Thereafter cunning, or mind, gained the day, and again the criterion of survival had changed.

It would thus appear that successive, broadly marked stages in the evolution of life have been dominated by strongly developed features—assimilation, sexual reproduction, muscular force, cunning or mind—each of which has been in its turn the survival-determining factor *par excellence*. The rising into power of one of these factors does not, of course, mean the disappearance of the one that held sway previous to it. It still continues to function, but in a subordinate way. Further, this cycle or rhythm may be traced not merely in the history of life as a whole, but to a lesser degree in such a group as the vertebrates, or even the mammals. There was, for example, a day when the carnivorous group, representing the stage of muscular force, was dominant amongst the mammals, while in the tree-tops the ancestral primate developed hand and brain. Now each of these stages has implied in the progressive forms a growing independence of the proximate physical elements of the Environment,[1] and at the same time an increasing range of commerce with, and conformity to, some deeper element in it, not, of course, fully understood by them. On the other hand, all along, other forms have settled down in an equilibrium of complete adaptation to some immediate aspect of the Environment. It has always been the easy thing to do, but such over-specialisation on their part has inevitably spelled their evolutionary doom. At whatever point we, as it were, look in on the process, we become aware of the Environment, either in its aspect of inorganic nature or other organic life, acting on living forms through pressure or stimulus, moulding, challenging, directing, developing,

[1] Cf. chap. xii.

selecting, by ever higher criteria. So we may perhaps think, with Professor J. M. Tyler,[1] of the minute ancestral vertebrate as also forced into maintaining the swimming habit, which resulted in the development first of the notochord and latterly of the backbone, by the pressure from the physically stronger invertebrate forms that crowded the rich feeding grounds at the bottom. Similarly also, in addition to the climatic factor already noticed, the pressure from more powerful marine enemies like the sharks may have been an element in pushing the earliest air-breathing vertebrates towards, and so latterly on to, the land, just as later the apes remained and developed in the trees because the ground was unsafe with carnivores. Yet in all this reaction to the Environment there has also been co-operation between forms in a growing degree from the beginning. The way of life has not been a *Via Dolorosa* throughout, in spite of the continual policing injunction of the Environment to move on and move up. If growing freedom has been used in many cases to escape from the pressure, to get out of the narrow, upward way that was to lead to man, by complete adaptation to some trivial or temporary aspect as in parasitism or in some other way, such a condition of static equilibrium has always in the end meant stagnation and degeneration for the forms in question. At every stage there have been these varied types of response to the stimulating, beckoning Environment : throughout it is only by ' a very small remnant ' that the advance has been maintained.

Finally, in this particular connection it is worthy of notice that that which was to be essentially the dominating survival character of a later stage, was, before it had come into the mastery of life, in bondage to the immediately lower character. As soon as it was sensed and acted upon —although this could not be deliberately so before the arrival of man—it ensured racial survival to those that

[1] *The New Stone Age*, p. 5. Cf. also by the same authority, *The Whence and the Whither of Man*, pp. 194, 195.

followed it, although the present belonged to those who still conformed to the criterion that was passing away. That is to say, every creature at any stage, has been a bundle of possibilities, which increased in number with the advance of life, and this is supremely true of man. For him, as for all the forms leading up to him, to conform to the criteria of the past has been to imperil his own existence ; to conform to the vanishing criterion of the present has been to risk his racial existence. The only way in which the future progress has been successively and triumphantly secured has been by conformity to some as yet dimly appreciated but higher element revealed in the unmasking Environment, which in its ultimate aspect is God.

We have seen something of the method by which Life has with difficulty, because of the intractableness of her material, pushed forward in her creative mission, striving to overcome and progress, at first by increase in the mere size of her representatives, or in the complexity of their organisation, or the lengthening of their span of days. And when these methods have become exhausted, it is as if she had once more changed her method, and tried to advance by means of that miracle of comprehension before and after, a human consciousness, which increases the organism's size by all kinds of mechanical devices, manifolds its activities by an infinity of crafts, and places its conquests outside of the destructive tendencies of time in written record or objective representation. Nevertheless when we regard this latest product of the process, history shows us that the earliest groupings of man in family or tribe or nation have come into existence and in many cases completely disappeared, just like some animal species of the past, under conditions that look as if the criterion of survival were again changing and now becoming increasingly a moral one. Recorded human history covers but a very small fraction of the period of man's existence on the earth, but it deals with a period in which he is still in process of attaining *in*dividuality, a period in which survival as the result of physical force has been already transcended, and survival as due to mental capacity is slowly being replaced by survival due to moral character.   Human history shows as matter of the most literal fact that with regard to the larger aggregates of mankind, ' righteousness exalteth a nation,' [1] in the ultimate sense that righteousness alone is gradually coming to mean survival for peoples, and that there is an 'Eternal Power, not ourselves, making for righteousness,' [2] in alignment or relationship with which, as revealed in the unmasking Environment, progress and survival are alone secured.   But if this is true of the aggregates of men, it is also most probably true of the individual man. That is to say, while man physically regarded is not wholly free from dividuality, so that no valid conception of the persistent *in*dividual can be formed on physical lines, yet in association with that physical stream of life throughout the ages there has not merely developed a sentient and spiritual life in gradual attainment of *In*dividuality, but with man has come into existence the possibility of a manner of life with survival-value, that as far transcends the life of cunning, as the latter transcended or had survival-value over the life of muscular force.   Than this spiritual life which has throughout organic history been gradually coming to light and dominance we can imagine nothing higher, therefore if *in*dividuality, which will from this point of view be equivalent to immortality, is attainable by man, we can only suppose that it is in some way related to this manner of life ; in some way it is attained as the result of it.

The opposing view is that which considers man to be inherently an immortal soul.   This is essentially an Orphic-Platonic conception ; it does not appear to be the Christian idea.[3]   And the more clearly it is realised that the process of evolution has been selective throughout, with a

[1] Prov. 14 [34].
[2] Matthew Arnold, *Literature and Dogma*, pp. 137, 143.
[3] Cf. chap. xiii.

gradually rising criterion of survival, the more will the onus of proof of any such break in the continuity of evolutionary method be thrown on those who maintain an inherent immortality for man. To-day we are aware of a long evolutionary history of forms that led directly to what at a certain stage we recognise as man, but it is impossible to lay our finger, as it were, on one particular point in that history and say that thereafter we are dealing with an inherently immortal being. There is no argument for the inherent immortality of man that would not be valid for the immortality of all created life, for while the sentiency of an Amoeba and the self-consciousness of Man seem so removed as to make each *sui generis*, yet the study of comparative psychology is slowly but surely showing that the difference is but one of degree, with no intermediate stage unaccounted for. The stages represented by (1) awareness on the part of the creature of what it is doing, (2) that awareness coupled with recollection of past behaviour and the results of such behaviour, and (3) that awareness and memory used as a basis for determining future behaviour, in the light of the ability to estimate consequences and of some sense of partnership in, or responsibility to, Reality as growingly understood, are progressive enrichments of the same spiritual life. They are the result of developed powers, of more knowledge, of deeper understanding. They are expressions of a growing and developing centre or self, which is however moulded and made, or unmade, as the result of its activity. Nor is there any intrinsic reason why a being that has developed the power to choose between good and evil should be immortal simply because it has developed this capacity ; surely what must be determinative of the future is the actual relationship chosen and realised. And, finally, with growing knowledge of the kind of world in which we find ourselves, it becomes increasingly impossible to believe—to take a recent example—that the creation of immortal souls could be contingent upon the passage of lustful

German soldiery through French and Belgian villages.[1]
In many different kinds of ways and under differing
conditions human beings are brought into the world who
represent, if the above deductions are sound, no more and
yet no less than potentially immortal souls.   The possibilities, that is to say, of *in*dividuality or immortality,
are not directly related to any origin by fusion of two
particular cells—they are beyond all merely genetic
relationship—nor yet to any particular structure in grey
matter.   They do not have their origin in any special
feature of the taxonomist, anatomist, or psychologist.
Such continued persistence can therefore only be essentially in virtue of a spiritual relationship.[2]   All advance ultimately means that the organism has entered
into some new relationship with the Environment, and
it is only one part of the result of this new relationship
that other aspects with which it was previously in relationship now appear in a new light.   Now the most
distinctive feature about the evolutionary process as a
whole is just the fact of the successive emergence of new
kinds of relationship at ever higher levels in that process,
as may be indicated by the terms physico-chemical,
vital, and mental.   Is it not probable, therefore, that
with man there emerges the possibility of some new relationship—a moral linkage with that which is ultimate
in the Environment, and which involves wholeness and
persistence of spiritual being—in short, that *In*dividuality
which is Immortality ?

[1] This is a reflex of certain incidents in the early stages of the Great
War, and is intended to convey no aspersion upon the German people
or army as a whole ; nor has the situation been confined to this war in
particular, nor even to days of war.

[2] The case of those dying in infancy presents no particular difficulty
on this view ; these innocents could not have willed themselves out of
relationship to God.

# CHAPTER XI

## EVOLUTION AS THE WINNING OF FREEDOM

OF philosophies of Evolution there is no end, some of them being the products of a false simplification of the facts. There is little wonder if the human mind fails in its grasp and appreciation of the facts of organic development as a whole. Nevertheless it becomes increasingly clear that things organic and inorganic are, because of their significance. In so far as they are lacking in significance they are deficient in reality. 'Evolution itself,' in Professor G. T. Ladd's words, 'cannot even be conceived of except in connection with the postulate of some Unitary Being, immanent in the evolutionary process, which reveals its own Nature by the nature of the Idea which, in fact, is progressively set into reality by the process.' [1]

Amongst these different philosophies of Evolution, that of the primordial germ, containing within it the promise and potency of all that followed, and sifting itself out in the various forms of life through the passage of the aeons, maintained its practically unchallenged place through half a century. To a biological generation that is just escaping from the thraldom of the Weismannian dominion, and wondering how it ever came to be so enslaved, it was only logical that all the characters of later forms had to be traced back to the Protozoa, and thus reduce the theory to its inevitable absurdity so far as this particular point is concerned. Professor Bateson's later modification, based on a wide range of brilliant experimental research, regards Evolution as ' an unpacking of an

[1] *Knowledge, Life, and Reality*, p. 522.

original complex which contained within itself the whole range of diversity which living things present.' [1] The outstanding feature about both of these views is that they tend to regard the organism, and indeed the whole course of organic evolution, as developing so mechanically as practically to be *in vacuo*. Everything is given ; acquired modifications are not transmitted ; there is no real enrichment of life or new creation ; the Environment has little more than a stimulating effect. On the contrary, and likewise based upon experimental and observational data, the proof is slowly accumulating, as we have seen, that the relationship between the organism and its Environment has been at every stage so close that we more correctly think of the two as one system undergoing change, and that the Environment has been a directive and selective agent in Evolution, operating throughout upon active responsive agents, whose relation to it has become increasingly intelligent. It is very difficult to suppose that the two phases in the individual life of an animal like the frog, which are adaptations to two very different sets of environmental conditions, were due to mutations with the production of which these different sets of conditions had nothing directly to do : yet this is what the former explanation involves.

Now on every form of evolutionary philosophy it has been difficult to find any reasonable explanation of that feature of Organic Evolution which is only less noticeable than its broadly progressive character, viz. the instances of retrogression, of apparently harmful adaptation, of arrested development, and those particular lines of evolution that apparently have led nowhere. In the recent revolt, however, from the distinctively mechanistic and determinate interpretations of the evolutionary process, no fact has come into greater prominence than the reality of the living organism as an agent in its own evolution. Life appears as a continually expansive, manifoldly expressive phenomenon, and all along, from

[1] Presidential Address, *B. A. Report*, 1914, p. 17.

the beginning, the assertive, often rebellious, living organism has manifestly throughout the ages been gradually winning ever greater freedom from, and control over, the more proximate physical aspects of the Environment. The mere fact of progress shows that there has been a tendency to break away from the limitations of the past. Rudimentary organs, larval forms, every new type of adaptation and variation, each an evidence of change, all testify to a certain degree of initiative in freedom, as if even the germ cells now and again made essays in self-expression.[1]

The history of freedom, then, may be said to begin with the first peculiar or special reaction or activity of the simplest organism which meant some new departure, favourable or unfavourable, first in its own life, and so, gradually, in the expression of the subsequent different forms of life. These earliest steps were probably taken while life was yet molecular in structure, but even in that condition it is not difficult to realise how a similar stimulus acting upon a considerable number of such living molecules may have been followed by a peculiarity of reaction in some one or several of them, that fundamentally affected the subsequent course of their existence. Wherever Life is, there is indeterminism, at first in a minimal degree, and the history of Evolution is the history of the gradual emancipation of the organism from the physical determinative aspects of the Environment. It is a history of a growing consciousness of such emancipation, until in moral freedom it becomes the peculiar characteristic, although in very varying degrees, of man. The life-history of any organism is the result of three factors, the living energy of the organism, the impressed traits—so many latent possibilities—of its ancestral past, and the stimulating, directing, and actively surrounding Environment. What actually is realised depends on the degree of individual

[1] Cf. Prof. J. Arthur Thomson, *The System of Animate Nature*, vol. i. pp. 98, 326.

activity of the organism itself—the degree in which it transcends, or liberates itself, so to speak, from its ancestral past and from the compulsion of the more physical aspects of the Environment. Such liberty can never be complete on this plane, but the history of life shows growing emancipation over the whole. It looks as if the purpose of Evolution were to create free beings in the world.

This tendency towards the acquirement of freedom may be traced in connection with the development of these psychophysical centres disclosed by the study alike of comparative anatomy and comparative psychology.[1] From the sheer determinism of the inorganic we pass to the comparatively simple unicellular forms where, just because there is life, there is a certain measure of indeterminism. In mechanism and finalism alike, ' all is given,' although it may be in different ways : in life alone there is the indeterminate, even the simplest organisms bringing to the ' given ' which they represent, that peculiar activity which, in the past as in the present, may mean a new departure in life. With the simplest forms, whose unicellular body is at once the unit of function and of structure, and is in the most direct relation with the determining environment, it seems as if there were a total powerlessness in relation to it and a dependence upon it that are not merely the result of minute physical size. It is not bulk alone that decides the comparative helplessness of the protozoon as compared with the fish in the stream, for it is obvious that there is also a minimum of relation between these simplest forms themselves : they have next to no knowledge of themselves or one another. Indeed nothing seemed more certain to the earlier observers than just the sheer determinateness of protozoan life : response followed on stimulus with mechanical regularity, and only that single particular response. The Environment literally

[1] Reference may be made to chapter iv. of a suggestive work entitled *L'Evolution, Doctrine de Liberté*, by Prof. F. Leenhardt.

controlled and determined protozoan life, from whose persistent pressure it was unable to get free. More exact study [1] has shown that the life of the protozoon is not thus absolutely bound, that on the contrary such a form as *Stentor* will try at least half a dozen different ways of responding to objectionable or injurious stimuli, and persists in trying, till relief or freedom is obtained from the particular situation. Professor Jennings' years of study of the behaviour of the lowest organisms have shown ' that in these creatures the behaviour is not as a rule on the tropism plan—a set, forced method of reacting to each particular agent—but takes place in a much more flexible, less directly machine-like way, by the method of trial and error.' [2]   ' In no other group of organisms,' he says, ' does the method of trial and error so completely dominate behaviour, perhaps, as in the infusoria ' [3] (ciliate Protozoa) ; something of the nature of mind has counted from the beginning.

A progressive study of the forms of life shows that with each advance a greater degree of freedom is obtained. Thus Jennings,[4] for example, made friends with a starfish, and spent a considerable amount of time—eighteen days with ten lessons per day—in successfully training it to use two particular rays in the process of turning itself over, after being placed upon its back. The pair of rays in question had never been observed to be ordinarily employed by this individual for this purpose. After a forty-eight hours' vacation the starfish still used this particular pair more frequently than any other combination. Even after a further five days' rest, or seven in all, without any further training, the influence of its past education was still noticeable. Starfish have no concentration of nervous elements even into ganglia, and yet are just as variable in their learning abilities as many

---

[1] Cf. *e.g.* Prof. H. S. Jennings' *Behaviour of the Lower Organisms.* The quotations are from his earlier *Contributions to the Study of the Behaviour of the Lower Organisms.*

[2] *Op. cit.* p. 252.        [3] *Op. cit.* p. 243.        [4] *Ibid.*

higher organisms.  Similarly R. M. Yerkes,[1] after giving instruction to an earthworm from October 12, 1911, to April 30, 1912, by means of an apparatus devised to test its ability to ' learn ' to follow a simple path so as to avoid an injurious stimulation, succeeded in getting positive results.  Objective study discloses that in the method of ' trial and error,' as evinced in the behaviour of lower organisms—and the whole search for food may be included under this category—' error ' implies that which is injurious to them, and so eventually to the race. Exactly the same types of reaction objectively regarded, occur in the higher animals : subjectively we know that the stimuli causing these negative reactions are accompanied by what we speak of as pain.  It is difficult to avoid the conclusion that there is some ' organic analogue of pain ' or pleasure in the lower organisms.

In the simplest multicellular forms function is already located in distinct organs, and with the division of labour thereby effected, which in its turn means so much increased capacity for doing work, following on the increased specialisation and centralisation in these organs, greater independence is secured.  In itself, the acquisition of sight, developed out of a sensory spot in the epithelium, every stage of which can be traced, meant an incalculable advance in the development of individuality and the winning of independence, for with it came the possibility of a more distinct conception than mere touch could afford, of that which is other than the perceiving subject. The evolution of the nervous system—the organ of relationship—can be clearly traced [2] out of a series of isolated ganglia enervating local regions of the body, which by their gradual linkage and centralisation in a ' brain ' bring the various local centres of the body into relationship, so that it responds henceforward as a whole. At a still later stage, as the result of increasing growth

[1] 'The Intelligence of Earthworms,' *Journal of Animal Behaviour*, vol. ii. no. 5.
[2] Cf. *e.g.* Prof. G. H. Parker, *The Elementary Nervous System*.

in the association centres of the brain, in connection with which the past is in some way enregistered, subsequent responses have no longer the direct immediate character of a reflex or tropism, but that typical reaction modified by the experience of the past.

The brain is thus an organ which, by its enregistration of the actions and reactions provoked by the Environment and the peripheral nervous system, and its recombination of them in new and more complex association, permits of the organism expressing itself in some new and unforeseen way, and in that degree manifesting its independence. And not merely does the organism exhibit these new actions and reactions, but it behaves at times in such a way as to suggest that it can do so more or less at its pleasure, indicating that not merely has it a power of inhibition, but can also in a measure initiate activity of itself, and is in that degree autonomous and self-determining. The higher organisms gradually substitute internal for external stimuli, the former being in great part the summed results of previous experience of the latter. Associated with the highest development of this cerebro-psychic centre is a suggestion of individuality and wholeness, and of self-assertive independence especially, to begin with, of the physical aspects of the Environment. This development has, of course, taken place particularly in the vertebrates, where the various stages in the winning of increasing independence are well marked. Thus while the cold-blooded vertebrates are so directly dependent on the environmental temperature that their functioning rises and falls in correspondence with it, the warm-blooded vertebrates, as it were, carry their own weather about with them in the form of their uniform high internal temperature, and are thus independent to a marked degree of the vagaries and sustained extremes alike, of external climate. The cold-blooded forms are historically older than the warm-blooded : there is thus in this related aspect also a marked advance in independence with the evolution of life. No phenomenon of organic functioning is more individual and less susceptible of complete explanation in terms of physics and chemistry alone, than the process by which the highest warm-blooded forms maintain their temperature at what is virtually a specific constant for each individual.

A detailed comparative study of the phylogenetic development of the central nervous system shows that each advance has led towards the gradual association of supremacy, in the sense of the co-ordination and control of life, with the cerebral hemispheres, more especially with the cortical area or neopallium. Not merely have modern species of reptiles a greater brain capacity on the whole than the Mesozoic representatives of these particular species, and modern mammals than the corresponding species of Tertiary days, but there has been the absolute advance in the various types of Primate brain. Life could probably have maintained itself in automatic subsistence at any particular level, but the actual observed advance in complexity of cerebral structure, being the concomitant of increased activity, power of adaptation, and ability through new responses to surmount new and difficult environmental experiences that might otherwise have meant extinction, looks as if this progress had been part of a purposive possibility, an intention of something higher. The increased cerebral development involves in some way a wider and more complex range of enregistration and combination of action and reaction, and so, through the presence of alternatives, of choice. In the highest forms of all, this independence becomes most marked, for not merely is there considered response to stimuli in the light of past experience, but there appears to be evidence of the initiative directly proceeding from this cerebro-psychic centre without the previous immediate impact of some external stimulus. Thus Leenhardt draws attention [1] to the fact that the brain sends out centrifugal fibres into the sensorial elements of the sense organs, *e.g.* the plexus of the retina, and apparently has the power

[1] *Op. cit.* p. 65.

of directly increasing the impressionability of these receptive organs, if not of putting them into this condition even in the absence of all external stimulation. Now it is in the misuse of this capacity to win freedom, this process in which the organism as an active agent has increasingly and gradually throughout historic time become a factor in its own elevation, that it is possible to find a reasonable explanation of the irregularities, impasses, retrogressions, and dysteleologies that become evident in the course of Evolution. But while this may be true of forms that are apparently organic *culs-de-sac* or actually degenerate, yet it would obviously be a misreading of the facts to class as dysteleological all forms of life that failed to maintain themselves in the narrow upward way that led to man's estate. No one could thus think of the plant world as a whole, or numerous groups (*e.g.* herbivores) in the regimented forms of animal life. In themselves, such as they are, they have proved essential to the higher forms, in a sense doing them service. Man could not have evolved if every other form of life had consistently progressed towards humanity. Nature has many ends, and the conception of teleology only becomes the more profound.

Man, as the present *terminus ad quem* of the vertebrate series, gives a meaning, which is otherwise lacking, to the whole of the preceding stages. He is directly linked with them, and the tendency noticeable throughout, towards the winning of liberty and the development of an increasingly self-activated centre, reaches its highest expression in him. Individuality has reached a stage in which general awareness has now become awareness of self. What exactly was the nature and manner of the last advance we do not entirely know. The study of even the highest type of purely animal brain is always limited by the fact of the indirectness of such study, although it becomes increasingly apparent that we have far from exhausted the mental capacities of those mammalian forms that have been longest and most directly associated with man, *e.g.* dog and horse, while those of the simian group have hardly been investigated at all. No naturalist doubts that the rudiments of every feature in the mental organisation of man exist in the cerebro-psychic centre of the higher animals : there is even an elemental self-consciousness in the negative sense that the animal recognises others of its kind as distinct from, and other than, itself. But the clearest proof of this development is seen in the recapitulated life-history of each human individual, in which the passage is made in every case in early childhood from proconsciousness through consciousness to self-consciousness. There are, for example, the months in which the child persistently speaks of itself in the third person, not having as yet attained to vital consciousness of self. As also indeed there is the still earlier, and as yet little studied, history, mainly instinctive and full of simple, reflex actions, not to speak of the embryonic and germ-cell stages, in which even Socrates must have reacted simply as a germ cell, although the limitations of our conventional thought have hitherto refused to be interested in the thought of him at this earliest period.

In the case of man this liberty of independence is shown supremely as the result of will, or, in other words, the integrated system of the mind in action. Such activity is thus seen by its racial development to be the most central and deep-rooted aspect of the life of the organism, amounting in man to a virtual, although as yet only partial, self-determination. The internal motives and springs of action are in himself, moulding and making the self. If, as on a misleading analogy it is sometimes stated, there is a struggle between conflicting motives in which the stronger wins, it is the man after all who decides which shall be the stronger. The reasons for his action are ultimately of his own making. But towards this dénouement the whole of the racial past has contributed and moved in preparation. Without that past, both individual and racial alike, the freedom to decide at any specific moment would not be what it is. In this sense man is literally the heir of all the ages. In his brain there is enregistered something of the experience of the past, for the cerebro-psychic centre has throughout constituted itself a synthesis of the actions and reactions and the method of life or habits based on, and resulting from them, in the age-long history. The Freudian may or may not be right in tracing ' the occasional dreams one has of falling through space with the violent instinctive effort often undergone to prevent disastrous consequences,' [1] to enregistered reminiscences of arboreal life ; but the suggestion of continuity and of the impact and reverberation, so to speak, of waking experience, at any rate, through the whole being, is sound. These registered experiences and infinite possibilities constitute the material out of which the developing organism realises itself and becomes itself, as the result of its own activity, freeing itself from bondage to the past and the immediate Environment or allying itself with the best it finds in both. Apparently the highest mammalian forms, from whose type of brain the human brain has been developed by gradual stages, regard the external world in much the same general way as man, for they react to it in the same way. But in his case internal motives, ideas, and reactions, stored as the result of the marked development of the cerebral hemispheres and contributing to a basis for self-activity, come more and more to play the determining part, in contrast to immediate purely external stimulation, although ultimately even these internal stimuli can all be traced to experience of something spiritual and active in that Environment.

In the long, sub-human stages of life there has been from the beginning undoubtedly an urge or push towards ever higher manifestations of life. The method followed is one whereby the creature's own activity becomes increasingly a definite factor in its evolution; pain and physical evil represent the results in great part of inefficient adaptation, poor reaction, or violation of what

[1] Prof. R. S. Lull, *Organic Evolution*, p. 667.

has been found to be a successful mode of living—in short, of misuse of growing freedom—and often involve arrest in development, actual degeneration and elimination. At the same time, these identical conditions have also had the effect of stimulating other forms in the direction of some new line of development, an activity which has had a mutual effect on the cerebro-psychic centre, registering and consolidating the results of this new activity. The capacity for pain and suffering, which has been an accompaniment of the process throughout, also bears a direct relation to the development of the central nervous system.[1] When man began to be conscious of himself and of the character of the process as a whole, the higher degree of independence which was his, although a direct development of the growing self-activity of the sub-human forms of life, became a real moral liberty, at least in possibility. The essential development throughout the course of life has been that of the cerebro-psychic centre with which in the end has come to be directly associated the expression of even the moral life of man.

The evolutionary process comes to an end in man, a being peculiarly conscious of himself, independent, self-active, and self-determining as is no other organism in creation, ' the master of his fate, the captain of his soul.' Typically these are the possibilities, although in very varying degrees of actual realisation. But in our ordinary associations with the word ' man,' we envisage a stage that is too abruptly separated from the higher animals. It is really necessary to make objective and concrete to ourselves the stage corresponding to the Pliocene *Homosimius,* or even earlier—at present theoretical, but of which the actual proofs will one day be in our hands—represented to-day in mentality by the child of tenderest years, and think of this stage, immediately above the higher mammals, as that of the sub-personal animal. It is the stage, long enough doubtless

[1] Cf. *The Spiritual Interpretation of Nature,* pp. 154-160.

in the racial history, though brief in the recapitulated individual history of to-day, when *Homosimius* was gradually arriving at ever fuller consciousness of himself, gaining it perhaps for a moment and losing it again temporarily in the manifold activities of life on the purely animal plane. But once permanently gained, that assertion of the self, particularly as it came to be opposed in thought to the conception of an object other than self, and so standing, when fully developed, in contrast with the mental equipment of a lower mammal, seems like a new creation. This affirmation of the self is the origin of a whole new series of relations amongst the elements accumulated in the cerebro-psychic centre. It is to this stage that racially and individually the origins of speech, doubtless monosyllabic at first, are referable, and it is not difficult to see how by its expression and fixation of ideas, the latter were given a certain independence and objective existence which made intercourse and progress possible in a manner hitherto unrealisable. When self-consciousness has come to full and clear cognisance, and the animal self-activity has become conscious liberty, the sub-personal animal stage has passed over into that of man.

It is now many years since Fiske drew attention to the significance of the long period of human gestation and infancy,[1] not merely in the development of family life, but in the development of the individual life. Man comes into the world with his brain relatively less developed than that of any other mammal. It is indeed remarkably adapted to the extended period of infancy, while that of the higher animals is practically ready for complete functioning from the moment of birth. The facts almost look as if there were some deliberate intention that the developing self or personality should have the principal share in the later moulding of its instrument of expression, and certainly it is only in the measure in which it has had a hand, so to speak, in the

[1] John Fiske, *Man's Destiny*, pp. 35-57.

shaping of itself that responsibility can be attributed to it. In this way there is an evident method for the development of distinct personalities, or individuality in the ordinary sense of that term. The development of personality has consisted in the gradual conscious appropriation and assimilation by an increasingly assertive self, conscious of itself, and in continuous reaction with the Environment, of all the innumerable elements stored in the cerebro-psychic centre of the sub-personal animal which are primarily the elements of the subconscious life of the self. In this growing recognition and establishment of a self as a spiritual centre of initiation and determination, man rises historically above the stage of the sub-personal animal, much as to-day he develops individually out of the infant. Of that long stage we have already outlined what is known about the development both of the cortical areas and of the lower jaw, with the implications of a rudimentary tongue, and an incipient capacity for speech in Early Pleistocene man and even his predecessors. But throughout the whole history, as the direct consequence of the growing independence, the course of evolution has never been representable by a direct line of progress moving as a whole unerringly towards some specific end, but rather by a general direction and tendency, often thwarted indeed and lost in many details, full of detours and deviations, yet always represented in some forms, that contrived to keep in the narrow upward way. To them, in the midst of the process, the fact of progress would have often seemed obscure for long periods at a time, even had they had the ability to reflect on its character in that particular early phase in which they lived.

Of the later stages in this winning of independence it is unnecessary for our purpose to supply further detail. Most interesting of all, as we have seen, is that one in which the animal with incipient personality, or *Homosimius*, evolved into the distinctive man. The struggle with the forces of nature, the growing sense of need, the realisation of the efficacy of team work and social life generally, all following on the development of reason, with the power to form conceptions, constituted various elements in the process. How closely the development of these characters was related to the power of speech is evidenced, as Leenhardt points out, by the double meaning of the Greek word ' logos.' [1] The use of fire, utensils, arms, agriculture, the keeping of domestic animals, roughly represent different stages in this progressive conquest of Nature, this greater freedom which came from knowledge and obedience to the laws and rhythms discovered. It is a movement in the midst of which man stands to-day, still growing towards fuller personality, becoming progressively free. With the invention of writing, the experience of previous generations became available for their successors, and the loneliness and isolation of the greater minds of the race were at an end. If their immediate followers did not understand them, it now became possible for them to find appreciation in a wider circle. The holding or binding elements in the social structure were in the beginning, as throughout, however, the moral and religious elements. But the method of evolution has continued the same, and the evidence of history shows that the evolution of the higher mammals, characterised by the acquirement of their typical cerebro-psychic centre, has issued in the evolution of humanity, which in turn is growingly characterised by the formation of a society of personalities developing along ethical lines. Organic evolution is supplemented by ethical evolution, and in this connection the altruistic factor has played an increasingly important part. Just as surely as mental development was the characteristic feature of mammalian evolution, so is ethical development the characteristic feature of human evolution first racially and then individually. It is outlined in the gradual replacement of the wandering tribe by the settled group, developing the more productive and constructive

[1] *Op. cit.* p. 107.

sides of primitive civilisation, as by a social environment in which the conception of rights, and law, and the family became more securely fixed, for these groups alone tended to survive.

To-day man is a being possessed of a high degree of conscious activity, with great possibilities of mastery of himself and of Nature. There is no doubt of his success in the latter field, but calm consideration of the results of history compels us to admit that this ethical progress which would issue in complete mastery of himself, has not kept pace with his psychical development. It becomes evident, when we consider the products of the human spirit in art and science, that man's intellectual development has outrun his moral development ; the former in itself has little power to produce the latter. Man may attain to a high degree of mastery over Nature without having secured any corresponding control of himself. Very little observation shows that neither science nor philosophy, intelligence nor any form of human power, necessarily carries with it mastery of the self, or has the ability to set man free from bondage to the physical or mental characteristics that he has inherited. The latter are elements or instruments that may be used by the self in strengthening that affirmation in virtue of which man made the advance upon the purely animal stage ; they may also be so used that in the end the self tends to be lost or submerged. In a general way, in the public control of morals and in education, a standard is set which, however, as yet to a very slight degree affects that self-mastery in the individual life which is the evident aim, the inherent possibility in every human life.

The stage of *Homosimius*, the sub-personal animal, is reached by a measure of gradual personalisation of the psychical inheritance received from the representatives of the previous stage, and this has gone on assisted by the further advances secured by the initial development of language, and even the use of the hands. The complete dominance of all these inherited ideas and impulses, the mastery of the developing self over all these elements and itself alike—that relative goal towards which the whole evolutionary process seems to be intended to move—is, however, far from established, is indeed only now in process of being worked out. As yet in multitudes of instances, the incipient self, so far from being master, is dominated by the products of its own activity in the regions of the mind, some of them wakened into activity from their enregistration during the ancestral past, others due to new and fresh combinations of these elements. As a matter of simple fact man has, as a whole, as yet evolved but a very slight distance in the direction of real and perfect manhood : he is just a very little way beyond the stage of the higher mammal, whose action is characterised, as Leenhardt well remarks,[1] by the predominance of psychical automatism in place of genuinely voluntary and conscious activity, always desired and approved by the self. In man, at the stage of his present evolution, there is still to a large extent a higher-grade automatism of action that is opposed to that complete mastery and possession—that final liberty—of the self which would appear to be the end of evolution. Man, growingly intelligent and free in his actions, yet finds that that very acquisition of self-consciousness in virtue of which he developed out of the sub-human stage is in itself not unified or harmonised. St. Paul describes this phenomenon in the moral aspect in his passage about the two laws warring in his members ;[2] Ovid knew the experience ;[3] Greek tragedy is based upon it.[4] In another aspect we have the same phenomenon in the psychical and pathological cases of dual personality, which in less advanced forms are much more common than is ordinarily supposed. In every man, in fact, to some extent there are a Doctor Jekyll and a Mr. Hyde. His mental life may be distributed between two or even more secondary

[1] *Op. cit.* p. 115.    [2] Rom. 7[23].
[3] 'Video meliora proboque, deteriora sequor,' (*Metam.*, vii. 20).
[4] *e.g.* Euripides, *Hippol.*, 380 ff.

selves ; there is as yet no real attainment of *in*dividuality.
Man is still only on the way towards self-harmony and
*in*dividuality, and his journey is a series of struggles
against these secondary centres for the establishment
of unity and control.   Such complete and permanent
control, in full self-consciousness, of his whole psychical
inheritance from the higher animals, as also of these new
elements that result from his own mental activity as
man, would constitute true mastery of the self.   It would
mean that he would repress those elements that were
unfavourable to his moral advance, and favour and con-
firm these that were useful, and in this way make of himself, by continual definite and fully conscious acts of will,
a spiritual organism of which he would be completely
master, and as the result of which he would be better
able to achieve that in himself and for others which his
reading of the world process indicates to him as its end.
At this stage humanity has not arrived.   We see indeed
that while amongst the most civilised peoples there is
evidence of movement towards a greater deliverance of
humanity from the organic, intellectual or social servi-
tudes that bound humanity at its first appearance, and
still binds its more backward sections,[1] even in the best
individual lives, which ought ever to be in advance of
those of the masses of mankind, there is even as yet but
an approximation towards this complete self-mastery,
independence and *in*dividuality.

In these earlier stages of humanity, out of which we are
just beginning to emerge, man has on the whole tended
rather to be a passive participant in his evolution, in a
considerably less degree, of course, than his animal predecessors, yet apparently interested more in the assertion
than in the control of the self, and living his life to a great
degree on that level of organic and psychical activity which
characterised the immediately preceding stage.   But now
with the ability to read, and reflect upon, the process of
which he is a product, and to set aims steadily before his

[1] Leenhardt, *op. cit.* p. 117.

mind, his part in the assistance of the process ought to become more active and intelligent, and his duty to achieve its end in himself more clear and binding. Indeed his realisation of a purpose in the process is just what in great part constitutes the Ought for him. He may see the purpose in things and be conscious of it in many ways, but until he acts in such a way that his life expresses what he believes that purpose to be, he has not aligned his will with his knowledge.

In the case of this sense of duty and responsibility, we have characters of which adumbrations can be recognised in the animal world, although principally in connection with those forms that have been closely associated with man. Thus the dog to which some object has been entrusted, or which shows signs of 'repentance,' in that degree, manifests a glimmer of a moral sense. There is, of course, in its case no abstract idea of responsibility, and the tokens are only developed in presence of some concrete object or situation relative to man, and never as between dogs alone. Nevertheless, at whatever stage in the ascent of man this sense of obligation began to be defined in his mind, it was of the nature of an urge or stimulus to development comparable to the sense of need on a lower plane of animality, or the inherited tendencies on the psychical plane in the case of the higher mammals. On the ethical plane this urge becomes obligation, and is in evidence with the moment when the sub-personal animal or *Homosimius* first begins to realise that he ought to be master of himself. But the question inevitably follows on any sincere reflection upon the course of things as to how far man—who has in the course of his evolution developed the ability to resolve upon, and carry out this or that external activity—has developed at the same time the power of self-determination and control, enabling him to become that which he wishes to be in his real and inmost being. It is possible that there is a type of self-satisfaction to which such a consideration will be unwelcome. But evolution has never been through the self-satisfied, or those completely conformed to the Environment of the moment. The fact that he has not become completely *in*dividual, independent, master of himself is testified to by the question itself : he has not yet reached a perfected or complete humanity. He is still in great measure in bondage to his organism, however that organism may mark an advance upon that of the higher animals. This seems to be the testimony of man at his best, *i.e.* in his moments of greatest independence and self-mastery, to-day. The higher course appeals ; man feels that he ought to follow it just because he feels he has the possibility within him of being something better than he is. It is the testimony of humanity itself to its incomplete, if not arrested, development : in some instances there is all too evident degeneration. Humanity is not that which it might have been or ought to be, or in its highest representatives wishes to be. This missing of the mark, this failure to advance by self-mastery as the result of a personal activity directed by that internal conscience or higher sensitivity or God-consciousness which is the form which the urge of evolution henceforth assumes for man, is sin.

It has been maintained that from the evolutionary point of view human liberty in the degree already attained is but the development of the growing liberty of the animal cerebro-psychic centre : it is in fact the liberty of that centre become conscious of itself as free. And just as the former opened the road to organic and psychic accident, impasse, and degeneration, so also the latter opens the way to moral accident or sin. As Leenhardt truly says,[1] they are fundamentally the same kind of facts, but considered at different orders or stages of being, and so, however, with very different content and implication. But whether we speak of the fact as abnormal development, or use the terminology of theology and speak of a 'Fall' and sin, does not much matter : in any case,

[1] *Op. cit.* p. 132.

nomenclature cannot affect the facts. On the whole, the former terminology is preferable as indicating the definite relation of these later stages in man's history to what preceded man.

The serious difficulty in connection with all attempts to reconstruct the real nature and possibilities of man is that we have no very direct means of learning about the stage that represents the infancy of the race—corresponding to the first two or three years of the individual life. While the fossil remains are as yet comparatively scant, and every modern race is markedly human, and possessed of characteristics representing development greatly advanced beyond the stage in question, neither can any modern higher animal give us much idea of the forms immediately preceding the animal with incipient personality : they are all long gone out of the narrow upward way. It becomes, therefore, a more or less speculative matter when one attempts to reconstruct the process through which the higher animal became the animal with incipient personality, a moral creature. To-day it is almost impossible for us to think of man except as an individual surrounded by a moral atmosphere, with his mind the arena of conflicting motives. The stage, however, that we must reconstruct is something slightly in advance of the higher animal, with no background or reserve of moral motives *at all* in the developing mind. The life of the higher animals in default of any general moral sense of obligation, however incipient, is, *broadly speaking*, amoral, an existence with a very high degree of internal harmony simply because there is no possibility of internal discord, a life characterised by an increasingly high degree of spontaneity of action. The qualification, however, must be made, for, as Henry Drummond [1] and others have shown, from an early period in the history of animal life, there has been behaviour favourable to the good of others, at first all unconscious, which offset the instinctive tendency to self-preservation, and as involving the welfare of the species,

[1] *The Ascent of Man,* chap. vii.

tended ultimately to prove the more influential factor of the two. We may even hold with Professor J. Arthur Thomson [1] that Animate Nature ' makes for ' the Beautiful, the Good, and the True, for, to take the last character, the creatures that have faced the facts of life and tried to learn them—the truth-seekers and the knowing ones —are on the whole most likely to survive.

Yet we have been compelled to look on all this as a preparation for a later stage with the possibility of fuller independence, and so completer mastery of the developing self. Out of these conditions the next stage develops, *but without any bias in one direction or another*. There is no possibility of strongly developed motive, no pressure from below so to speak, or from above : there is no inevitability in the character of the process as to whether man should be, so to speak, good or bad. The so-called animal passions have nothing wrong in themselves : there is little misuse of them in nature. The conditions of the first moral act are possibly entirely unrepresentable to our minds to-day : they were in themselves, so far as the rest of the animal creation was concerned, practically those of an amoral world. The slightest degree of ability to consider and pass judgment on behaviour, a situation involving a challenging alternative to be that which for some reason he approves or disapproves, an elementary, indefinable sense of obligation which is the new form of the evolutionary urge, less immediately compelling than in the previous stages because liberty is on the point of meaning more and being more realised than ever it was before—our developed conceptions make it difficult to represent these undeveloped beginnings. But in whatever degree man follows this feeling of obligation, he shows himself master of himself since he has made himself that which he approves : there is harmony and independence in an incipient degree. It is a new type of self-assertion, grounded in and based upon the lower physical assertiveness of life, but determined by a new environmental

[1] *The Control of Life*, p. 267.

relationship. His world is now a moral world and he can never henceforward step out of it, nor pass beyond its determining hold on him.

Notwithstanding the inherent difficulties of the problem, the question as to how this incipiently moral self did actually come into being in the early stages of man's development has been made the subject of much consideration.[1] The instinct of preservation which antedates the development of self-consciousness may with the development of self-consciousness become increasingly self-ish. On the other hand, the sense of the self could only have been developed in some living form that was gregarious in habit and had accordingly reached a certain social level, for it is only by direct contact, relationship, and contrast with others that the idea of the self comes into clear recognition. Fixed relationships or customs must often have come at first into being without any very deep reason, for the power of reflection at this stage can only have been of the simplest. We can but look for guidance in study to the mind of the child, regarding it as recapitulating the mental history of the race. As children who have built a castle in the sand with more than one entrance will, after a short discussion that evinces no sound reason other than that of whimsical fancies, decide that visitors may enter only by one particular passage, so originally custom and habits may have arisen for which there was, and could have been, no reason worth the name. Later reflection might consider how these customs affected different individuals, whether, that is to say, they were just in their incidence or otherwise, whether they were indeed supportable. At the same time, in these relationships with others that fashioned the sense of self into being, thought as in the mind of the child would be mainly occupied with the objective action of others : their behaviour relation to the developing self would be the subject of criticism and judgment long before such judg-

[1] For a good account see James Ward, *The Realm of Ends*, chap. xvii.

ment was seriously turned upon the self itself. Introspection is a later development, a harder business than direct observation. Accordingly conduct that might seem reprehensible in others would continue to be indulged in, all unconsciously, by the criticising subject. At the same time, a distinct factor in the promotion of introspection would be any communication to an individual of the impression made by his conduct upon others.

Again, previous to this development of the ability to reflect on action either as it affected others or the self, actions as in the childhood of the human individual to-day, reprehensible in older people because, as we say, ' they ought to know better,' are rightly held to be those of innocent and guiltless individuals. And the same holds true *a fortiori* of the similar activities in the case of the lower creation. At many stages previous to man there have been possibilities of behaviour, and even habits, which the experience of more developed forms shows to be contrary to the welfare of the race and of the individual and which are therefore disapproved by them, but which cannot be held to be blameworthy in the case of those forms that have not yet developed the mental apparatus which makes reflective experience possible. In the constitution of things the adaptability of life has prevented these traits from obtaining any absolute domination in the world of life as a whole—the deer can escape from the devouring carnivore by fleetness—but the impulses remain. The interest for the evolutionist is in the question, which is part of the general fact of progress, as to how activities which are not blameworthy at one stage or on one level do become so at another.

The ability to pass judgment on the conduct of others then probably antedated self-criticism. The latter would only come with the developed self-consciousness. Such self-judgment or conscience thus necessarily implies self-consciousness. And in the known judgment of the family or tribe upon courses of action—the public opinion of those nearest to him—primitive man probably found his first moral standard. A ban is set upon certain lines of conduct, and the individual facing alternatives comes to realise that one is considered worthier than the other, and henceforth it *is* worthier for him. Actions that before were non-moral have now become such as should be avoided, and are in that measure evil. He knows things as good and evil, and things done before without reflection are now done under a self-judgment, approving or disapproving. The origin of the so-called tribal conscience can only in the end be set down to the influence of some individuals—possibly one—more prescient, more sensitive, more quick than the rest in attaining this higher consciousness. From such a point of view ideas of 'total depravity' as an inherent condition of the race at any period are seen to be purely misanthropic. The various impulses lying at the basis of the actions referred to are not in themselves moral or immoral, but man's use of them from the dawn of self-consciousness is. It has always been the easy thing to conform to some Environmental aspect of the moment, to seek some equilibrium on a lower level, to give up the struggle, but to do so is the unnatural thing ; it is infidelity to the character of the process.

How slow has been the advance, the following of the upward way, is the sad reflection of those who are interested in the welfare of the race. All along it has been a struggle, veritably a matter of life and death. And yet it is difficult to see how ' a world in which the possibility of wrong-doing was prevented by the exclusion of all temptations that were really such '[1] could ever be or become a moral world at all. But the world that we know is a world in which conscience is a reality whether men always obey it or not, and its interests are those of righteousness. There is the liberty to follow or not to follow, and the growing liberty implies a moral order in which moral evil is a possibility. But that possibility however realised has been powerless to prevent the moral

---

[1] James Ward, *op. cit.* p. 372

progress of the race. Morality is not so much *in* the nature of things as it actually *is* the nature of things : the moral order is *the* order of the world.

It is perhaps idle to speculate how if man had consistently and determinedly aligned himself with the promptings of that ' still small voice ' of obligation, how if, in that first moral use of the growing liberty which marked the transition from the animal with incipient personality to man, he had affirmed his self-mastery in an affirmation of the self as his duty, there would have proceeded more rapidly that liberation of himself from the inherited psychic organism, and his transformation of it into an instrument better suited to his internal harmonious development.   Physical evil would have retained that character of a stimulus, warning token and test which it has for the lower creation, but it would have been more rapidly overcome.   What is more important is to note as objective historical fact that man being as we have actually seen him to be, some half a million of years after the period in which the higher mammal was becoming the sub-personal animal, and while yet humanity was in its childhood, there appeared in Palestine One who in His person exhibited perfect manhood, and whose life was at once full of the completest internal harmony, and liberty, and independence.   No other life has ever given such a sense of perfect freedom.   His absolute mastery of Himself in face of every kind of temptation, and throughout a series of situations that finally involved His execution, never failed.   He realised in every particular that towards which the whole evolutionary process has been evidently tending.   At first it seems inexplicable that this perfect type should appear unique in the midst of historic humanity,[1] all of whom are separated from Him if in nothing else than that in every other human soul there is internal disharmony.   His appearance, which is the most remarkable fact in human history, is yet in itself in one sense of the same order as that of the appearance

[1] See later, p. 315.

of personality in animality : that is to say, it marks the introduction of a new era in human history.  But the change is so profound as to constitute Him the turning-point or pivot in all history.  As a matter of simple observation civilisation moved manifestly in Him from a Self-regarding basis, as exemplified at that time in the Roman State, to an Other-regarding basis, represented in the Church.  Christianity gave a new direction to human history.  For in Him there came to light and actuality for the first and only time that for which the whole process from the beginning had evidently been purposed, and He is the fulfilment of all that went before.  The more that process is seen to be a unity, the more clearly will this eternal and absolute significance of Jesus Christ become apparent.  In Him the specifically human characteristic of Love came for the first and only time to perfect and victorious expression over the organi-cally derived complex of human nature, *i.e.* over the selfishness of the individual, with the result that His personality and teaching thereafter acted as a trans-forming elemental energy in the world.  He was the first and only perfect man—*the* Son of man : He was the first and only One in Whom Love, the fundamental character of God, found perfect expression—*the* Son of God.  So that He is unique whether we look backwards or forwards —backwards, for never man spake or lived or died as He did ; forwards, for history can only once traverse such a turning-point.  In a very real sense He is the Alpha and Omega of strictly human history, and to Him every successive generation turns in seeking its ideal.

Another remarkable fact is that in some kind of a direct relation to Him, men of all races and civilisations have found that they are freed from the tormenting internal dualism so characteristic of humanity, and begin to become masters of themselves through some moral energy that is associated with Him.  He gives liberty to the captive : the spiritual life of men, as often indeed their physical life also in some measure, is renewed in every aspect, through this relation with Him.  It is a transformation that reaches to the very core of a man's being, to the self that has been struggling for affirmation and control : a spiritual Power is at work which is an expression of this new relation.   It may be difficult to explain the fact, but it is there.   Throughout the world there is an increasing race of men—the word is not too strong, although the characteristics are not physical but spiritual—who by an act of will, bringing themselves into relation with Him, attain to yet greater liberty and begin to develop a quality of life which, if His words are true, is eternal.

Accordingly, then, we may really see a double move-  ≥ ment in human evolution, which goes far deeper than the superficial siftings of nationality.   The one concerns those individuals and masses of individuals whose evolution will end like other lines of previous evolutionary history, in an impasse, just because the individual is at once cause and effect, without spiritual relationship, and a prey to a disrupting inward disharmony of mind :  the other, a new line which tends towards increasing self-mastery, freedom, and inward harmony.   The former line will long persist, enriching civilisation and itself evolving to some extent, but with no ultimate future beyond that of the limits of terrestrial existence, except in so far as its members come to realise their true destiny :  it constitutes a divergent evolutionary branch.   The other branch is in the true line of continued evolution.   Its members while sharing in and contributing to the advance of science and art and literature, and in every way helping to raise the standard of civilisation, realise that terrestrial conditions are a determining phase in that process of attaining self-mastery, inward harmony, *in*dividuality, and freedom :  for love has no value in God or man except in so far as the lover is completely master of himself, is really free.   At the same time, there is little doubt, to judge by the progress of the past, that human evolution as a whole even in its terrestrial phase will become increasingly spiritual, that is to say, that humanity will more and more show in its members 'a unity of that which man is and of that which he wishes to be.'[1] Such a stage when achieved terrestrially will be the Kingdom of God upon earth—that condition when the Will of God will be done on earth as it is done in heaven.

[1] Leenhardt, *op. cit.* p. 152.

# CHAPTER XII

## GOD AND THE WORLD

THE evolutionary history of the origin of man, however far back we care to trace it, presents us with a series of stages with considerable gaps. Even in the most recent series of events from the Pliocene onwards, the number of these lacunae is not insignificant. On the other hand, every year contributes something to making the story more of a connected whole. Every decade the explanation of the growing number of stages appears more reasonable in terms of Evolution, than on the alternative of the Special Creation of each one of them from some ancestral pair. With the further realisation of the course of each individual human history as a progress from the initial stage of the fertilised egg-cell to adult manhood, a process will be seen in which that ancestral history is resumed or rehearsed without a gap or break, and it will become increasingly probable that what is true of the individual must have been true of the race—in fact, is true of the individual, because it was true of the race.

At the same time, such an explanation is after all only proximate and methodological. The mind is still unsatisfied. It pushes further back in its effort to reach some interpretation of the series as a whole, to find some thread whereon to string this impressive cluster of data, some clue to the meaning of it all. The impression is ever one of activity, of process ; it is dynamic throughout. With no absolute beginning, so far as we can see, the process takes the form in the case of our planet of a long period of inorganic evolution preparatory to a second stage which is characterised by life, and leads directly to a third, of which man is the distinguishing feature and culmination. It gives an impression of purposiveness throughout. There has also been everywhere the indication of order, which inevitably suggests mind. At no point is there insuperable evidence of a complete and absolute break, or *ab initio* creation of the whole. There are expression points, moments whose implications are greater than their actual advent, increments, points after which everything moved upon a higher plane, but in every such change, transformation or epiphany, there is always something carried over from the previous stage. Life builds upon the basis of the inorganic elements ; self-consciousness after all posits consciousness ; Jesus is the Son of Mary. The new character or grace is supervenient, the outcome of ' emergent evolution,' in active relationship at every moment with a stimulating, supporting, and revealing Environment, and it is always in some way directly linked with what preceded.

While, then, the proof of such continuity, *e.g.* in the evolution of man, may be still incomplete at certain points, yet it is maintained that all the indications, inorganic and organic alike, point in the direction of such continuity both of physical and spiritual life, and that such a view gives the more satisfying explanation. It has been suggested that the real continuity lies in the realm of energetic relations, and as the process seems to develop in one particular principal direction, viz. the evolution of man, and is apparently not reversible, it gives the impression of being in a general way controlled and directed, that is to say, of being under the influence of mind not indeed necessarily knowing and intending everything in advance, but working persistently towards a specific consummation. The existence of the different forms of energy, however interpretable in terms one of the other, leads back in thought to some common Source.

Of mind as influencing the direction of energy, controlling it so that the expenditure of it takes place in ways which would not otherwise have been the case, and pro-

ducing changes in the distribution of matter and energy, we
have sufficient evidence in the case of man.   Accordingly
it is difficult to suppose that some kind of selective and
purposeful activity does not at least ground and condition
that energetic process of which man is the final product.
Using the word to express the basis of all the phenomena
of consciousness in man and the higher animals, and
of that proconsciousness which accompanies the self-
preservative activities of even the lowliest of organisms,
we find a continuity of something that becomes enriched
and expansive in its relations with the Environment as
life advances.   Now this evolution of mind and the development of the individual cannot have come about
from matter, if the earlier statements on the relations of
energy and matter and mind are true ; they may, however, well be the result of the activities of a World-Ground
that is itself of the essence of a self-determining Mind.
In this way, while we are pushed towards a theistic interpretation as the most reasonable, it must be a self-
consistent Theism.

In this connection the age-long yet unsolved problem
of the relationship of mind and brain will be viewed, in
virtue of our other data, in terms of the primacy of mind.
No quantitative relationship has been established, or is
ever likely to be established, between the two entities.
Consciousness, as we ordinarily know it, is associated
in a certain relation with a brain : but this does not
necessarily mean that a brain is an indispensable accompaniment of consciousness.   We know that lower grades
of consciousness are present in the case of organisms that
have no brain, and in the case of man consciousness waxes
and wanes in intensity in very varying degrees.   The
detailed proof by Professor Bergson of the theses that
' there is infinitely more, in a human consciousness, than
in the corresponding brain,' [1] that ' the mind overflows
the brain on all sides, and that cerebral activity responds

---

[1] *Mind-Energy*, p. 41 ; cf. also *Matter and Memory*, chaps. ii.
and iii.

only to a very small part of mental activity,' [1] seems convincing. In fact we are just on the threshold of knowledge with regard to the effects of thought upon the nervous system, and the associated field of phenomena like hypnosis, stigmata, and possibly even telepathy has as yet been only scratched on the surface. From vasodilatations like blushing to actual metabolic changes in nerve-cells there lies a whole range of phenomena definitely inducible by thought, although assuredly there is also much evidence of the effect of body upon mind. The Two-Aspect or Identity Hypothesis of the relations of mind and body,[2] while it permits of the envisaging of organic Evolution as a general development from mind-bodies to body-minds, and looks on psychosis and neurosis as the convex and concave sides, so to speak, of the same curve, does not perhaps so easily provide for that degree of initiative that is at any rate in evidence all along, tending to suggest the predominance of mind, and would appear to involve a degree of exact correlation between states of mind and body that does not in point of fact always exist.

Of Mind, however, or more particularly Will, *i.e.* the mind in deliberate action, as *creative* of energy—a conception which would resolve for us the final dualism of Mind and Energy—the evidence is not as yet direct. At the same time, there are some considerations that make such a solution at any rate conceivable. Thus the doctrine of the Conservation of Energy while experimentally true of any detached or abstracted portion of Reality, and so a useful and necessary working hypothesis, is a mere unproved assumption when applied to the Universe as a whole, and as a matter of fact in those cases where equivalence in work compels belief in actual transformation of energy, we have as yet no knowledge of the exact nature of the physical change involved in such

---

[1] *Mind-Energy*, p. 57.

[2] For an admirable summary of present-day theories see Prof. J. Arthur Thomson, *The System of Animate Nature*, vol. i. chap. vii.

transmutation. There is the further assumption that the physical is only and always physical, and there is no suggested ultimate physical source for the infinite energy of the Universe. On the other hand, the view which regards Mind or Will as creative of Energy, or Energy as a manifestation of Will, helps to make intelligible the specificity of action, the directedness, the working out of what looks like purpose. It is also the case that the very conception of Energy comes to us historically ' from a depersonalising of human will, and . . . implies a direct experience of a sense of effort.' [1]

However these things may be, the evolutionary process of creation with its suggestion of urge or drive in a definite and culminating direction, gives the impression of a Supreme Mind going forth in creative and directive energetic activity, as the result of which physical organisations are built up ' of ever-increasing complexity suitable for the reception of its ever-increasing influx.' [2] In Bergson's phraseology, ' I see in the whole evolution of life on our planet a crossing of matter by a creative consciousness, an effort to set free, by force of ingenuity and invention, something which in the animal still remains imprisoned and is only finally released when we reach man.' [3] The process consists, then, in the preparation of an inorganic environment composed of matter with strictly determinate relationships, forming the foundational substructure or matrix in association with which life came into being. Now matter is ultimately explicable in terms of energy,[4] and in that whole process of self-emptying or kenosis which is Creation, the self-limitation of God nowhere so markedly appears as in this relatively fixed, proximate, physical aspect of Environment, from the domination of which life has ever been struggling into freedom and union with the deeper ultimate Source or Ground of it all, which is God. Objectively, then, the

[1] J. E. Mercer, *The Problem of Creation*, p. 107.
[2] G. W. de Tunzelmann, *God and the Universe*, p. 131.
[3] *Mind-Energy*, p. 18. [4] P. 9.

result of Evolution at every stage is seen to be a growing freedom from the domination of the proximate physical aspects of the Environment, which develops in the case of man into a progressive control of them through growing commerce, rapport, and union with the ultimate spiritual Reality in that Environment. With him, moreover, the freedom to be won covers the whole range of his inherited animal past. Progress, Life, Evolution throughout, have depended on growing adaptation to ever deeper and wider aspects of the Environment : complete adaptation to the proximate material aspect has always meant stagnation, and destruction sooner or later. The aim of the process is the development of perfect, *i.e.* truly free, personality—conscious of volitional choice between alternatives, conscious that it is not compelled to choose at once, but can do so in deliberate review of its whole experience. Perfect freedom is perfect self-determination from within, as opposed to rigid compulsion from without. The forces of what seemed to be the inevitable are increasingly controlled by the developing will.

The process, therefore, is interpretable as one through which, as the result of this self-limitation of God in a creative activity providing both the principle which issues in self-realised spirit and the Environment which renders such self-realisation possible, living organisms progressively come into being which are stages in the development of self-conscious spirit. God creates that which by interaction with the Environment, likewise a manifestation of Himself, may win freedom, may issue in free self-realised spirit. In the earlier stages there is no consciousness as we know it, but the process leads towards consciousness. The lowest organisms are mainly ' conscious ' of matter—the proximate physical aspect of the Environment. Higher organisms are conscious of matter and of other organisms, but even they react principally to discontinuous stimuli of limited range, as compared with man. Their mental life is largely a series of discrete experiences and disconnected moments ; their world is a world of percepts. With memory, continuity of conscious experience becomes for the first time possible, as also sustained action according to a plan, and that developed form of intelligence that realises the continuity in the Environment. Freedom is found to be in direct relation to the development of spirit : growth in the latter is growth in freedom. Growing freedom on the mental side means emergence from discontinuity into coherent unity, advance towards the *in*dividual. As his mental development proceeds, man realises more and more that the spiritual is ultimate : indeed, according to Bergson, spirit is progress in duration.

We have seen how a progressive gaining of freedom is of the very core of the evolutionary process. Yet even in the slowly growing degree in which it is manifest at every stage in life, increase in freedom is not given to all : indeed, it is given to none, but all have had the opportunity and power of attaining it, and while even the complete self-realisation of the developed spirit in perfect goodness and love is dependent upon freedom, yet is there no compulsion towards freedom. There is the impulse or urge and the possibilities at every stage, but all this is often nullified by the impulse towards equilibrium, and no advance is made. The material aspect of the Environment is always there, and different creatures respond to its stimuli in different ways : nevertheless throughout there is selection by the Environment of a ' saving remnant ' who responded to its spiritual beckonings. Progress in freedom could only be won by struggle with, extrication from, and gradual conquest of, that which is not free, hence the necessity for the proximate physical aspects of the Environment. As M'Dowall points out in a very suggestive book, ' freedom must necessarily be based on determination of some sort.' [1] It means the achievement of self-determination out of the press of external factors which would constrain the plastic growing spirit. Also it involves utilisation of the

[1] Stewart A. M'Dowall, *Evolution and Spiritual Life*, p. 154.

gains of others, of past efforts, and that may mean pain and suffering for these others. Yet except on the principle of such economy, it is difficult to see how there could be progress. Forms that did not make for progress, having turned out of the narrow, upward way, have either filled a humbler but far from valueless rôle, or were killed out, or found their end in *culs-de-sac* of parasitism or actual degeneration. Hence the pain and suffering incidental to all advance, and we can only believe—and are confirmed in that belief by the Incarnation—that God suffers as things go wrong, whether in the case of the unconscious lower creation or of man. If freedom is the goal, then struggle and suffering are inevitable, for freedom means extrication and transcendence.

Creation, then, is a definite self-limitation of God, a surrender in part of His freedom, which is restored as His creatures are perfected : nevertheless, just in the degree in which even man's partial freedom is real, God is self-limited in relation to him. Perfect spirits cannot be *made* : the whole idea of being *made* is incompatible with the idea of freedom. Because God is Love, He must be self-communicating, and that for Him means creation. He is eternally Love, and so in virtue of His nature, eternally a Creator : it is His Love, so to speak, that supplies the driving force or urge or impulse, and the more we consider the world process, the more we are constrained to admit that it is all of grace, that indeed, in a very real sense, as Erigena long ago maintained, 'Nature and Grace are one, the ways of Nature being manifestations of Grace, and Grace achieving its purposes through the eternal orderliness of Nature.' [1] Love is God in activity, and 'where Love is, there God is also.' There is, therefore, an eternal impulse towards creation in God, since a desire for fellowship or union always craves expansion as well as intensification. He creates the conditions under

[1] From a chapter on 'Erigena : the Division of Nature,' by G. J. Blewett in *The Study of Nature and the Vision of God*, p. 329.

which freedom can be won by spiritual beings, and then in a measure leaves to them the winning of their freedom. ' Work out your own salvation,' says the Apostle,[1] but immediately he adds, ' it is God that worketh in you to will and to do of His good pleasure.' We see the actual method ; we do not know enough to say that it was the only method possible, but we do know that it is achieving the end. And this end is the perfecting of beings who are acquiring the attributes of personality, and their final union with Him, not indeed by way of absorption, but in an existence of communion whose basis and object shall still be activity and love in alignment with His will. The process, that is to say, issues supremely in other self-determining personalities who differ from Him as distinct individual personalities, each with its own experience, which, however, can never be of the same degree as that of Him in whom they find their cause, differing from Him, as they do, also, in that while they began to be in time, He is from all eternity. The evolution of personality when perfected means ' unity of experience between the perfected soul and the Creator so far as the experience of the former reaches, while yet the persons remain distinct,' [2] and unity comes when the evolving spirit of man has become wholly assimilated to, though never absorbed in, the Spirit of Divine Love. Unity with God, in perfect mutual spiritual experience, free from all limitations, *is* Eternal Life, and this means an enrichment of the experience of God Himself through ' the reciprocal fulfilment of love.' [3]

The winning of freedom, however, leaves the way open, as we have seen, for the introduction of wrong methods in the lower creation : in the case of man the gaining of freedom means the possibility of sin. That possibility first comes into being when man can make a right decision, knowing it to be such. Hence, while pain and suffering are inevitable elements in the process, sin is no necessary

---

[1] Phil. 2 [12].                    [2] M'Dowall, *op. cit.* p. 49.
[3] M'Dowall, *op. cit.* p. 138.

product of evolution.   It is misdirection of personality,
' a misdirection of the will in *time*, which adds to Reality
only when the issue in conduct is actually consum-
mated. . . . God suffers in the consequences of man's
sin, but sin itself has no part in Him.' [1]   He is affected by
it as it affects Reality.   Sin is failure to continue to win
freedom, an acceptance of dynamic equilibrium, definite
rejection of the purpose of life, treason to the purpose of
the process.   Sin is knowledge rejected, and it is knowledge that makes sin possible.   It is deliberate wilful failure to achieve the purpose of the whole process in relation
to the individual life.   The sinner remains bound.   It
is in the creature, not in his surroundings, that we must
look for the significance of sin.   It is the rebellious refusal
to progress—acceptance of the present.   ' Sin is any
want of conformity unto or transgression of the law of
God,'—the law of progress, and true self-realisation.

The self-limitation of God in creation is, then, finite ;
it affects only a portion of His experience.   Matter
may be regarded as the result of the elimination of
freedom from a certain portion of the experience of
God.   In the fulness of His experience He is transcendent.   Duration is characteristic of that which is
becoming, of the process, of God as Immanent.   God
is, we have said ; the World becomes.   He is the Being
in the Becoming—that is God as immanent.   But He
is not exhausted by the process : He *is*—that is God as
transcendent, as simultaneous.   It is peculiarly difficult
to represent the situation clearly to ourselves, yet we get
a hint of it in our own personality, and man being a
genetic product of the process, there is no illegitimacy in
arguing from man to the character of the process.   If we
make God in our image, it is because He first made us in
His.   Now every human individual can say of himself,
' I am, and I become.'   There is something of him that
is not subject to the law of change in the degree in which
this is true of the physical and certain mental aspects of

---

[1] M'Dowall, *op. cit.* p. 138.

his being. Further, that which is persistent through these changes—that self-identity or measure of *in*dividuality that gives him a sense of transcendence to the rest of himself—is the basis on which his existence and his freedom rest, and his freedom is his power to create and initiate change. In this he differs from the inorganic and markedly in degree from all other organic forms. The consciousness of transcendence comes out also in self-consciousness—in the ability to separate himself as subject from himself as object.[1] The activity of God as Transcendent is internal, within Himself, or with the spirits of just men made perfect, for the meaning of communion is activity without change. On the other hand, His activity in relation to the cosmic process and the gradual development of beings towards greater freedom and perfection is in time, durational, and in that limited sense God is becoming, becoming man, a limitation that is removed as men become perfect. God has been becoming man in order that man may become as God. He became man in Jesus Christ, the Incarnate Logos. So in thinking of the Transcendence of God we strive to represent and express to ourselves His persistence through change, His wisdom and fulness of power.

In thinking of God as Transcendent we think of His internal self-determination and perfect freedom, and in thinking of Him as Immanent we have in mind His creative activity based on volition externally directed. The last follows from His nature which is Love, and Love means the desire to share experience. And the movement is towards the development of personalities because God Himself is Transcendent Personality, the Suprapersonal. Union is the entering of other personalities into His experience as far as that is possible for beings who have had a beginning in time. Now we can see as objective fact evidences of the striv-

[1] Telepathy, the ability of one mind to influence another at a distance, if a fact, would also give a certain sense of transcendence.

ing of the human soul throughout the ages to enter into relationship with that Power which, by its characteristics revealed in the world process, we are driven to think of as God. And just because we know ourselves as on the way towards complete personality we cannot be content with anything less than a Personal God, and feel the insufficiency of a view which conceives of God as no more than ' unceasing life, action, and freedom,' having ' nothing of the already made.' [1] Such a view includes no conception of Transcendence : it is Pantheism, as sterile a creed as Unitarianism. But man is a product of the process, which we have related to God, and God cannot be less than man ; and therefore Personality in some suprapersonal sense must be predicated of God. Now Love is the most characteristic feature of personality, so that we can believe that God is Love, and that the creative movement, an expression of His Personality, is directed towards the development of a plurality of persons in perfect union with Him and completely free, and so enriching and completing the experience of Him who filleth all things. Finally, in this connection, while we must believe that the Transcendence of God is complete in spite of the fact of His Immanence, yet in man that which we have seen to be suggestive of, and in a measure capable of, transcendence —his developing *in*dividuality or self—is imperfect just because of its physical immanence. Now to become more self-determined from within, *i.e.* more free, is for the human spirit to pass from immanence to transcendence, from the temporal to the eternal. Man's freedom *is* his transcendence. And it is just here that the struggle for freedom and *in*dividuality against bondage and dissolution or annihilation is most severe and most critical, for on it would appear to depend the attainment or non-attainment of that condition which is Eternal Life.

[1] Prof. Bergson, *Creative Evolution*, p. 262.

# CHAPTER XIII

### THE SCRIPTURAL DOCTRINE OF IMMORTALITY

IN bringing the conclusions of the previous chapters to
the test of Scriptural teaching, that is to say, in attempting to estimate how far they are in accordance with the
views set forth in the greatest religious handbook of all
time, we are following a course which is as necessary as
it is crucial. Briefly summarised the situation is as
follows. It is maintained that the method of Organic
Evolution has been one throughout—that of selection ;
what has changed is the criterion of selection. Organic
Evolution has been a process of continued adaptation to
Environment, the resultant of various factors, but at
marked stages in the progress of life the character of the
conditioning, *i.e.* the survival-determining, factor, has
changed. At first it was power of food-assimilation,
then advance in methods of reproduction, thereafter
physical force, then cunning or mind, and with the
appearance of man the criterion has become increasingly
a moral one. There seems to be no reason why with the
appearance of man the general method of evolution
should change. There is nothing in the history of man,
physical or spiritual, to indicate either that it should
change or that it has changed. Further, we have seen
reason to believe that man is only now in process of
attaining *in*dividuality, and that this must be essentially
a spiritual process. Does Scripture, then, in any way
support the contention that eternal life—continuity of
personal existence—is morally conditioned, that man, in
short, is immortable rather than immortal, and can only
realise his true destiny as he fulfils his place in the moral
order ?

The answer to this question—for the problem is not new—can be attempted with a greater measure of certainty to-day than in any previous period, and not merely because we know so much better what the teaching of Scripture is. Just as in an earlier age ignorance of any other mode of creation compelled interpretation of the opening verses of Genesis in terms of a doctrine of Special and Immediate Creation,[1] so lack of knowledge of the conditions of life left other passages of Scripture open to interpretations that seem henceforth untenable. But, in particular, study of the mental presuppositions and general religious outlook of the hitherto little known period between the Old and New Testaments has furnished us with many of the elements out of which the various eschatological schemes of the later book were woven, and enables us to understand what exactly was in the mind of the writers and speakers in the use of certain phrases and the enunciation of certain statements. The wonder of it, the proof of the deep and lasting truth— the inspiration—of Scripture is seen in the fact that there is no disharmony between these statements and the conclusions that appear forced upon us on the strength of other considerations.

The supreme contribution of Israel to the world was its monotheistic doctrine of God. In the collection of writings known as the Old Testament, apart from those books and sections of books that profess to deal primarily with the actual history of Israel, we have a record of the religious experiences of some of the choicest souls amongst a people who were led through them to a unique conception of God. How this knowledge of God, at first crude and realistically anthropomorphic, was purified and deepened as the result of national and personal experience is one of the special interests of the Scriptural page. But from the beginning this consciousness of God is represented as something peculiarly vivid and direct, and so completely satisfying as to constitute in itself the

[1] *The Spiritual Interpretation of Nature*, p. 280.

very essence of life. At every stage in the history there is also evidence of the reaction of the religious Hebrew not merely against the ideas and ideals of the peoples living amongst and around him in Palestine, but against the more impressionable of his own race who failed to hold to the conception of the true God amidst the welter of superstition, debasing folklore, and general low moral level of the age. At the same time, so far as there was any idea of immortality in the mind of the Hebrew, it took the form principally of the thought of the identification or corporate solidarity of himself with his people— God's chosen people. In the earlier stage of Israel's history there was little developed sense of the value of the individual life. Not indeed before the time of Jeremiah and Ezekiel, after the seventh century B.C., was there clear recognition of individual responsibility and retribution. The unit was the family, and Achan's sons and daughters suffered with him in expiation of his guilt.[1] Yet it was just in these sons and daughters that as a rule the Hebrew felt his immortality to lie—in the merging of himself in his family and tribe and nation. And as there could be no question about the continuance of his people—for they represented the Kingdom of God amongst men—and as its destiny, however subjected to change, was always envisaged as worked out upon the earth, the thought of death and what came after it did not play any outstanding part in this connection. God was at work in His world, and men received at His hands judgment and retribution here and now. To the Hebrew mind as expressed particularly in the Psalms, the consciousness of God was so real, and so ultimate a factor in this present life, that its thought busied itself little with the question of a future state or of the future at all except in relation to the nation. It was only when the experience of the Exile threatened and ultimately seemed to destroy the outlook for the nation that the pious soul was more and more driven in upon itself and God. Re-

[1] Joshua 7 24.

flections that must have been bitter to a developing sense
of individuality—as that death would after all prevent
a man from sharing in the hopes of the nation—became
poignant when these very hopes themselves vanished in
thin air.   Then it was that, troubled also by the manifest
lack, as it appeared, of the retributive element in life, the
consciousness of God and fellowship with Him became
even more than ever the solace of the disquieted heart,
until the thought became intolerable that such fellowship
could be interrupted by death—' Thou wilt not leave my
soul to Sheol; neither wilt thou suffer thine holy one to
see corruption.' [1]

Apart then from the patriotic ideas outlined above,
Hebrew thought was not at first much concerned with the
future, and still less, speculatively, with the state of the
dead, otherwise than to acquiesce, on the whole indiffer-
ently, in the popular beliefs which it shared by inheritance
with the surrounding and autochthonous peoples.   These
were connected with Sheol, the place of the dead, a con-
struct of the imagination even to the localising of it in
' the lower parts of the earth.' [2]   To this region of gloom
and darkness all went at death, the great ones of the earth
as well as their servants, the prisoner together with his
taskmaster.   It was an apathetic condition of mere
existence, void of all moral distinctions : all that we
associate with the word vitality was gone.   Sheol was
an abode of flaccid, shadowy, dream-like beings—what
Odysseus calls ' the pithless heads of the dead.' [3]   ' Thou
too art made weak as we ' are the words with which they
greet a regal newcomer.[4]   Much as in the Homeric conception, the dead were thought of as going on existing
in some sense or another,[5] but it was not the ' soul' that

[1] Ps. 16 [10].                                    [2] Ps. 63 [9].
[3] Odyss. ii. 24-55.  The rendering is by Prof. H. A. A. Kennedy
In several respects the Hebrew and Homeric conceptions were akin.
[4] Is. 14 [9-11].
[5] At the same time it seems futile to attempt to draw distinctions,
as is sometimes done, between ' life ' and ' existence ' where personality
is concerned.  The only existence that means anything even in the
case of animals is a condition of life.  ' But, in fact,' says Dr. R. F

survived; the dead are called 'shades' rather than
'souls' or 'spirits' in the Old Testament. The early
Hebrew did not think of annihilation as we conceive the
term : this conception did not appear till late, and then
perhaps rather by implication so far as the actual records
go. Yet Sheol was so much the land of silence and for-
getfulness that existence there practically amounted to
nonentity. It was perhaps a sort of outgrowth of the
family grave. Originally it was not thought of as
within Yahweh's jurisdiction,[1] although later thought
on the omnipresence of God could not consider Him as
excluded even there.[2] Nevertheless the character of
Sheol was unaffected. The stories of translations, e.g. of
Elijah, show that no real life beyond death was expected
for the average man.[3] The whole pathos of the appeals
and protests, and of the ventures of hope, e.g. in the Book
of Job and the Psalms, lies in the belief that God was not
there, and that death as involving existence there meant
separation from Him.

It is important therefore to note that the Old Testament is not really interested in personal immortality
except so far as that involves a personal relationship to
God. There is indeed no suggestion in the Old Testament
that man was created immortal.[4] To the Hebrew way
of thinking, any idea of an inherent immortality would
have made man too independent of God. The whole
doctrine of Sheol is but a pagan survival of the pre-
Yahwistic beliefs of Israel, held in common with their
prehistoric kinsfolk ; there is nothing of revelation about
it. Such teaching as there is was simply the definitely
expressed conviction that those who are in complete

Weymouth (in a statement quoted in *The Problem of Immortality*, by
Dr. E. Petavel, pp. 492, 493), 'the Greek mind did not reckon the
existence of the disembodied spirit as existence at all. . . . The soul
existed, a Greek would tell you, but only " as a shadow or a dream "
(Hom. *Odyss.* xi. 206).'

[1] Ps. 6 [5], Is. 38 [18], [19].     [2] Amos 9 [2], Ps. 139 [8].     [3] Cf. Ps. 89 [48].

[4] Eccles. 12 [7] might appear to supply an exception, but the very
late date of that work and the general drift of its teaching remove it
far from the main current of O. T. thought.

communion and perfect fellowship with God would overleap Sheol—'God will redeem my soul from the power of Sheol : for he shall receive me.' [1] The sense of reality of present personal union with God was so great as to make the thought of death shrink into the background. The question arose, ' Why should death interrupt this fellowship with God ? ' and gradually the position was reached that there is a certain relationship which implies immortality as a natural result : a man in correspondence with God, ' as a righteous, religious being,' [2] cannot but be immortal. Immortality then, in the Old Testament sense, is morally conditioned. ' The essential thing is the relation of men to God. This contains in it the fate of men. And this fate will yet reveal itself.' [3]

The scant references to the idea of resurrection in the Old Testament are connected with an entirely different train of thought. In spite of all appearances, the religious Hebrew held fast to his idea of the eventual establishment of the Messianic Kingdom, the Kingdom of God, upon earth. It was simply the expression of his belief that after all the world in which he found himself was God's world, that He was ' the decisive moral force in the universe ' [4] and would one day vindicate Himself as such. The Day of the Lord meant the inauguration of this Messianic Kingdom of righteousness upon earth with Jerusalem as its capital, and Israel as the elect people in whom all the nations of the earth were to be blessed. It was felt that the happiness of that reign would not be complete unless it was shared in by those who in the past had been loyal to the hope, but had died before it was realised. Plainly such participation involved a resurrection—the body had to be reanimated by the ' shade ' which was in Sheol — and the idea is first associated

---

[1] Ps. 49 [15] ; cf. also 73 [24].
[2] A. B. Davidson, *Theology of the Old Testament*, p. 519.
[3] A. B. Davidson, *op. cit.* p. 461.
[4] Prof. R. G. Macintyre, *The Other Side of Death*, p. 346.

in the Old Testament with the people rather than with individuals. But it is a resurrection of righteous Israelites only. ' *Thy* dead men (Israel) shall arise : the inhabitants of the dust shall awake and shout for joy ; for a dew of lights is thy dew, and the earth shall bring to life the shades.' [1] On the other hand, it is stated just as definitely that the heathen oppressors ' are dead, they shall not live ; they are shades, they shall not rise.' [2] But consequent upon the actual course of the national history, so full of unmerited suffering at the hands of oppressors, the conviction gained ground that in this future order inequalities must be put right in order that the vindication of the oppressed be complete. As early as 350 B.C. a shaping of the doctrine of retribution can be traced. In Daniel 12 [2] the thought is developed of ' many of them that sleep in the dust ' as awaking, ' some to everlasting life, and some to shame and everlasting contempt '—a selective resurrection of the good and of the evil. But here again the reference is distinctly to the establishment of the Messianic Kingdom upon earth ; it is in this that the saints of God will share, while the wicked are raised for judgment in vindication of the inauguration of that Kingdom. Apart from this single reference, there is no suggestion in the Old Testament of any destiny for the wicked. [3] So far as it is concerned they simply cease to be, in any sense that has meaning or content for personality : they merely ' maunder on in Sheol, and may maunder on eternally.' [4] Behind all these subjective hopes and fancies, however, there was this rooted conviction that active relationship with God meant life, immortality, something that death could not really affect. This is the positive viewpoint of the Old Testament, and in a sense there is no other ; for to speak of ' a

---

[1] Is. 26 [19] (trans. as in Prof. Charles' art. Eschatology, *Encyc. Bib.* pt. ii. col. 1354), a late passage, probably of the fourth century B.C.

[2] Is. 26 [14] (R.V. marg.).

[3] Unless such a passage as Ps. 49 [14] can be interpreted apart from the preceding verse 12. But see Ps. 146 [4].

[4] For the phrase the writer is indebted to Prof. A. C. Welch.

doctrine of immortality' in connection with an existence in which there is neither remembrance of God,[1] nor of former things,[2] seems like playing with words.  The Old Testament writers manifestly show that they were not otherwise interested in the question of immortality—as if the implication of their message was that God did not wish men to think of a future existence as a refuge, that the future was just a continuation of this life, and that if a man could not and did not find God here and now, he was not likely to find him elsewhere or in any other existence.  That only was life where a man was in vital fellowship with God ; anything else was mere existence. Heaven was just the presence of God, a condition that the Old Testament saint felt he could experience in the completest measure here on earth.  There might be, must be, change on the occasion of the Day of the Lord, but the perfect Messianic Kingdom was to be on earth.  It was the Hebrew conception of God that determined all the rest of their thinking, and while the bent of the Hebrew mind may not have lain in the direction of speculative construction, they nevertheless mediated a knowledge of God through a direct experience of Him, that produced in them a conviction that was greater and more helpful to mankind than any mere system of thought.

In the Apocalyptic period which stretches from the last two centuries B.C. to past the end of the first century A.D., there were further modifications of some of the preceding conceptions, again under the stress of actual historical events which tried the faith of the righteous. Apocalyptic was really a sort of Jewish philosophy of religion, an attempt to reveal the future purpose of God for the world with a view to the establishment of faith in difficult days.  In the terminology of another field, it may be said that the writers of Apocalyptic books were Catastrophists as opposed to the older Uniformitarians (the prophets) who, on the whole, looked for a gradual moral reformation in the life of the nation, although some

---

[1] Ps. 6 6.                    [2] Eccles. 1 11.

of them, as *e.g.* Amos and Isaiah, were not forgetful of
'the day of the Lord.' To the Apocalyptic mind things
had gone too far; the world was too evil to be the possible
subject of moral change. Nothing short of a complete
ending of the present dispensation, and the commencement of a new age visibly inaugurated by God Himself,
would be of any avail. But the Apocalyptist was more
supermundane in his ideas of the Messianic Kingdom
than the Old Testament prophet : he tended on the
whole to push the consummation more and more into
the future. There was, however, strictly no advance
on the Old Testament conception of the attainment of
immortality, although in a few instances ideas are ex-
pounded about the manner of resurrection which recall
St. Paul's teaching about the spiritual body (1 Cor.
15 $^{35-40}$). The doctrine of retribution, which became a
leading tenet of the Pharisees, appears in all the Apocalypses
amidst a plethora of speculations, some of which are very
confusing. In connection with the doctrine of a resurrection the Jews in their exclusiveness were inclined at
first, as we have seen, to identify the righteous with
righteous Jews. Nevertheless throughout the Apocalyptic
development, the contrast between Jews and non-Jews
(*i.e.* Gentiles) becomes less strongly emphasised than
formerly. The contrast now was rather between righteous
and sinner. Sheol has become an intermediate state
where souls await the Final Judgment : formerly it had
represented the one state in death. Added to it also are
Gehenna, a place of torment and the abode of the worst
type of sinners, and Paradise, the home of the righteous—
heaven. On this view Gehenna was the end for the
wicked, although it is not always easy to say if their
punishment was clearly thought of as 'everlasting,' or
whether rather the idea of annihilation was not directly
expressed. Josephus, interpreting the view of the Pharisees in the time of our Lord, states that they believed
'that souls have an immortal vigour in them and that
under the earth there will be rewards and punishments,

according as they have lived virtuously or viciously in this life ; and the latter are to be detained in an ever-lasting prison, but that the former shall have power to revive and live again.' [1]

It will not be surprising if we find in the canonical writings of the New Testament a certain correspondence with this rapid progressive development of popular religious thought, but it is not germane to our purpose to attempt to trace the influence of Apocalyptic in the New Testament.[2] This brief survey of the development of thought in the Old Testament and Apocalyptic times will, however, have made it clear that we need not expect a complete and final system of doctrine in the New Testament, and it is useless to pretend that we find one. It is, however, of vital importance to attempt to reach the actual standpoint of these inspired pages upon the question of the attainment of immortality. With vague speculations about ' a larger hope ' we are not concerned.[3] Nothing so robs life of its tremendous seriousness and meaning, reducing it to the level of a marionette-show, and belittling man's fateful capacity to choose life or death, as the amiable outlook of Universalism. Yet Scripture is sufficiently and gravely clear in its indications as to the way of life.

Let us take first the teaching of our Lord. Considered as a whole it is pre-eminently a treatise upon the attainment of eternal life. There is, our Lord teaches, a physical life and a spiritual life, but the latter is the real life. The former is terrestrially conditioned and relatively unimportant : its conditions do not persist in the hereafter. There is nowhere any unequivocal suggestion in His teaching of the inherent immortality of the soul.[4] ' The

---

[1] *Antiquities*, book xviii. chap. i. (Whiston's trans.).

[2] For an excellent summary see Dr. J. H. Leckie, *The World to Come and Final Destiny*.

[3] Dr. Leckie states that he is ' not disposed to agree with those who find the idea of universal salvation in any one of the sayings of Jesus ' (*op. cit.* p. 155).

[4] There is only one instance in the Synoptic Gospels (Matt. 10 [28]) where Jesus is represented as using the word ψυχή, soul, so as to

immortality of the soul ' in fact is not a Biblical phrase :
it is not even a Biblical conception. ' At the resurrection,' [1]
says our Lord, using the expression of the Sadducees,
which meant nothing to them, but which they had employed for the sake of an argument, ' at the resurrection
(*i.e.* in the future life), people neither marry nor are
married.  As for the resurrection of the dead—Abraham
and Isaac and Jacob are alive *now*, because God was
their God : they were and are in a conscious vital relationship to Him, and therefore they live.'  Further,
the story of the Transfiguration brings before us, as
Professor Macintyre points out,[2] Moses and Elijah in full
possession of what St. Paul terms ' the spiritual body.'
What is true of these patriarchs may be true for all.

Jesus Christ then set before men the conditions of life
or of death in the ultimate senses of these words, warning
them of the difficulty of attaining life.  ' Enter ye in by
the narrow gate : for wide is the gate, and broad is the
way, that leadeth to destruction, and many be they that
enter in thereby.  For narrow is the gate, and straitened
the way, that leadeth unto life, and few be they that
find it.' [3]  In clearest and sharpest contrast Jesus distinguishes between  the alternatives, ' life ' (ζωή) and
' destruction '  (ἀπώλεια).  Similarly  in  majestic  simplicity and unassailable directness, He says : ' Whosoever
would save his life (ψυχή, soul, or life) shall lose it ; and
whosoever shall lose his life for my sake and the gospel's
shall save it.' [4]  By the ' soul ' or ' life ' Jesus means the
core of a man's personality, his very self, the citadel of
his being.  But there is nothing static in His thought
about the ψυχή.  It is something charged with potenti-

suggest a reference to the future.  Scholars, however, give what seem
to be cogent reasons for considering that the more exact rendering of
our Lord's words is found in the corresponding passage in Luke (12 [4, 5])
where the reference is to a double possible fate for the body in the
present.  The Matthew version is apparently later, and expanded in
keeping with certain well-marked theological tendencies of the writer.
Cf. H. B. Sharman, *The Teaching of Jesus About the Future*, p. 267.

[1] Matt. 22[23-33]; Luke 20 [27-40].     [2] *The Other Side of Death*, p. 170.
[3] Matt. 7 [13, 14].                              [4] Mark 8 [35].

ality and a capacity for self-realisation, something that
may be ' won.' [1] The full attainment and possession of
it are correlated by Him with a certain manner of life.
To closely hold and attempt to realise the ψυχή in selfish
satisfaction is to starve it into non-existence ; it is to
lose or forfeit oneself. There is no direct reference of
Jesus to the ψυχή in which He speaks as if He thought
of it as necessarily having a life other than that of the
present. He thought of it rather as something capable
indeed of self-realisation under certain conditions, but
' fearfully liable to self-destruction by becoming self-
centred.' [2] A man's life, then, may be *lost* : he may be
' mulcted of his soul.' This is the heaviest penalty—the
loss of all that possible development means. Nor was
His teaching on this matter directly connected with
any question of rewards and punishments. Indeed, any
statements in the Gospels along this particular line are
largely secondary, if not late additions.[3] Eternal life is
a matter of union with, of keeping hold of, God. The
reward of the good life simply is its persistence, because
it is in relationship with God. The soul that does not
understand the worth of God understands nothing. If
to any human being, God the reality is nothing, the fear
of eternal punishment will mean still less.[4]

---

[1] Luke 21 [19].

[2] H. B. Sharman, *The Teaching of Jesus About the Future*, p. 269.

[3] *E.g.* Matt. 25 [31] ff., a poetical and parabolic passage dealing with
a judgment of the nations prior to the inauguration of the Messianic
Kingdom upon earth, and probably Luke 16 [27] ff.—a parable, whose
primary teaching, if not decisively clear, is certainly not intended to
be informative of the conditions of a future existence. Jesus often
used old frameworks into which He fitted new conceptions, just as one
may see captured howitzer shells set up in public places as collecting
boxes for charitable objects.

[4] After a careful study of the different texts, Dr. Sharman concludes
that ' Jesus never used " Gehenna " in any other sense than the valley
of Hinnom, that is, the valley of Hinnom as the depository of the
offal of Jerusalem, the carcasses of animals, and the bodies of criminals
who by the special nature of their crimes were refused the rites of
burial so sacred to the Jews. Wherever Gehenna appears in any other
sense in the gospels, most especially when it is conceived of as the place
of future and eternal punishment, the comparative study of documents

Again, we read, ' Jesus said unto them, The sons of this world marry, and are given in marriage : but they that are accounted worthy to attain to that world, and the resurrection from the dead, neither marry, nor are given in marriage.' [1] ' *They that are accounted worthy to attain* ' : our Lord, according to St. Luke, spoke of a resurrection of the righteous only : it is they who have attained. The resurrection is not a universal thing : it deals only with the righteous.[2] St. Luke's enlargement of the incident is Pauline.[3] The whole Pauline system, as we shall see, indeed the whole Christian system, is opposed to a resurrection of the wicked.[4] Or, yet once again, when the rich young ruler asked, ' Good Master, what shall I do to inherit eternal life ? ' [5] our Lord's answer is framed on acceptance of the basal assumption of the question, viz. that eternal life is a morally conditioned survival or continuation of being. Luke in this passage interchanges the expression ' eternal life ' with ' the Kingdom of God,' implying in either case the condition of sonship. A corresponding situation with the tempting lawyer is similarly resolved—' This do, and thou shalt live.' [6]

In many passages in the Fourth Gospel the nature and conditions of Eternal Life are set forth. ' For God so loved the world that he gave his only begotten (unique) Son, that whosoever believeth on him should not perish, but have eternal life.' [7] ' *I* am the resurrection and the life,' [8] said Jesus to Martha, trying to get

---

seems to show with clearness that this sense is derived by subsequent modification of the original words of Jesus ' (*op. cit.* pp. 262-263). Dr. Sharman also adds : ' Jesus himself never referred to " torment " or " fire " as the form of future fate for the unrighteous ' (p. 265), *i.e.* apart from the indirect reference in the story of Dives and Lazarus.

[1] Luke 20 [34-35].
[2] There is also a distinct sense of limitation in Luke 14 [14].
[3] Cf. parallel passages Matt. 22 [29] ff., Mark 12 [18] ff.
[4] ' As regards the resurrection itself, the teaching of Christ seems clearly to have been that only the righteous attain thereto ' (Dr. R. H. Charles, *A Critical History of the Doctrine of a Future Life*, p. 396).
[5] Luke 18 [18] ff.    [6] Luke 10 [28].
[7] John 3 [16].    [8] John 11 [25] (R.V.).

her mind away from the 'Last-day-resurrection' conceptions of her early upbringing : '*I* am the resurrection and the life . . . whosoever liveth and believeth on
me shall never die.' Living union with Christ and
obedience to Him make eternal life a present possession.
' He that believeth on the Son *hath* eternal life ; but he
that obeyeth not the Son shall not see life, but the wrath
of God abideth on him.'[1] Throughout this Gospel the
idea underlying the word ' eternal ' loses all sense of
duration. It expresses quality, the life of God, the life
that belongs to the divine order. The question is primarily
one of the attainment or non-attainment of life through
union with God, *i.e.* morally conditioned.[2]

In the writings of the Apostle Paul[3] the view in question
is very remarkably developed. He may be said to start
from the position that God ' alone hath immortality,'[4]
*i.e.* is alone essentially immortal. As for himself, he
desires to share in the experiences of Christ—' if by any
means I may attain unto the resurrection from the dead.'[5]
For St. Paul salvation is a process—a present possession
by the grace of God, but a future one also accomplished
in ' the day of Christ.' Life ($\zeta\omega\eta$) in St. Paul's large synthetic sense begins here, and goes on without a break.
' Because ye are sons,' he says in another place,[6] ' God
sent forth the Spirit of his Son into our hearts.' The
Spirit implies sonship, or assimilation to the Divine
Being. The process then is quite clear. ' If the Spirit
of him that raised up Jesus from the dead dwelleth in
you, he that raised up Christ Jesus from the dead shall
quicken also your mortal bodies through his Spirit that

[1] John 3 [36] (R.V.).

[2] John 5 [28-29] is a difficult passage, unrelated to the immediate con-
text and foreign to the general teaching of the Gospel. N.T. scholars
like Wendt (*The Teaching of Jesus*, vol. i. p. 256 *n.*) consider it a later
addition.

[3] Cf. throughout Prof. H. A. A. Kennedy, *St. Paul's Conceptions of
the Last Things.*

[4] 1 Tim. 6 [16] (R.V.). Cf. John 5 [26], Rom. 1 [23].   [5] Phil. 3 [11].

[6] Gal. 4 [6]. The idea is an expansion of that referred to above under
Luke 18 [18] ff.

dwelleth in you.'¹ 'In either case' (for there are
different readings), said Principal Denney, 'a share in
the Christian resurrection is conditioned by the Spirit
of Christ.'² Spiritual union with Jesus Christ *is* the
Resurrection, involves eternal life.³ But what is the
alternative? If the Spirit of him that raised up Jesus
from the dead does not dwell in a human heart, what
happens? St. Paul faces the situation. He realises that
this process may not be achieved: it may never even
commence. To begin with, the 'natural' man, 'flesh
and blood,' cannot inherit the Kingdom of God.⁴ 'Many
walk whose end is destruction.'⁵ 'Then sudden destruction cometh upon them.'⁶ In none of St. Paul's writings
is there any suggestion of a resurrection of the wicked.
In fact such an idea would seem to go contrary to his
positive conception that it is the 'Spirit of life in Christ
Jesus' which sets men free from the law of sin and of
death.⁷ Eternal life is the natural result of a vital relationship with God, or with God through Jesus Christ. St. Paul
never distinguishes between physical and moral destruction. His ideas of destruction and life are synthetic,
just as the Old Testament ideas were. Our subtle and
often laboured distinctions were not before his mind.
Nor can it be maintained that the phrase 'everlasting
destruction' (2 Thess. 1⁹) differs radically from ἀπώλεια
(destruction). The term represents the common Apocalyptic belief, and a restoration of all Israelites is nowhere
expressly stated in Apocalyptic literature.⁸ It may
be illegitimate to urge on the evidence available, that
the term 'destruction' clearly indicates immediate
extinction.⁹ We may associate with the word the idea

¹ Rom. 8 ¹¹.                              ² *The Expositor's Greek Testament* in loco.
³ Rom. 6 ³⁻⁶.                             ⁴ 1 Cor. 15 ⁴⁷, ⁵⁰.
⁵ Phil. 3 ¹⁸, ¹⁹. Cf. also the very positive statement in Eph. 5 ⁵.
⁶ 1 Thess. 5 ³; cf. also 1 Tim. 6 ⁹; Rom. 9 ²², 2 ⁷⁻⁸.
⁷ Rom. 8 ².
⁸ Volz, *Jüdische Eschatologie*, referred to in Kennedy, *op. cit.* p. 278.
⁹ It may, perhaps, refer to a final disintegration and extinction of
personal life in Sheol. But cf. W. Morgan, *The Religion and Theology
of Paul*: 'If a study of these terms θάνατος (death), ἀπώλεια (de-

of being robbed of all that life means, complete paralysis of being, physical and ethical, arrested development in some pagan conception of an underworld ; we may even allow that the idea of extinction in our sense of the term was never clearly before the Hebrew mind, although much of their phraseology seems to involve it. The fact of the matter is that it is difficult to extract a positive idea out of the word, for the New Testament leaves it unanalysed. But it is gratuitous in face of this great range of statements to insist on schemes of Universalism or even on views of a general resurrection to rewards and punishments, as the central line of Scripture teaching upon this question.[1] ' Die Weltgeschichte ist das Weltgericht,' said Schiller,[2] with profoundest truth. Every day is a day of judgment, nationally and individually. Any day may be for nation or individual alike a Great Last Day. History does not go back on itself, and the evident vindication of God in history—so evident that he who runs may read—as the moral decisive force does not require that it should. Ultimate destiny is a matter of spiritual condition. ' Verily, verily, I say unto you, He that heareth my word, and believeth him that sent me, hath eternal life, and cometh not into judgement, but hath passed out of death into life.' [3]

It may be felt that some further qualification is required because there are undoubtedly a few passages in the Pauline and Lucan writings which have a contrary significance. There is indeed in all the New Testament writers a certain clashing of conceptions borrowed or

struction), leaves the question of annihilation or endless suffering an open one, the general turn of the Apostle's thought points conclusively to the former ' (p. 238).

[1] The unscriptural doctrine of Purgatory probably arose in great part through the reflection of the Early Church upon the significance of martyrdom. Part of the martyr's reward was his immediate translation to heaven : but for other members of the Church was required a period of education and purification which for the martyr, in consequence of his blood-bath, was unnecessary. The whole belief is really an effect of the Martyr Period on dogma.

[2] In his poem of the Second Period, entitled *Resignation*.

[3] John 5 [24] ; cf. also 3 [18, 19] and 9 [39].

inherited from very different sources. Thus there sometimes seems to be a hesitancy between accepting the Platonic conception of immortality or the conception of the Davidic Kingdom. These writers were not so acutely analytic as more modern generations, and felt no difficulty in entertaining ideas that seem to later thought mutually incompatible. Bearing, then, in mind that neither in Gospels nor Pauline writings is there any system of clear self-consistent teaching on the future state, we can only consider these isolated passages and attempt to reconstruct the particular conditions under which they came into being. Such a passage is Acts 24 [14, 15], in which St. Paul is reported as speaking thus of himself, ' After the Way which they call a sect, so serve I the God of our fathers, believing all things which are according to the law, and which are written in the prophets : having hope toward God, which these also themselves look for, that there shall be a resurrection both of the just and unjust.' Nothing that St. Paul himself writes agrees with this last view, and we can only suppose with Professor H. A. A. Kennedy that in his report of that speech, St. Luke's great aim was to show that St. Paul was not such an anti-Judaist as the distinctively Christian doctrine of his epistles made him out to be. St. Paul evidently kept some of the old eschatological pictures of his early days in his mind, but our duty in interpretation is to follow the main line of his religious experience.[1] Another passage whose tenor is similar, is the following : ' We shall all stand before the judgment-seat of God.' [2] This, however, should be read in close association with the immediately succeeding

---

[1] This passage may be linked with John 5 [28, 29] and Rev. 20 [12, 13] as running counter to the general N.T. teaching of a resurrection of the righteous only. According to Dr. R. H. Charles, the Revelation passage ' occurs in a Judaistic source of that book. . . . In all Jewish books which teach a resurrection of the wicked, the resurrection is not conceived as a result of spiritual oneness with God, but merely as an eschatological arrangement for the furtherance of divine justice or some other divine end ' (*op. cit.* p. 444 *n.*).

[2] Rom. 14 [10].

verse : ' For it is written, As I live, saith the Lord, to
me every knee shall bow, and every tongue shall confess
to God.' The verse is a free translation of Isaiah 45 [23],
which refers to the coming of the Messianic Kingdom,
when every nation shall worship Him. That is to say,
in the passage in question we see a survival in St. Paul's
mind of his old Jewish eschatology, a reminiscence in
eschatological picture language of a Jewish conception of
a universal judgment. For St. Paul, however, the verdict
of God is given *now* : that indeed is justification. In the
corresponding passage, 2 Cor. 5 [10], he is speaking only
of Christians, just as in I Cor. 15 he is dealing solely
with ' the dead in Christ.' [1]  It is of the utmost importance to note throughout that resurrection in the New
Testament is ' resurrection unto life,' that in this fundamental sense, immortality and resurrection are really
synonymous terms,[2] with less relation to a future point
in time than they have to the present, full experience
of which is entered upon at death, and that a ' resurrection body ' is a very different conception from that of 'the
resurrection of the body.' St. Paul's practical interest,
the interest growing out of his own experience, is with
those who are ' united with Christ.' Hence, perhaps,
in part the reason of the obscurity in his teaching regarding
the fate of the wicked.

Nor is there any indication that the other New Testament writers thought otherwise on this great topic.
' We are not of them that shrink back unto perdition '
($\dot{a}\pi\acute{\omega}\lambda\epsilon\iota a$) says the unknown writer of the Epistle to the
Hebrews,[3] ' but of them that have faith unto the gaining
(or acquisition, $\pi\epsilon\rho\iota\pi o\acute{\iota}\eta\sigma\iota s$) of the soul.' The sugges-

---

[1] The passage I Cor. 3 [11-15] appears to be associated with the imagery
of 2 Thess. I [7-10], which certainly does not represent the Apostle's most
mature thought upon this transcendent theme (cf. *e.g.* 2 Cor. 5 [1-10]).
Rom. 2 [6-8] is a passage that seems to conflict with the Apostle's own
doctrine of Justification by Faith, unless it be again an instance of the
earlier eschatology remaining with him, and still supplying the setting
for his scant and obscure teaching concerning the fate of the wicked.

[2] This comes out especially in St. Paul's latest teaching, 2 Cor. 5 [1-10].

[3] Heb. 10 [39] (R.V. marg.).

tion surely is that eternal life is an achievement through relationship with God. Nor is the other side of the alternative less clearly depicted in this and the other epistolary writings. ' For if we sin wilfully,' says this same writer, in his straightforward way, ' after that we have received the knowledge of the truth, there remaineth no more a sacrifice for sins, but a certain fearful expectation of judgment, and a fierceness of fire which shall devour the adversaries.' [1] ' The only sacrifice,' says Dr. Dods,[2] ' has been rejected, and there is no other sacrifice which can atone for the rejection of this sacrifice.' And then he proceeds to quote from Delitzsch as follows : ' The meaning is not merely that the Jewish sacrifices to which the apostate has returned have in themselves no sin-destroying power, nor even that there is no second sacrifice additional to that of Christ, but further that for a sinner of this kind the very sacrifice of Christ itself has no more atoning or reconciling power.' Or again, ' But these people !—like irrational animals, creatures of mere instinct, born for capture and corruption, they scoff at what they are ignorant of : and like animals they will suffer corruption and ruin, done out of the profits of their evil-doing.' [3] Throughout the Johannine Epistles there is maintained the solemn contrast, ultimate, and ethically determined, between those ' who are of the cosmos ' and those who ' are of God.' One and all the Apostolic writers postulate eternal life solely for those who in their terminology are ' in Christ,' ' have passed from dead unto living,' ' have been born again,' have been made ' new creatures.' They think of such individuals as the subjects of some qualitative and determining change in the relationships of their inmost being, their real life, so that it is now responsive to the true environment of souls, which is God, in a survival-determining degree—' If '—

---

[1] Heb. 10 [26, 27] ; cf. also 6 [6] : ' it is impossible to renew them again (Moffatt's trans.) unto repentance.'

[2] *The Expositor's Greek Testament* in loco.

[3] 2 Peter 2 [12] (Moffatt's trans.) ; cf. also James 1 [15].

it is a conditional ' if '—' the Spirit of him that raised up Jesus from the dead dwelleth in you, he that raised up Christ Jesus from the dead shall quicken also your mortal bodies through his Spirit that dwelleth in you.' [1] There may be dispute as to the validity of the contention : but as to what the contention is, there surely can be none.

Relief is sometimes sought from what is felt to be the inconvenient and uncompromising character of these apostolic affirmations in other supposed ' reconciling elements ' in their teaching. But this is only attained by means of a literalism which is deprecated in the case of those who accept the statements as to the attainment of eternal life at their face value, if for no other reason than that they are consonant with the method of the organic world order as a whole. The simple fact is that God's purposes of salvation are not, and cannot be, achieved in the individual life in face of the persistent refusal of the individual, inasmuch as God's gift to men of the possibility of winning freedom is the necessary *prius* to the possibility of becoming a son of God in the sense of the apostolic writers. Love is the one thing in the world that cannot be forced and does not force : the moment compulsion or pressure enters, it ceases to be Love. Man can only respond spontaneously to the Love of God as a free being, otherwise the response can have no value even to God Himself. The heart of God as revealed in Christ embraces the world of men in purpose and intention, and all human souls are precious and of infinite potentiality and worth, but the gift of God can always be refused in virtue of those very capacities, themselves a prior gift, which alone enable men to be what God expects of them. It is no surrender of the Divine Omnipotence thus to realise and acknowledge the possibilities in a situation which only arises as the result of a self-limited expression of the most fundamental character of God, viz. His Love.

The force of the Conditional presentation is perhaps most strongly felt when consideration is directed to the

[1] Rom. 8 [11].

arguments usually urged against it. To insist that all analogy fails because in organic evolution selected and un-selected forms alike eventually perish, is really to affirm a belief in the physical proximate aspects of the selecting Environment—organic and inorganic alike—as ultimate and permanent, instead of realising that they are but temporary manifestations of the Real Environment which is spiritual, and with which man is primarily concerned and can come into relationship by means of these other aspects. Further, the Conditional view stands in line, as we have seen, with the general method of evolution which has been selective throughout, with a gradual advance in the character of the survival-conditioning factor. What was the nature of the specific mental mutation whereby the man-like ape became the ape-like man we do not know, or even exactly in what period it occurred. But we do know enough of the process to represent to ourselves its general character. We know that whatever mental and, later, moral development we recognise in these ancestral forms, as in the forms of to-day, took place as the result of the interplay of elements—potentialities—in these forms with the En-vironment in its deepest and most spiritual sense, as it beckoned and unmasked Itself to the developing human intelligence. It is therefore surprising to find the statement made in criticism of Sabatier's brilliant if somewhat unconvincing theory of Immortality that ' the human species, on Sabatier's theory, has for one of its chief characteristics, not the actual possession of a certain quality, but the power of attaining it. Surely, if this be the case, mankind stands alone among all the species of creation. Every member of every other race and kind must conform itself to its type.' [1] Every mem-ber of every other race and kind has done nothing of the kind, else had there been no evolution. It is in virtue of the nonconformists that there has been progress—those forms that did not conform completely to their present Environment, to do which meant stagnation and death

[1] Dr. J. H. Leckie, *The World to Come and Final Destiny*, p. 229.

—but conforming to other elements in that Environment, not responded to by the others, were literally metamorphosed,[1] transformed, into the new type. It is further stated [2] in the same work that ' the real weakness of Conditionalism lies in its two great denials,' of which the first is that of the indestructibility of the soul. But this dogma is maintained merely on the basis of an unconvincing sort of higher pantheism, of which it is difficult to offer anything in the nature of proof. The other denial is that of a supposed organic unity of the human race. In Leckie's words, ' Every essential property of any species is found in all its members. A quality which is the possession of some individuals only, of any given kind, or is capable of being developed by these, but is not the necessary characteristic of all the species, cannot be one of the distinguishing marks of that kind of creature. . . . But the idea that such a great thing as immortality can be a merely contingent and accidental quality is surely out of the question. The possession of unending life by any number of individuals really constitutes them a different species. . . . And so it is evident that Conditionalism really destroys the unity of the race and divides it into two distinct and separate species. If there exist, at any given time, some men who are already immortal, or destined to achieve an endless life, and others who are, and will remain, evanescent and mortal, these two classes are so distinct as to belong to different orders of being.' [3] Now it would only lead to confusion to point out that in the opinion of some competent authorities, Neanderthal man did as a matter of fact constitute a separate species. The real reply to the above position is that it misrepresents the issue, and in any case the idea of ' essential properties ' belongs rather to the realm of physics than to that of biology. On the Conditional view all men are immortable—potentially immortal : whether that characteristic is developed and attained is a matter of a moral relationship to God. Those who are in this relationship cannot really die :

[1] Cf. Rom. 12 [2].　　[2] *Op. cit.* p. 245.　　[3] *Cp. cit.* p. 248.

those who are not, do die, if there is any truth in the Bible. There is indeed a great distinction. But it is simply a travesty of 'the evolutionary form of the Conditionalist theory' to state that it 'regards the end and purpose of the world's history to be, not the creation of a redeemed humanity, but the production of a selected number of perfect individuals.' [1] On the Conditional view the purpose of God as indicated above is clear and manifest and recognised as all of grace, but it maintains that it cannot be achieved in the case of those who deliberately put themselves out of all relationship to Him. 'From our standpoint,' says Dr. Leckie, 'it is incredible that the human spirit can be divested of moral life, any more than of actual existence. To us it seems that freedom, the power to choose the right, belongs to the very idea of the soul and cannot be taken away.' [2] Exactly, but how is freedom merely the power to choose the *right* ?

When now we attempt to represent to ourselves the nature and dynamics of this change, wrought in the secret parts of a man's being, we quickly reach the limits of our present human understanding. All progress has been by way of change, and moral change as latest will naturally be concerned with the highest elements in man's being. Yet if we are unable to indicate with precision the actual moment at which the developing consciousness of the child expands into self-consciousness and are in great ignorance as to the character and agency of this change, it is not remarkable that we experience difficulty in making clear to ourselves the inward working in moral change. It is like dealing with a new dimension. Moral relationship being dependent on the attainment of self-consciousness is an even more complex and subtle process than thought, and the issues of the latter are complex enough. There is something so fundamental even in them, that they affect the physical life of the individual. 'As he thinketh in his heart, *so is* he,' [3] physically and spiritually alike : it is the kernel of truth in all theories of suggestion and auto-suggestion.

[1] *Op. cit.* p. 231.   [2] *Op. cit.* p. 209.   [3] Prov. 23 [7].

All moral advance, both racial and individual, has been directly dependent on the development of conscience, that moral sensitivity to the Ultimate Environment in virtue of which the individual decides his actions or reviews them in relation to the highest that he knows, a condition which, if Freud is right, is operative even in our dream life.[1]  But man, as we have seen, appears not yet as an *in*dividual, self-determined and full of inward peace and harmony, but rather as a being in process of attaining individuality, full of disharmony and inward disquiet as the dividuals higher and lower—and they may be legion—struggle for mastery.  If then immortality be indeed a function of goodness [2] as we have been driven to believe, the attainment of it will be directly related with a manner of life resulting from a changed outlook and inward experience which, by inducing inward peace and harmony, and that overcoming of the divided self with freedom from the dominance of the lower self, will issue in *in*dividuality.  Now relationship is of the very texture of Reality, and man just because of his mental and moral constitution is able to come into relationship with God and the fellowman.  But the selfish or self-filled life is a life bereft of spiritual ties or relationship, which when its physical metabolism comes to an end, must by reason of its separateness and apartness, its actual spiritual unrelatedness, perish.  The selfish being, in his chosen apartness and spiritual isolation, fails to develop the higher potentialities in human life, degeneration follows, and slipping back to the level of the predominantly self-centred, wellnigh sub-human stage, he may live and die on that level.  On the other hand, nothing can so unify and integrate a human life—make it *in*dividual—as Love.  To have and to hold for oneself implies apartness and unrelatedness ; to give oneself implies

---

[1] Cf. his account of the intervention of what he calls ' the censor within the soul ' in preventing the gratification of desires in the tragedies and comedies of dream life.

[2] Cf. Proverbs 12 [28], could we be sure of the text.

relationship and union, and in its highest and completest form that relationship to God which means eternal life. Thus is it literally true that he that would save his life shall lose it. Just in proportion as we give ourselves to the service of others in love do we find the Spirit of God dwelling in us in such a way that so far from losing our sense of distinct being, we only become more really and fully and individually ourselves. In conscious dependence on Him we realise ourselves. In a very direct way ' the development of self-sacrifice and the development of the sense of personal distinctness go together.' [1] This was the experience of the Apostle Paul : his sacrifice of himself for Christ's sake just in that measure made him feel sure of his being united with Him, and at the same time aware of his own distinctive developing individuality. ' Not I live,' he said, ' but Christ liveth in me ' : he did not say, ' I live in Christ.' It is an experience which resolves the inner disharmony—' to be spiritually minded is life and peace.' [2] There is a degree of conscious willed relationship with God—' I am in my Father and my Father in me '—in which it is not possible that he who has attained it can be holden of death. ' We *know* that we have passed out of death into life, because we love the brethren.' [3]

Now the proof of all this is our Lord and Saviour Jesus Christ. It was natural for the apostles to correlate immortality with Him because He was perfectly good, and, as a matter of simple fact, He brought life and immortality to light. As related to the disciples, the Resurrection implies their objective certainty that He whom they had known and loved, and with whom they had companied in the days of His flesh, was still alive and communicating to them the mind of God, and His purpose for the world. The basis of the Resurrection faith was not so much the Empty Tomb as the conviction of the disciples that in these post-resurrection ex-

---

[1] O. C. Quick, *Essays in Orthodoxy*, p. 168.
[2] Rom. 8 [6].                              [3] 1 John 3 [14]

periences they had been seeing, hearing, and speaking with the same historic Personality whom they had followed during these three years, and thought they had lost for ever. At the same time, the fact that we are just beginning to understand the effects of mind and particularly of emotion upon the metabolism and actual constitution of the body, that we are only on the threshold of our knowledge of what is involved in the far from static conception of personality, and that we have no ability whatever to estimate what would be the effect of a sinless spiritual life upon its physical concomitant, forbids us to relegate the story of the Empty Tomb to the realm of legend. However regarded, the Resurrection is the supreme proof of the triumph of spirit over matter.

As related to Himself, our Lord's death was the death of that particular life, the great climactic act of a life of sacrifice, lived in the closest relationship to God. Such a relationship is eternal : ' it was not possible that he should be holden ' of death.[1] Such a relationship we believe to be creative. Our Lord's Resurrection body was made by His Spirit, and therefore could not see corruption. His post-resurrection life was the proof that the world needed of the supremacy of the spiritual over the physical. ' I *am* the Resurrection and the Life,' He says, and in the case of every Christ-filled individual, the Resurrection is taking place *now*. The spiritual body is being prepared and provided *now*, and death is only an incident, no more the end of life than the moment of birth was the beginning of it. The Spirit of God working in those who are related to Him shall ' quicken their mortal bodies ' [2] so that at death the corruptible is, so to speak, sloughed off. There is no break in the continuity on the spiritual side, and St. Paul most distinctly states that the body laid in the grave is not that which shall be.[3] To be ' united with Christ ' then represents a spiritually and morally tempered condition of prepotency, whose

[1] Acts 2 [24].        [2] Rom. 8 [11].        [3] I Cor. 15 [37].

survival of death is natural. It represents a moral attainment that was likewise open to those who in spirit saw the day of the Lord Christ afar off and were glad. For the love of the Eternal to man is essentially eternal, and the possibility of the religious relationship began when man's mind was able even dimly to comprehend the existence of God. The ' power of an indissoluble life ' [1] has been at man's disposal from the beginning, and this also is of grace.

Finally, it may well be asked whether in an age whose conceptions of Hell and of ' a certain fearful looking for of judgment,' [2] can never be exactly those of our fathers, there is not just that element of appeal applicable to the thought of to-day in the aspects of Scriptural teaching emphasised in the preceding pages. For if this world in which we find ourselves is ultimately a spiritual process, shot through with purpose and possibility for man who is its fairest fruitage, does he not miss the whole meaning of life in so far as he does not definitely set his will and energy in line with the Eternal Purpose ? Does he not, if living a mere selfish existence, with no sense of responsibility to himself or his fellows, in that measure lose that relationship with God which is the sole condition of spiritual existence ? If a man can make his soul, may he not also unmake it ? And if into that process came One who supremely revealed to men the heart of God and so the purpose of life, and gives men power to ' walk in newness of life,' [3] ' how shall we escape if we neglect so great salvation ? ' [4] It may be that *we do not escape*—that *it is the end*, for that we have destroyed ourselves.[5]

---

[1] Heb. 7 [16].    [2] Heb. 10 [27].    [3] Rom. 6 [4].    [4] Heb. 2 [3].
[5] Such a possibility indeed is literally suggested in the words of our Lord ; cf. Luke 9 [25] (ἐαυτὸν δὲ ἀπολέσας), a passage which seems toned down in the Authorised and other English versions, apparently under the influence of Platonic preconceptions.

# CHAPTER XIV

## THE HISTORIC JESUS AND THE COSMIC CHRIST

At this stage our study of Individuality, its import, and attainment might have ceased, were it not that into the field of human history has come, as we have seen, One in whom the perfect life was manifested while on earth, and about whom it was even said that ' He brought life and immortality to light.' [1] In some way or other all thought upon ultimate problems, in so far as it makes any claim to completeness, inevitably leads back to the question, What think ye of Christ ? for He stands forth as the most momentous fact in the whole world process, and in the realms alike of fact and of thought that process reveals itself increasingly as a unity. It is evident, however, from what is involved in the nature of personality, that the judgment in answer to that question may differ according as the individual offering it gives it with a part of his being or with the whole. The answer may be mainly an intellectual judgment—' a judgment of the head,' so to speak, or it may be an active determining judgment of the whole man, including ' a judgment of the heart,' to designate it by the dominating aspect. Thus of Napoleon it is related [2] how one day in St. Helena he turned to General Bertrand and said, ' Bertrand, I know men ; and I tell you that Jesus Christ is no mere man. . . . Between him and every other person in the world there is no possible term of comparison. . . . Alexander, Caesar, Charlemagne, and myself founded empires.

[1] 2 Tim. i [10].

[2] Robert-Antoine de Beauterne, *Sentiments de Napoléon sur le Christianisme* (1840).

But on what did we rest the creations of our genius ?
Upon force. Jesus Christ alone founded His empire
upon love ; and, at this hour, millions of men would die
for him.' [1]   It is a great pronouncement, and yet, as a
'judgment of the head,' is infinitely removed from the
'judgment of the heart' set forth in such a saying as that
of St. Thomas—' My Lord and my God.' [2]   We cannot
get away from the fact that in judging Jesus Christ—
just as, in a lesser way, in offering criticism of any artistic
masterpiece—it is himself that a man judges,[3] and every
one who essays a determination of that unique figure
inevitably lays himself open to the haunting Samaritan
reflection, ' Sir, thou hast nothing to draw with, and the
well is deep.' [4]

To many the mere raising of ultimate issues implies a
predetermined ' judgment of the head,' which is sometimes
feared, sometimes resented.   Of the work of scholars
digging amidst the records of past ages, and critically
reconstructing modern ideas of Scripture, many have
said in sorrow and in anger, ' They have taken away my
Lord, and I know not where they have laid Him.' [5]   If
that is really true for them, it may be good that they
should thus be compelled to start afresh on the quest of
the living Christ.   Others, for whom a certain personal
experience is not less the most direct and impressive
thing for them with regard to Jesus Christ, sometimes

[1] The narrative concludes : ' The Emperor became silent, and, as
General Bertrand remained equally still, he resumed : " If you do
not understand that Jesus Christ is God, well—I was wrong in making
you a general." '   It is only right to say, however, that the famous
monologue from which the above extracts are taken ' does not strike
the careful student of Napoleon's acts and sayings as representing his
inmost thoughts on religion.'   Cf. J. Holland Rose, *Napoleonic Studies*,
pp. 102-110, and, *per contra*, Philip Schaff, *The Person of Christ*, pp.
219-250, 288-289.

[2] John 20 28.

[3] ' The man who, more than any other, has shaped learning and set
the paths in which it should go onward for twenty-four centuries was,
to those who knew him, " the vain and chattering little Aristotle." '
(Prof. N. S. Shaler, *The Individual*, p. 173.)

[4] John 4 11.                              [5] John 20 13.

let that experience determine their unthinking relation to all those questions which often are decisive for those who never pass beyond a 'judgment of the head.' That experience when interpreted in the light of the Gospel narratives does not suffer them to find any difficulty in connection with circumstances such as the Virgin Birth or Resurrection. They are credible of Jesus Christ because Scripturally certified. To their mind the greater marvel would be if it could be shown that Jesus Christ was a mere man : the virgin life seems to demand the Virgin Birth. Yet others who have also found in Him ' the power of God unto salvation ' realise that through the revelations of science and the teachings of philosophy, the world in which they think of Him as operative now must be regarded very differently from the way in which it was thought of two thousand years ago. The long, slow history of man himself and the conditions under which he has attained his present stage of evolution are better understood. If the process has been a process towards the development of immortable Individuality, then this achievement of the highest moral individuality— the perfect life—in Jesus Christ must have some definite relation to the process as a whole. They recognise that if Evolution is postulated as the divine method of cosmic development, a final criterion of its claim as universal truth will be found in its relation to Jesus Christ. How may they think of Him in connection with the world process as revealed in science and philosophy ?

The fact that our Christian era is dated—and incorrectly dated [1]—from the supposed year of the birth of our Lord has inevitably tended to concentrate attention on that particular point of time as the moment of the world's greatest uplift, and also, on some theological constructions, as the climax of human sinfulness. One im-

---

[1] ' The data appear to be best harmonised by attributing the census of the Nativity to B.C. 7 or the beginning of B.C. 6 ' (Hastings' *Dictionary of the Bible*, vol. i. p. 405). It is placed even earlier on some theories, *e.g.* B.C. 9-8 : cf. G. H. Box, *The Virgin Birth of Jesus*, p. 119. In the *Encyclopaedia Biblica*, vol. i. col. 809, the date is given ' *circa* B.C. 4 ? '.

mediate result is that even the fact of the development of our Lord's self-consciousness—in short, the recognition that He lived a human life—tends straightway to be obscured. An opposite tendency is illustrated in the case of those who would attempt to find a basis for the life and work of Jesus Christ that shall be wholly outside of, or independent of, history. This endeavour is as impracticable as that essayed by those who would destroy or obliterate the history that we have. Historical fixation in some measure is necessary because we are dealing with a process, and with a progressive process : but complete success in this direction is not an absolute necessity for a view of things under which it is believed that the same Purposive Energy is at work to-day as in the past.

The task of history is to attempt to explain as far as possible how under, and indeed in spite of, the universality of law, that which is unique arises. Scientific explanation, in terms of natural law, often seems to make it more difficult to realise how the special and unique can arise. Yet in an evolutionary process, once it is proved to be a progressive process, there is more reason to consider everything unique : there is no duplication, no repetition. But in any case universal laws, which are statistically based, can never explain or, in the realm of the organic, enable us to predict completely with reference to the particular or individual case. The tasks of the man of science and of the historian are different. The former is in search of the universal causality in what has happened : the latter endeavours to trace the particular causality of the individual happening.

Dependent merely on his power of criticism of sources to which it is quite possible that additions may be made at any time which might compel revision of previous estimates, the historian readily realises the relative and approximate character of even the soundest of his conclusions. He progressively attains various degrees of probability, but rarely does he reach certainty. There is usually a residuum of uncertainty which can never be completely dispelled. He does not and cannot know every detail, and in that measure his account is incomplete. To this hour certain important details about the battle of Waterloo have not been satisfactorily cleared up. No tenable theory of inspiration can prevent these considerations applying with equal force to the Gospel narratives. Here also the historian must apply his critical canons of analogy and correlation. But if in the course of investigation it is found that these resources fail, it is simply an error of judgment immediately to rule out as unhistorical that which thus stands out unique and apparently unrelated. It is gratuitous to assume that the limits of a self-imposed method are necessarily the limits of Reality. That an incident lacks confirmation or is without analogy does not necessarily disprove its actuality. ' Historical standards are not constitutive of Reality ; they merely regulate authentication.' [1]

Further, into history there enters in the case of personality something which ultimately, at any rate as yet, is only partially explicable in scientific categories alone, something which is no finished product, and so the great spiritual turning-points in history associated with it are at bottom scientifically inexplicable in a complete degree in themselves. If the view propounded in these pages of the Evolutionary process as a purposive development of individual personalities is correct, and if their dependence on the Environment be a more vital factor at any moment than their Heredity, no man can profess to attempt to set down what range of spiritual commerce with the Ultimate Environment—what degree of communion with God and its consequent results—is possible. The man who knows nothing of this experience is handicapped in any endeavour to interpret a life in which spiritual communion has been the distinctive feature, and even if he is aware of what is implied in it, he knows just in that degree that it is something of which no complete, strictly scientific explanation can be given. The relations dis-

[1] A. W. Hunzinger, *Das Wunder*, p. 136.

cerned in history between a personality or the uprisings of spiritual life and the general immediate Environment, provide the means of ascertaining the conditions under which the appearance of such spiritual factors is rendered possible, *i.e.* intelligible : they do not constitute a strictly causal derivation.[1]  Such conditions can never amount to a pure causal explanation : they do not directly represent that Supreme Energy which at critical stages in the world process has produced the striking changes—the big lifts—that we recognise there.  In personality, indeed, we recognise the depths of spiritual life, and the thought of the divine immanence is readily suggested to us.  But the compulsion of the divine power we feel only in the presence of experiences which seize us with immediate force as the revelation of the actuality and activity of God.  This occurs supremely and uniquely in the person of Jesus Christ.  In His case the ordinary canons of analogy and correlation fail.  There is something here that has never been known before, something about which we can say—just because we understand the world process so much better—that it will never, in that particular form, be known again.

The uniqueness of the person and work of Jesus Christ cannot be explained away along historico-critical lines. This does not mean that there is actual unassailable proof of every recorded fact concerning Him, but it does mean that critically He cannot be put away out of reality. History takes care for itself that when criticism oversteps its limits it shall always be brought back within its justifiable limits : in other words, truth is invincible.  Historical criticism may do much by way of explaining historically the local form and time of the appearance of Jesus, but these will never supply in themselves a sufficient ground for His actual appearance and active significance.  Sir Leslie Stephen once wrote : ' Apologists labour to point out how precisely Christianity was adapted to the various wants of the time.  The obvious inference

[1] A. W. Hunzinger, *Das Wunder*, p. 138.

is that Christianity was developed by the instincts of the
people who felt those wants.' [1]   If this contention is
right, it is very strange that the most discerning of the
people, in response to the needs of whose instincts Christianity was developed, in the end ' all forsook Him and
fled.' [2]   Is it probable that even the twentieth century
could in this sort of a way produce the Christ ?   Incon-
ceivably No : still less could the Palestinian environment
of two thousand years ago in itself have done so.  Further,
historical criticism must also recognise the insufficiency
and incompleteness of its canons, and admit, if it is true
to itself, much as mysterious and problematic which
faith, however, will recognise as God, the living worker,
the Redeemer, meeting it in the actuality of things.
History can establish the spatial, temporal, and psychological relations, conditions, and occasions under which
the Divine Energy expresses itself in history, but it cannot
explain the increments or even the convergences out of
which spring the great lifts in history : it cannot integrate
what it collects together.   This transcends the empirical
' hang ' of things, although expressing itself in and through
time and space, and notably in the human consciousness.
But the point at which the highest values and realities
come to light, incontestably clear to faith, and recognised
in some measure by all, is the Person of Jesus Christ.

The whole question is best approached by considering
in the first instance what our Lord said about Himself.
In the case of any great achievement it is probable that
he can give the most accurate account who has achieved.
In Jesus Christ, whatever else we may say, we have a
unique moral achievement, and on this ground we have
confidence in adopting prior to any other, and as one by
which to test all others, our Lord's own explanation of
Himself.
    Concerning his relation to God, our Lord is most ex-

---

[1] *An Agnostic's Apology and other Essays*, p. 299.
[2] Mark 14 [50].

plicit.[1] ' The Father,' He says, ' is greater than I.' [2]
' One there is who is good.' [3] ' My meat is to do the will
of Him that sent me, and to accomplish His work.' [4]
' My teaching is not mine, but His that sent me.' [5] ' I
can of mine own self do nothing.' [6] And so on through
many passages,[7] in which He freely and fully declares
His dependence on God and His subordination to Him.
We recollect His audible appeals to the Father previous
to His exercise of that power which, as man, He felt
was derived, *e.g.* at the raising of Lazarus. Nor is this
attitude contradicted by such a statement as, ' I and the
Father are one.' [8] Although the analogy fails beyond
a certain narrow range, we can imagine a pool testifying
to the oneness of its relation with a river which is, however, at the same time ' greater ' than it. In the same
sense St. Paul keeps a clear distinction between ' God our
Father and the Lord Jesus Christ,' [9] referring again and
again to ' the God of our Lord Jesus Christ, the Father
of Glory.' [10] Nevertheless, in spite of all that evidenced
this subordination to the Father—for He Himself declared that He was neither omniscient [11] nor omnipotent,[12]
—He revealed the Father to men : He was the thought,
the heart, the self of God, made audible and visible to
men.

Yet He was conscious from the beginning of a unique

---

[1] In the following paragraphs no attempt will be made to differ-
entiate in value between the Synoptics and the Fourth Gospel. They
are one and all records and impressions, it may be of different value,
but it does not follow, as is too often assumed, that the more exact
recorder or the one nearest to the facts is necessarily the better interpreter, or best endowed with the power to comprehend most fully the
significance of the phenomena which he records. At the same time it
must be recognised that the Fourth Gospel is more akin to St. Paul's
writings than the Synoptics so far as Christology is concerned, in that
it is largely interpretation, rather than record.

[2] John 14 [25].          [3] Matt. 19 [17].               [4] John 4 [34].
[5] John 7 [16].           [6] John 5 [30].
[7] Cf. further Matt. 26 [39] ; John 5 [19] ; 6 [38] ; 12 [44] ; 14 [10, 31] ; 18 [11] ;
20 [21].
[8] John 10 [30].          [9] Ephes. 1 [2].
[10] Ephes. 1 [17] ; cf. also Col. 1 [3, 12] ; 3 [17] ; and 1 Cor. 8 [6].
[11] Mark 13 [32].          [12] John 5 [19] ; Matt. 20 [23].

relationship to God. This developed into a peculiar self-consciousness of Himself as the Messiah, the Christ, with which there came into ever clearer association that supreme sense of a divine and eternal mission to mankind. As men come to understand God as He reveals Himself in nature and in history, they understand Jesus Christ better, and He in turn reveals God to men. Knowledge of the one interprets the other. ' All things have been delivered unto me of my Father; and no one knoweth the Son, save the Father ; neither doth any one know the Father save the Son, and he to whomsoever the Son willeth to reveal Him.'[1] ' He that hath seen me hath seen the Father.'[2] The history of experience shows this to be the case. ' Is not this the carpenter ? ' was a common reflection from minds that recognised in Him nothing more than a mere man. ' Thou art the Christ, the Son of the living God,' avowed a deeper understanding. ' For me to live is Christ,' was the expression of a heart that found in Him the ' very essence of the Unseen and the living influence of the Eternal.'[3] And so throughout the ages it has been. A progressive deepening of insight into the Person and work of Christ follows upon growing realisation of the work of God in the world, in ourselves, and in our fellowmen, and will continue to follow. There is no change in Christ : the difference is in the beholder.[4] Our age sees the divinity of Christ primarily in His moral and spiritual influence upon human history, rather than in the recorded miracles that helped the incipient faith of an earlier period. ' Even though

---

[1] Matt. 11 27.    [2] John 14 9.
[3] Dr. Marshall Talling, *The Science of Spiritual Life*, p. 101.
[4] This progressive deepening of faith is strikingly illustrated in the serial confessions of ' the man born blind ' (John 9) : thus :
*v.* 11. The *man* that is called Jesus made clay and anointed mine eyes.
*v.* 17. They say therefore unto the blind man again, What sayest thou of Him, in that He opened thine eyes ? And he said, He is a *prophet.*
*v.* 35. Jesus said, Dost thou believe on *the Son of God* ? And he said, Lord, I believe. And he worshipped Him.

we have known Christ after the flesh, yet now we know Him so no more,' said St. Paul.[1] That which convinced him was not records, but an experience in which Christ came to him. It is the ultimate test to-day.

But our present interest is in the attempt to relate the evolutionary conception of the world process to Jesus Christ. That process has shown itself interpretable as a continuous progressive, purposive manifestation of God, of which at a certain stage man is the crown, yet man struggling, largely failing, misusing his hardly and slowly won freedom. From the side of the Divine purpose one more stage was necessary to complete the process of revelation and enablement, when the human mind was partially ready to understand it. If then that ultimate view of God's relation to the world and to man, from which we started, is supportable ; if, that is to say, we are right in thinking of the Divine Mind or Spirit, which is also Love, in virtue of its very essence realising itself in the gradual creation, through process, of organisms of ever-increasing complexity suitable for the reception of its ever-increasing influx, which should issue in free spiritual beings capable of coming into union and fellow-ship with it ; if God has indeed been becoming man throughout the ages ; then it is reasonable to suppose that this purpose would be made clear to man when he had reached the stage at which he was able to begin to understand and appreciate all that was implied in it. Doubtless in the previous aeons multitudes of men had lived and died, partially understanding, some more clearly than others, what was the purpose of God's gift of human life, and it was counted unto them for righteousness.[2] 'But when the fulness of the time came, God sent forth His Son, born of a woman.'[3] His coming

---

[1] 2 Cor. 5 [16].
[2] See Acts 10 [34, 35], where St. Peter definitely states this point of view.
[3] Gal. 4 [4] (R.V.)

was no more, but also no less, ' a special intervention ' than the appearance of life, or self-consciousness, or any of the other big lifts in the cosmic process. If this progressive view of the evolutionary process is true, there simply had to be a fulness of the times, and while the fact of the world's sin can afford no special reason for the appearance of our Lord at one time rather than another, the stage of man's evolution, in relation to God's ultimate purpose for him, does. That is to say, the Incarnation is to be thought of as a great primary fact in itself, which would have taken place in any case quite apart from any particular thought of man's sin.

For if the original purpose of God is complete self-communication to a being who can come into fellowship with Him, that purpose cannot be set aside by anything that man can do. Such a glorious manifestation of His love as that which is seen in the Incarnation cannot be dependent on man's sin : in that case it makes man's sin necessary to it. It means that man merited less of God before ' the Fall ' than after it. In terms of some philosophies sin is a natural and necessary factor in the development of man's spiritual nature. On such a view it would be difficult to see when it would cease to be necessary. On the contrary, sin is the deliberate refusal to accept the purpose of God in human life. It is at once treason to the world process as a whole and ingratitude to God : accordingly with the progress of knowledge sin deepens in character. But it has never changed the purpose of God : it only turns revelation into redemption. The source of the Incarnation is in the heart of God : baffled in one way, it finds expression in another. But His purpose has been the same from the beginning, although His methods of dealing with mankind may change. The Incarnation, then, is not dependent on ' the Fall,' for that would make it an afterthought. To think of it in the character of an emergency policy rather than as the natural development of the Divine purpose is to obscure its central and climactic place in human history. Redemption springs from it, not it from redemption. The original idea of the Incarnation lies in the prophetic words—' they shall call his name Immanuel ; which is, being interpreted, *God with us* ' :[1] it is only later that the development comes— ' thou shalt call his name Jesus ; for it is He that shall save His people from their sins.'[2] That which is true historically of the race is also true individually. The Incarnation is not merely the assurance that the pitying God is with mankind in the long, upward struggle, but it is the revelation of His very heart, showing Him as Love, seeking men, able to save, waiting to forgive. Or, in the language of philosophy, the ultimate purpose and plan belong to the wider Reality, not to us ; it seeks us.

Creation is the primary Kenosis (self-emptying or self-limitation) of which the Incarnation is the central and most significant fact—central, because Jesus Christ made real that for which the whole process came into being. It is the insistence of Scripture that the redeeming God is the creating God,[3]—' in bringing many sons to glory it was *befitting* that He for whom and by whom the universe exists should perfect the Pioneer of their salvation by suffering.'[4] The religious life, that is to say— redemption—is not something apart from the rest of Nature and things. The process of Nature from the side of the Divine intention has been throughout—in inception and general conduct alike—a process of grace, and it is fulfilled in grace. For, broadly conceived, it has been a process of progress with possibilities opening out at every stage as the result of growing freedom, with constant support from the Environment in the maintenance of whatever advance was secured. It is not remarkable that in the degree in which men in the past entered into appreciation of the meaning and purpose of

---

[1] Matt. 1 [23].  [2] Matt. 1 [21].
[3] Prof. J. Moffatt, *The Approach to the New Testament*, p. 32.
[4] Heb. 2 [10] (Moffatt's trans.).  Cf. also Ps. 124 [8] ; Matt. 11 [26].

life, they felt sure that that meaning and purpose would be still more clearly revealed.

In the perfect manhood of Jesus Christ, the creative spirit of God which throughout the ages had been becoming man came to full and complete expression as a revealing, energising and saving power. Without the Incarnation the process of human evolution had been checked and hindered, just as if, at earlier stages, any of the other environmental elements, such as light or oxygen, had failed to be developed when they were required. In some such manner as the Carboniferous forests appeared and purified the dank, dense, carbon-dioxide laden atmosphere of the Devonian era, so that a new impulse was given to organic evolution, came Jesus Christ and purified the spiritual atmosphere, and man advanced in intercourse and fellowship with God. His life of love and sacrificial service created a new moral atmosphere. Or, as we can think of the origin of the human race as a marked discontinuous variation or mutation, a point emphasised by some notable impulse of the Divine energy raising life in such a way that henceforth it had the possibility of moving thereafter upon a higher plane, so may we perhaps in all reverence think of the historic appearance of Jesus Christ. In relation to man, the appearance of Jesus Christ is, then, an integral part of the evolutionary process in the purpose of the unmasking Environment which in its ultimate spiritual aspect is God.[1] He was perfectly adapted to it from the beginning. In Him Environment and process meet—reveal themselves as one. In Jesus Christ all of purpose and perfection that was implicit and struggling to expression, becomes once for all explicit. Thus the Other-regarding factor in Evolution, to the history of whose gradual emergence, all unconscious at first, reference has been made,[2] received its supreme expression in Him. In this way, as a matter of simple historical truth, Jesus Christ is the central

[1] *The Spiritual Interpretation of Nature*, chap. 10.
[2] Cf. p. 254.

pivotal fact of the world's history.[1]   In Jesus Christ
God visibly identifies Himself with the whole world
process in which suffering is seen to be service and
vicarious suffering its highest expression.[2]   To the man,
then, who says, 'We know enough of the process to say
that He can never be included,' the reply may be made
that when we know the process better, we may perhaps
see that He is included, not in the sense of being a product
of the process—in which case His appearance would
reasonably have been expected as its last term, which is
precisely what did not take place—but in being an expression, the supreme Revelation, definitely ordained
and in the fulness of the times appearing, of that Power
which is at work in the whole process.   And further,
if we believe, as we may, with Professor B. Moore, that
'it was no fortuitous combination of chances and no
cosmic dust which brought life to the bosom of our
ancient mother earth in the far distant pre-Cambrian
ages, but a well-regulated order of development, which
comes to every mother earth in the universe in the
maturity of its creation, when the conditions arrive
within the suitable limits,'[3] it is not impossible that
other worlds may know their Bethlehem, and their Calvary
too.   In a very real sense, the historic Jesus is for us the
cosmic Christ.

It may, however, well be questioned why this revelation
should be made, and this development reached, in course
of the process, and not rather at its end.   Now, close
investigation of the world conditions at the time of the
advent of our Lord shows that whilst commerce was
flourishing, and the rich culture of the Hellenic East had
penetrated throughout the Latin West, something was
lacking.   'The old gods are dethroned. . . . The world
is empty, because heaven is empty first.'[4]   Not that

[1] Cf. *antea*, p. 260.
[2] *The Spiritual Interpretation of Nature*, pp. 165-168.
[3] *Biochemistry*, p. 34.
[4] Prof. Rudolf Sohm, *Outlines of Church History*, pp. 2 and 3.

there was any lack of religions, but they had no power to elevate or recreate human life. The moral progress of man had reached a stage at which it was wellnigh spent, and there was serious danger of collapse if not of actual general retrogression. The moral life of man had not consolidated, and gave no promise of further development : it seemed exhausted and unable to bear the strain of continued advancement. Mankind in many of its representatives had reached a high stage of mental evolution, but its moral evolution had reached a point when definite personal intercourse with some personality loftier than any of the sons of men was needed to still further develop the potentialities in man. Just because he was becoming aware of himself as incipient personality, it was through such a medium that God would most naturally lead men on into fuller understanding of life and deeper fellowship with Him, and through a Person achieve that which the methods and limitations of earlier ages would less and less succeed in achieving. But further, as Le Conte brought out long ago, with the ability to work out his own salvation, to co-operate in his own evolution, the human individual is influenced by ideals. His evolution is not entirely externally determined. ' In organic evolution *species* are transformed by the *environment*. In human evolution *character* is transformed by *its own ideal*. . . . Organic evolution is *pushed* onward and upward from behind and below. Human evolution is *drawn* upward and forward from above and in front by the attractive force of ideals. Thus the ideal of organic evolution cannot appear until the end ; while the attractive ideals of human evolution *must* come—whether only in the imagination or realised in the flesh—but must come somehow *in the course*. The most powerfully attractive ideal ever presented to the human mind, and, therefore, the most potent agent in the evolution of human character, is *the* Christ.' [1]

---

[1] Joseph Le Conte, *Evolution and its Relation to Religious Thought*, p. 363.

Accordingly, in regarding the Incarnation as the central fact of the world's history, we must think of its primary purpose as one of revelation.   As such it is an integral part of the process, necessary for the further spiritual evolution of mankind.   Through it that became manifest which men had only dimly perceived before, viz. that God was with them in that ceaseless struggle which is life, and desired to enter into loving fellowship with them, that fellowship which means Eternal life.   In Jesus Christ men may see the perfect life which is, however, also a redeeming and recreative force—the direct response of God to the questing sense of man's deepest need, an answer in terms of revelation and of power.   And all this He achieved as the result of an identification of Himself with God and His purposes, so complete that He could feel Himself to be the fulfilment of the highest intuitions and yearnings of the past.[1]   The creation process has been a whole, and the close relation that St. Paul seeks to establish between it and Jesus Christ, in whom, he says, it all literally ' stands together,'[2] means this at least, that at no stage has it been a chance affair, but that from the beginning it had as end, man developing towards sonship, and so meant Jesus Christ—*meant* in the creative Divine Mind, with a meaning and significance which are existence itself.   As St. Peter said, He ' was foreknown indeed before the foundation of the world, but was manifested at the end of the times for your sake.'[3]

As the Revealer Jesus showed to men in time and space what is eternally true of God, focalising within the limitations of a human life the infinite love of God to man, His desire to share with them all the experiences of human life, and how He suffers because of sin and human suffering ; by His death Jesus revealed at what a cost alone can sin be overcome, and what forgiveness means. His was a life of perfect Love—a life that has for ever demonstrated that Love at any rate is very close to the

[1] Luke 10 [23, 24] ;  Matt. 13 [17].
[2] Col. 1 [18] ;  cf. also 2 Tim. 1 [9-10].          [3] 1 Pet. 1 [20].

secret of the Universe, and in some way controls the creative energy of the world. Creative and recreative evolution works in human life by Love ; ' they became,' said Hosea, ' like that which they loved.' [1] But while the death of Jesus supremely revealed the attitude of God, it did not change that attitude, which has always been the same. ' Light from the sun at night is streaming constantly through all parts of space, but only where a moon or a planet comes to reflect it does it become so that we can see and know it.' [2] The death of Jesus was the climactic act of a life of revelation and redemption, but we may find ourselves ' seeking the living among the dead ' if we focus too much into an event ' what ought to be perceived as a permanent and spiritual power, ever operative, and everywhere revealing the transforming life of God.' [3] Jesus saves men by His life as by His death ; in short, the Incarnation as a whole is the At-one-ment.[4]

Jesus Christ then proves to be the Reconciler, making men at one with God ; ' He is the Lamb of God which *is taking* away the sin of the world ' [5] as men become reconciled to God in Him ; He unites them to God in and through Himself. Organic life is at-one-ment with, or adaptation to, the more proximate aspects of the Environment ; Eternal life is at-one-ment with, or adaptation to, the ultimate aspect of the Environment, which is God. In either case it is a matter of necessary active relationship, which can easily be destroyed. That life of service and of sacrifice unto death which showed forth supremely the general law of all organic progress from the dawn of life, proves itself powerful, by ideal and in actuality through the direct transforming work of the Spirit

[1] Hos. 9 [10].
[2] Dr. D. A. Murray, *Christian Faith and the New Psychology*, p. 328
[3] Dr. Marshall Talling, *The Science of Spiritual Life*, p. 185.
[4] 2 Cor. 5 [19].
[5] John 1 [29]. The Greek tense is a present participle. The scope and purpose of this work do not admit of an examination of the various theological theories of Atonement, even were the writer competent to do so. It is important to notice that no one of them has ever received credal sanction.

of Jesus in human lives, to take away the sin of the world.
Love begets love, and there is wrought a repentance and
surrender in human lives which from the side of God implies
forgiveness.   Love begets love, supplanting selfish desire
as the dominating impulse in character.   Man attains to
immortality only as he loves, since it is love alone that can
produce wholeness and perfection of being, and is the only
enduring relationship.   It is not, then, so much a matter
of substitution as of identification.   God and man become reconciled, united, at one, in Jesus Christ, in an
eternal and indissoluble relationship.   And not merely
does He reconcile man to God, but also man to man, and
even nation to nation.   At a point in the Uspallata Pass,
on the boundary between Chile and Argentina, may be
seen ' an impressive statue . . . representing Christ extending the blessings of peace on either hand,' [1] set up by
the Governments of these two countries at the close of
the delicate frontier negotiations of 1902, as a symbol of
lasting reconciliation : ' He is our peace,' runs the in-
scription in part, ' who hath made both one.' [2]

In two of the four Gospels the story of the appearance
of Jesus Christ in human history is placed within the
setting of a Virgin Birth.[3]   Such an explanation or interpretation of His life is not distinctive of these Gospels,
although sound and far-reaching differences may be
established between the Gospel narratives and similar
accounts in pagan literature.   As records, the narratives
become subject to textual and other criticism,[4] but a

[1] Sir Thomas H. Holdich, *Political Frontiers and Boundary Making*,
p. 150.                                                  [2] Eph. 2 [14].
[3] To try and render the doctrine tenable by reference to the phenomenon of parthenogenesis in the animal kingdom is both to misunder-
stand the rôle of the phenomenon in nature and to miss the meaning
of the doctrine in question.   Between the biological phenomenon and
the Scriptural narrative there is nothing in common save the name.
[4] Thus, some scholars (*e.g.* Harnack, Schmiedel, Weiss, etc.) have
regarded Luke i. 34, 35, as an interpolation—it may be on insufficient
grounds.   On the other hand, such a psychological situation as is
depicted in Luke 2 [50] is not easy to understand, if these verses are not
later additions.   For critical examinations of the whole question, cf

more penetrating question is whether such an interpretation is necessary. With regard to the former line of study, it may be noticed that while the First Gospel recognises the Virgin Birth, yet it perhaps also gives a clue as to how this explanation first arose, and provides us with the atmosphere in which it naturally flourished. ' Now all this is come to pass, that it might be fulfilled which was spoken by the Lord through the prophet,' [1] and then a reference is given to a passage in Isaiah which can only be brought by a circumlocution into relation with the event which it was held to anticipate. It would be difficult to exaggerate the tremendous influence of the Old Testament upon the thought of the early Christians, or to over-estimate the exquisite sensitivity of their minds to the meaningfulness of its language. They ransacked the sacred writings for passages which might be supposed to shed light on the career of the Messiah. In this way references were found which came to be regarded as fundamental, not merely by the average early Christian, but by St. Paul himself. Thus it would appear [2] that his doctrine of the Lordship of Jesus Christ developed in his mind upon the basis of the first verse of the 110th Psalm, ' The Lord said unto my Lord.' This supposedly authoritative designation of the Messiah cleared away mountains of obscurity with regard to the Person of our Lord from the mind of the early Church. Similarly, Isaiah vii. 14 seemed to supply an astounding hint, although the word rendered ' virgin '[3] really means a young marriageable woman, with no special stress on virginity. After the Resurrection, when our Lord was put by His followers on the same level with God, the name of the child ' Immanuel '—God with us—came as a re-

G. H. Box, *The Virgin Birth of Jesus*, p. 35 ff. ; Professor J. F. Bethune-Baker, *The Faith of the Apostles' Creed*, p. 66 ff. ; and Vincent Taylor, *The Historical Evidence for the Virgin Birth*.

[1] Matt. 1 [22].

[2] On the authority of Prof. H. A. A. Kennedy.

[3] The Hebrew language has its own particular word for ' virgin '— (bĕthúlā).

discovery in the Old Testament, and a reinforcement of their own decision. But in particular to account for His sinlessness, what was more probable than that this beautiful story should spring up, and that religious minds should say of Mary, ' This is the Virgin of whom it was spoken as in Isaiah vii. 14 ' ? Further, the Birth narratives in the First and Third Gospels are closely associated with an angelology in which Judaism generally and Apocalyptic literature in particular were steeped, and of which no very clear or consistent account has been given. The whole conception of angelology was in part due to Deistic views of God that kept Him at a distance from the world, whether on account of its unworthiness or His exceeding transcendence. A ritual conception of holiness had pushed Him out of all direct communication with the world ; angels, consequently, were His intermediaries. Further, it seems to follow from Luke i. 35, that the paternal relationship is associated with the Divine Power, indicated by the name Holy Spirit, rather than with the First Person of the Trinity. And, finally, the Roman Church, by its logical doctrine of the Immaculate Conception of the Virgin, rightly realises the fact that, within the whole system of presuppositions and ideas in which this subject has been enshrined, the ' entail of heredity ' could not be broken even by such Virgin Birth from a human mother, while the idea that it could is only possible under the influence of the old-world fancy that in conception the male element plays the predominating rôle. On the other hand, the oldest Gospel knows nothing of such a story, and of the purpose of the latest Gospel it is expressly stated that ' These (signs) are written that ye may believe that Jesus is the Christ, the Son of God ; and that believing ye may have life in His name ' : [1] yet amongst these signs was not included that of a Virgin Birth. This does not indeed disprove the Virgin Birth ; that cannot be done, and in any case arguments from silence are always precarious. But it is apparent that

[1] John 20 31.

X

the writer of the Fourth Gospel did not think of it as a primary faith-eliciting factor, or necessary article of belief in relation to his idea of the Incarnation, and it is clear that the burden of the Apostolic preaching was the death and resurrection of Jesus rather than the manner of His birth.

The same is probably true of St. Paul. There is no reason to doubt that he held a natural generation for our Lord.[1] Although we find no definite argument for or against the doctrine in his writings, his was a mind that would certainly have laid great stress upon this conception if it had been prominent in the Church in his time ; for to his way of thinking the spirit came from God. The doctrine arose, however, at a comparatively late period in the Church's history, and by the time that St. Luke wrote his Gospel it was widely held. The silence of the earlier author of the Epistle to the Hebrews may be held to corroborate the point of view based on the writings of St. Paul. Apart from the question of fact, however, the immediate question is whether such a doctrine is necessary—whether a full doctrine of the Incarnation cannot be held without it. More relentlessly the query may be pressed, Is not such a belief pure Naturalism, an outcome of the old static conception of human nature or man, cut, so to speak, to a certain physical and spiritual specificity of type ? How can a physical happening be considered worthy proof or cause of a moral achievement ? ' He was not a physical production, but a spiritual bestowal ; the spirit-miracle of the ages, a special revelation of the Unseen Heart of the Universe. The man who cannot see Deity in Jesus, will see God nowhere.' [2] The motive in the doctrine is abundantly clear, but is it not possible that some of the forms or categories in which one generation moulded its highest expression of worship may be subsumed in, or replaced by, or held along with, those that have been elaborated as the result of the spiritual ex-

---

[1] Cf. especially Rom. 1 [3] ; 9 [5] ; Gal. 4 [4].
[2] Dr. Marshall Talling, *The Science of Spiritual Life*, p. 95.

perience of a later generation ? To the man who has
seen in Jesus Christ the very revelation of God there is
nothing too wonderful that he will not believe about
Him, although he will also never close his mind to what
he may accept as the results of reverent scholarship
concerning the accounts of His earthly life. When in
answer to our Lord's interrogation, St. Peter made his
supreme confession, he framed it in words that subsume
the heights and depth and length and breadth of faith.
And if the generations that follow us come to see that
just as the belief in Verbal Inspiration, based on such
a passage as Rev. 22 [18-19], has proved to be part of a
beneficent design whereby, in the dark days when as
yet the fixing power of the press was unknown, the
sacred text was safeguarded to a tolerable extent against
mutilation by careless copyists, so the belief in a Virgin
Birth was instrumental in awakening many minds
throughout the ages into a realisation that God had
sojourned amongst them in the flesh, ere yet they had
developed the insight to see the fact in the wonder and
spirituality of our Lord's moral character, it will not
lessen the force of their witness provided they too can
say from the heart of a personal experience, ' Thou art
the Christ, the Son of the living God.' [1]

When men's souls were flooded with the light and joy
and peace that came to them through knowledge of Jesus
Christ, it seemed to them as if His love must have been
eternal. He who so proved a Saviour to men must have
existed with God from the beginning. In reflections
such as these may have in part arisen the doctrine of
the pre-existence of Jesus. We have seen that Jesus
Christ revealed in human life what is eternally true of
God—His love to man, His hatred of sin, the cost to
Him in service and sacrifice by which alone it can be
put away. And we may well suppose that throughout
the ages, as men have lived consistently near to God,

[1] Matt. 16 [16].

they have felt in some dim and distant way that all these things were true of God. More prescient souls believed that one day He would make it absolutely clear to men —they saw afar off the day of the Lord Christ and were glad.[1] At any rate there is no doubt that some of the New Testament writers conceived religious history as having taken that form so far as it concerned the people of past generations. They went further, not merely in elaboration of distinctly Jewish ideas, as that all the Messianic actualities were pre-existent with God (e.g. the New Jerusalem, The Tabernacle,[2] the 'book of Life,'[3] the Messiah Himself), but sometimes they actually adapted traditional material to their purpose. Thus St. Paul, in a wonderful admonitory passage describing the propitious circumstances under which the Israelites nevertheless failed, says that 'all ate the same spiritual food, and all drank the same spiritual drink, for all the way they kept drinking of a spiritual rock which continually followed them, and this rock *was* the Christ' (ὁ χριστός, the Messiah ?).[4] In these words he emphasises the fact of the Divine in history, but few will maintain that they are intended to express his deliberate thought about Jesus Christ. So also the writer of the Epistle to the Hebrews thinks of Moses 'considering obloquy with the Messiah to be richer wealth than all Egypt's treasures.'[5] Moses suffered because he believed in God's saving purpose, says this writer, and in it all had some dim consciousness that

---

[1] John 8 56.  [2] Heb. 8 5.

[3] Rev. 13 8 (Moffatt's trans.).

[4] 1 Cor. 10 4. 'This thought may have been suggested to Paul by the Jewish tradition that the Israelites were accompanied on their march by a rock "globular, like a beehive," which rolled after the camp. The use of the word *spiritual* shows that Paul did not himself literally adopt this grotesque tradition, but he appears in this passage to have adapted it' (Prof. J. E. M'Fadyen, D.D., *The Interpreter's Commentary* in loco). Pre-existence, in the sense of his creation before the world, is even postulated of Moses in the apocalyptic work, *The Assumption of Moses*.

[5] Heb. 11 26 (Moffatt's trans.). The writer apparently has Ps. 89 10 in his mind.

God had an ultimate wider purpose of salvation, which would also be accomplished through suffering. He thinks of Moses as feeling that he is true to the eternal nature of God in his action, and that God would yet even more wonderfully manifest Himself in Christ than He was doing in him. Or, once again, in 1 Peter 1 [11], it is said of the prophets that ' the spirit of Messiah within them foretold all the suffering of Messiah and His afterglory, and they pondered when or how this was to come.' Scholars tell us that the phrase ' spirit of Messiah ' is simply here equivalent to the Spirit of God, and that we must think of the language of the epistles as hortatory rather than exact and definitive. If then these inter-pretations are correct, it will follow that the passages in question indicate a belief on the part of the writers in expressions in times past of that character and activity of God which were ultimately manifested in Jesus Christ, as also in the vigorous appreciation of these revelations by highly sensitive spiritual personalities of the past, not merely in their present but also dimly in relation to the future. But in themselves they can hardly be taken as evidence of the writers' belief in the pre-existence of that historic individuality which was known to men on earth as Jesus Christ.

On the other hand, in certain of the Pauline epistles there occur very familiar passages in which our Lord is thought of as a pre-existent separate individuality : ' the image of the invisible God ' is certainly not God Himself.[1] These passages comprise some of the most difficult in Scripture, and apparently yield very different results in different hands. The early effort to guard against tritheism was helped by the fact that the word ' person ' when first used, did not convey the meaning of personality as we now understand that word in the sense of distinct self-conscious individuality, but just in that measure it makes it difficult for us to formulate

[1] Col. 1 [15-20]; 2 [9-10]; Phil. 2 [6-11]; 2 Cor. 8 [9]. Cf. also Heb. 1 [2-3] John 1 [1-2].

a clear conception of pre-existence to-day.   The development of language has led us away from the original idea.[1] Conceptions of Trinity and Triunity must relate to divine manifestation or activity—a love in God that gives not merely the Son but the Spirit.   And it is important to remember in this connection, as Dr. Hastings Rashdall reminds us,[2] that it was ' part of the traditional doctrine of the Church ' that ' the human soul of Jesus did not exist before His birth in time.'   What the Church has taught is ' that the Second Person of the Holy Trinity, the Son or Word of God, existed from all eternity ; but the human soul to which that Word of God was united at His birth did not exist before that birth.' [3]   The Word, *i.e.* the Immanent Purpose or Wisdom of God, was *made flesh*.  How that Word was previously related to God—in what manner or form the eternal thoughts of God are *real* to Him—no human mind can conceive.[4]

Now St. Paul's statements in this particular are inferences from the tremendous impression of the exalted Lord upon Him.   His account of the process whereby that exaltation was attained is essentially dynamic, rather than static.   The state of being ' on an equality with God ' even for this pre-existent One is conceived as something to be achieved later as the result of suffering.

[1] That some forms of theological expression have departed far from Scriptural teaching is clear from these statements of Principal Denney : ' In spite of the creeds, there is no such expression in the New Testament as believing in the Holy Ghost.   The Spirit is not an object of faith like Christ or God, it is an experience which comes to people through faith. . . . There is no justification in this for representing the Spirit as a third person in the same sense as God and Christ ' (*The Christian Doctrine of Reconciliation*, pp. 308, 311).   The New Testament writers took their idea of the Spirit from the Old Testament, but interpreted it entirely in the light of their experience of Jesus.   In one passage (2 Cor. 3 [17]) St. Paul makes the identification complete.   ' Now the Lord,' he says, ' *is* the Spirit.' (Cf. also Rom. 8 [9-11].)

[2] *Jesus, Human and Divine*, p. 31.

[3] At the same time the New Testament nowhere expressly speaks of ' an eternal Son of God ' ; the conception is a logical inference from other statements.

[4] ' A Science without mystery is unknown ; a Religion without mystery is absurd ' (Henry Drummond, *Natural Law in the Spiritual World*, p. 28).

Our Lord did not think of it as a thing to be snatched, says St. Paul, but rather as something to be slowly attained.[1] The same point of view—' made perfect through sufferings '—is found to hold the mind of the author of the Epistle to the Hebrews.[2] Both writers start from a notion of pre-existence and regard the post-humiliation state as something higher than our Lord had ever attained before.   It would, however, be unwise to attempt to find any complete hard and fast system in St. Paul's teaching about our Lord, and it is worse than useless to try and tie him down to a theory.   Ultimately he was always governed by the facts of his own experience, and gives the impression of feeling out after things rather than of setting down fixed conclusions.   Thus even in his treatment of the Cross in the Epistle to the Ephesians (chap. 2), he seems to say, ' Do not attempt to rationalise : trust rather to the appeal it makes.'   The writings of St. Paul have this in common with the Synoptic Gospels, that they are both of the nature of first-hand impressions—in the one case of a life, in the other of an experience : in neither instance do the writers try to round off their ideas.

The majestic inevitability and the profound and understanding tribute of these passages will always remain, expressive of the deepest conviction that that which has superlatively appealed to men as Divine cannot have begun to be at any particular point in time, and illustrative of the truth that the imagination shall never exhaust itself in telling of the wonder of the grace of God in Jesus Christ.   And this conviction is unaffected however wide the difference in general outlook may be between a view of God's work in the world that considers man, conceived statically as of one fixed type mental and moral, and with a racial history of some 6000 years, to have fallen from a

---

[1] Phil. 2 [6]. Cf. Prof. H. A. A. Kennedy, D.D., *The Expositor's Greek Testament*, in loco, to whose understanding the writer is particularly indebted at this point.
[2] Heb. 2 [10] ; 5 [7-10].

stage of primitive innocence if not of goodness, so providing the occasion for a supreme manifestation of the divine love in the sacrifice of a pre-existent Christ, and a view that realises that that history has covered probably half a million years of slow, upward human progress, not unconnected with stages of animal history previous to these, through which man gradually has been growing in his knowledge of and likeness to God, until in the fulness of the times One came in whom men saw that God indeed dwelt and Who has helped above all others in deepening their likeness to Him.   Regarded from such a point of view, with its increasing sense of the value and potentiality of human individuality, the Incarnation becomes not so much a defeat as a relief, not so much a humiliation as an inspiration, not so much an exception as a perfection.   It is Revelation in that it showed men in time and space what is eternally true of God, and thus regarded, the work of Christ has been and is an eternal work.   It is Redemption in that the awakened individual who consciously and continuously puts his life in direct relationship with Jesus Christ, influenced and inspired by His purpose and consciousness of the divine, receives power to ' walk in newness of life.'   ' To bring the consciousness and the presence and the power of the divine into human life and work—this is the ultimate religious problem.   And the Man, Christ Jesus, is the solution of this problem.' [1]

In our Lord accordingly we see a unique consciousness of a unique filial relation, yet with self-admitted limitations of knowledge,[2] and the evidence of mental conflict and even of uncertainty at times in connection with the accomplishment of His life task.   We see a consciousness of a vocation which developed into the conviction that

[1] Prof. H. A. Youtz, *The Enlarging Conception of God*, p. 188.

[2] Matt. 24 [36], and the corresponding Mk. 13 [32] ; even more particularly Luke 12 [50], ' How am I straitened,' *i.e.* limited, until after the releasing baptism of death.—(See Prof. J. F. Bethune-Baker, *The Faith of the Apostles' Creed*, p. 17.)

He was the Messiah [1] in the sense that He would be a Deliverer [2]—would save His people from their misconceptions, from themselves, from their sins, and that He would inaugurate the Kingdom of God upon earth. We see a consciousness of a unique relation to His fellowmen as the One who had been chosen of God to reveal His very heart, and to introduce a new epoch in history, and there is nothing that He said about Himself which has not been justified by history. ' Christianity,' says Professor Albert Schweitzer in his remarkable missionary book,[3] ' is for him (*i.e.* the Central African) the light that shines amid the darkness of his fears ; it assures him that he is not in the power of nature-spirits, ancestral spirits, or fetishes, and that no human being has any sinister power over another, since the will of God really controls everything that goes on in the world—

> " I lay in cruel bondage,
> Thou cam'st and mad'st me free."

These words from Paul Gerhardt's Advent hymn express better than any others what Christianity means for primitive man. That is again and again the thought that fills my mind when I take part in a service on a mission station.' And what has proved true in the case of the coloured people by the Ogowe River is likewise verified by dwellers in Thames Valley and by the Seine. Joy and peace come into human lives in the degree in which they have been liberated from the ' demons ' of the age in which they live, and from the ' demons ' of their

---

[1] It should be borne in mind that ' no Jew thought of the Messiah as actually God or as equal with God.'—(Dr. Hastings Rashdall, *op. cit.* p. 38.)

[2] So, quite definitely in Matt. 20 [28], and the corresponding Mk. 10 [45], where it is stated that ' the Son of Man came . . . to give His life for the λύτρον, deliverance, of *many*.' In Acts 7 [35], Moses is described as a λυτρωτής, *i.e.* deliverer : there is no suggestion of ' ransom ' here. The same word is also used in the Septuagint in Ps. 19 [14] and 78 [35], and rendered ' deliverer ' in Wellhausen's translation ; cf. also Gen. 48 [16]. On the other hand, there are several passages (Lev. 25 [25], 27 [13], etc.) where the usage is in accordance with the primary idea of redemption.

[3] *On the Edge of the Primeval Forest*, p. 154.

own ' hearts.' It is simple matter of fact that the whole
progress of life, whether we regard it at the protozoan
level, at the stage of incipient humanity, or in the case of
nascent nationality, consists in the winning of liberty,
and that there is no real progress for humanity which is
not progress in the consciousness and exercise of freedom.
Christianity is thus of the very essence of progress.

Yet our Lord's own explanation of His life was that it
was one with the life of God—that He so lived and moved
and had His being in God that their character and purposes were one. That was the secret of His life, according to Himself—not a Virgin birth. Our Lord Himself
never gave that reason, never hinted at it. His life was
a human life of such a kind that it is only fully described
when spoken of as ' divine.' This does not mean that
the ' divine ' is merely the human made perfect or become
infinite : it is something more than that. In the case of
our Lord, ' as in no other, the Divine " personality "
expressed itself through a human " personality " : the
human personality was the personality of God under the
conditions of human life.' [1] The Christian narratives by
their use of the supremest categories and conceptions of
their day—crowning Him with many crowns—testify to
the overpowering impression that our Lord produced
upon His contemporaries and the immediately succeeding generations. That impression is a whole and it is
consistent in its ascription of absolute worth. Each of
the writers says in his own way, ' Thou art the Christ,
the Son of the Living God.' Yet it may be that they gave
these particular explanations because they could not
understand the reason that our Lord Himself gave, viz.
His constant fellowship with God. His life involved such
complete possession of Him by the Divine Energising
Spirit that it was completely in accord with the life of God
—in Him dwelt ' all the fulness of the Godhead bodily.' [2]
' I have meat to eat that ye know not of.' [3] None of His

---

[1] Prof. J. F. Bethune-Baker, *The Faith of the Apostles' Creed*, p. 94.
[2] Col. 2 [9]; cf. also John 3 [34], 2 Cor. 5 [19].          [3] John 4 [32].

disciples lived even for a moment on that spiritual plane of constant and absolute communion with God in complete surrender on which He had continuously lived.

This fulness and perfection of life have usually been expressed by the use of the word ' sinless,' [1] one of those negative and therefore inadequate conceptions which the theology of the future may discard. For it implies too much the idea of one moving down a stream and keeping clear of the shoals and snags by fixing his eyes on the buoys that mark them, whereas such willed and developed God-possession as was our Lord's, involves a moral supremacy to which failure is foreign, and which advances in permanently instinctive relationship to what is good. When the writer to the Hebrews speaks of Him as ' made perfect through sufferings,' [2] he is not working with the old classical idea of the ὁ παθὼν μάθων,—as if our Lord learned through suffering to avoid faults He had already committed. He did not become sinless through suffering, but He was thereby perfected or matured in sympathy. So filled was He with the Spirit of God that power streamed out of Him into other lives in physical and moral healing, and that through His will He could exercise a control over energy as it appears in the so-called forces of Nature of a character that we as yet do not directly or fully understand. And yet through it all He Himself made no difference between Himself and other men except in the degree in which He lived and moved and had His being in God. And unless we are in the same state of mind as those two hapless souls that dwelt amongst the tombs and asked, ' Art thou come hither to torment us ? ' [3] or take refuge in the position that He cannot have meant what He was saying, we must believe Him when He who knew so well what was in man, said, ' Verily, verily, I say unto you, He that believeth on me, the works that I do shall he do also ; and greater works than these shall he do, because I go unto the Father.' [4] We simply do not

---

[1] Cf. John 8 [46].
[3] Matt. 8 [29].

[2] Heb. 2 [19].
[4] John 14 [12].

begin to know what are the possibilities of a God-filled human life ; we may see them in Jesus Christ if we will but look. We look on other lives, and say His was not human, when as a matter of fact we are just on the threshold of understanding what personality is, and its possibilities in relation to God. We limit the word 'human' in terms of the knowledge of yesterday, which is the ignorance of to-day, and then we say that what is beyond that is 'divine.' Jesus is beyond that, and therefore He was divine, and the idea is even welcomed in partial excuse for our own failure. Surely it is truer to say with St. Paul that Jesus was man, and revealed to us both what man may be and what God really is, and thus He is the one Mediator between God and men.[1] We tend to think about Him in such a kind of way— which was not His way of thinking about Himself— as makes all His sayings impracticable and unreal : an unreal humanity is no humanity. We wrong our Lord and minimise the purpose and achievement of His life when we explain it, as He never did, in terms of some superinduced conception of divinity distinct from His humanity. He was a man ; from that we must start. He was a man, not a prodigy, ' the first born among many brethren.'[2] He lived a human life with all the aids and possibilities that other men have ; but He used them as no other man ever did. When He spoke to men the most daring words that ever fell from human lips, challenging them in the supreme moral imperative, ' Be ye perfect even as your Heavenly Father is perfect,'[3] He was telling of that which He had achieved through His own willing to be in perfect communion with God. When He said, ' Father, not my will but thine be done,'[4] He showed the reality of temptation for Himself in thus willing His own will into unison with that of God.

We have said that such doctrines as the Virgin Birth and Pre-existence were fundamentally important to the

---

[1] 1 Tim. 2 [5] (' Himself man,' R.V.).      [2] Rom. 8 [29].
[3] Matt. 5 [48].      [4] Luke 22 [42].

early Christian communities in that, in addition to constituting their supreme forms of homage to our Lord, they supplied *explanations* of His unique Personality. Now it is rather remarkable that there is no single New Testament writer who associates the doctrines of the Virgin Birth and of Pre-existence. As a matter of fact they are quite different and unrelated views, and yet they were held together without any sense of incongruity in that collection of writings which constitutes the New Testament. In the Gospels indeed we may find several lines of explanation of the Person of our Lord. The First and Third Gospels contain genealogies which suggest a spiritual heredity, both on His father's and His mother's side. It may prove a real evidence of the inspiration of the Bible to a generation which is just beginning to understand the scope and mechanism of Heredity, that genealogies which only puzzled previous generations should be included as part of the attempt to explain Him. Along with the genealogies they contain the story of His birth of the Holy Spirit and a virgin mother. A third explanation is given in terms of the idea of a pre-existent Heavenly One who comes to earth. The oldest of the Gospels gives as its explanation a narrative of the descent of the Spirit of God upon our Lord, accompanied by a voice which in the Third Gospel is represented as saying, ' *This day* have I become thy Father.' [1] That is to say, it suggests that Divine Sonship was conferred at our Lord's baptism, which was a crisis in His growing awareness of Himself and His mission.[2] The vague forecasts of His earlier days reached a climax when He put Himself side by side with the men and women at the Jordan and had the spiritual consciousness of a new and complete oneness with God ; with this there came a new consciousness of spiritual power, and He went forth. And this is practically what Justin Martyr taught in the Early

---

[1] Luke 3 [22]. See Moffatt's trans. and note *in loco*.
[2] This may also have been St. Peter's understanding : cf. Acts 10 [38], and the whole atmosphere of thought in 4 [27-31].

Church during the period when the doctrines of the Pre-existent Logos and Virgin Birth, which had taken shape as the result of further reflection, were still slowly making their way.[1] Nevertheless, the fact of Christ remains, solitary and salvatory, and it is quite certain that a generation that feels the insufficiency of any one attempted explanation will yet be unwilling to discard any particular Scriptural interpretation, being only the more conscious that all the generations in every land and all their distinctive conceptions will never exhaust the wonder that is in Christ Jesus, our Lord.

In conclusion ; any attempt to get behind the dogmas and formulae of Primitive Christianity, and so to reach the religious convictions which they represented for that time and generation, will always be subject to the control of the Christian experience of to-day.   We want to know, if the *tour de force* is possible, just what it is that would have made a modern believing man instinctively feel at home in the Church that met in the House of Cecilia.[2] There, just as now, assembled men and women whose hearts leapt up responsively to the story of the spiritual experiences, whether read from written records, or spoken at first or second hand report, of those who had companied with the Lord ; and under the action of the illuminating and informing Spirit of God they entered into the distinctively Christian experience of communion through Jesus Christ with God, communion with Jesus Christ in God.   In this way they were and are alike able to test for themselves all that He said about God, and they find it so true that He becomes their supreme religious authority.   They feel closest to God when they are nearest to Jesus.   He so perfectly interprets God to them that in the end they can only say, ' He is

---

[1] The doctrine of the Virgin Birth formed no part of the Nicene or Athanasian Creeds (A.D. 325) ; although there is ' no doubt of its great antiquity ' as a credal article.   See Prof. J. F. Bethune-Baker, *The Faith of the Apostles' Creed*, p. 66 ff.

[2] Cf. Walter Pater, *Marius the Epicurean*, vol. ii. p. 92 ff.

not merely the revelation of God—He *is* God, manifest in the flesh.' [1]  He is the One Who has gone ahead blazing the trail, ' the Pioneer of their salvation,' [2] yet saying to men ' Follow me,' and enabling them to follow.  He is the One Who has arrived, while they are but on the way.  And just so certainly as we know that we shall not attain to the stature of perfect manhood in Christ Jesus on this terrestrial plane of things, yet is it sure that that is the goal of our spiritual existence which He sets before us, drawing no absolute line between Himself and us in at any rate one fundamental respect,[3] yet proving in the experience of men to be a recreative and transforming power,—' the power of God unto salvation.' [4]  His thought of Himself in relation to us is that of a mountain peak which at some future stage we may scale : hitherto we have tended to think of it as a star.

And the Gospel, the ' Good News,' takes on a wider sweep, for the revelation of God is never complete.  Men have often crucified the Spirit of Truth, but from its lips they shall never hear the words ' It is finished.' For along with the realisation that the world in which we find ourselves is ultimately a spiritual world, goes the sense that Nature is actually rooted and only fulfilled in grace, because it is a world into which in the fulness of the times One came Who not only was the revelation of the heart of God but Who is now, as He was in the days of His flesh, the only Saviour of mankind.  We reach a point of view from which we begin to understand that the motive of the world process as a whole is Love, that from the time that the creative self-limitation or self-emptying of God culminated in the production of man, His Spirit has been striving with men throughout the ages—seeking for ever completer self-expression in the sons of men until this was perfectly attained in the Son of Man.  But so to think is to reconstruct

---

[1] Dr. H. S. Coffin, *Some Christian Convictions*, p. 90.
[2] Heb. 2 [10] (Moffatt's trans.).
[3] Mark 3 [33-35].          [4] Rom. 1 [16].

our thought of history. For it is to reaffirm that the life of the historic Jesus was a recapitulation in mundane setting of time and space of the eternal activity and character of God. God is eternally that which He showed Himself to be in Jesus Christ. Yet the God manifest in Him has been from the beginning of human history enlightening every man, laying down His life in some of them, and receiving it again. He is the reality underlying all these spiritual outgoings that in differing degrees have characterised epochs and nations and individuals. In human history He has been implicitly working from the beginning in increasing revelation, and humanity was represented in Him ere its divinity was represented on earth in Jesus Christ. Calvary itself was the complete and final expression of a law of life which had been in operation from the beginning of life, at first unconsciously and later in varying degrees of conscious imperfection and limitation—that only by service and sacrifice even unto death can sin be put away. And this is to realise that not once but many times has God been buffeted and bruised and spit upon and rejected and despised of men, laying down His life in many of His servants who saw the day of the Lord Christ afar off and were glad, that He might receive it again in the newer and better conditions that their lives of faith and service and suffering inaugurated. It is to remember with the writer of the Epistle to the Hebrews that still through the ages Jesus Christ is crucified afresh and put to an open shame, and that Christian men and women are called upon ' to fill up that which is lacking in the sufferings of Christ ' [1] and shall be until mankind comes to the knowledge of the truth, and is one in Him. ' Christ was crucified not to save us from crucifixion, but to show us how the perfect man submits to it, and how all of us are called to submit to it. He lays down His life in as many selves as He can find with consecration enough to let Him do it.' [2] Through Him men can come into an

[1] Col. 1 [24].          [2] J. W. Lee, *The Religion of Science*, p. 288.

experience of God which means salvation, moral renewal, and the true development of personality.   And when a man has come into this relation with the Eternal, understanding God fully in terms of that manifestation in Jesus which breaks our hearts by its tenderness and challenges our loyalty by its truth, he sees with St. Paul that in Him the whole purpose of the universe literally 'stands together,' [1] and comes to realise that he has missed the whole meaning of life, and life itself, if he has not entered into active living relationship with God through Him.   He also understands with St. John that ' all that is in the world, the desire of the flesh and the desire of the eyes and the proud glory of life (and thought), belongs not to the Father but to the world ; and the world is passing away with its desire, while he who does the will of God abideth for ever.' [2]

[1] Col. 1 [18].          [2] 1 John 2 [16, 17] (based on Moffatt's trans.).

# INDEX

Acheulean climate, 102 ; cultural phase, 56, 90, 91, 143 ; fossil remains, 100-101 ; implements, 99-100.

Acton, Lord, 186, 187, 190.

Africa, Palaeolithic man in, 104, 109, 110, 143, 144 ; primitive mammals in, 224.

Age of the earth, 48-50.

Ages, geological, 50, 51.

Alpine race, 169, 172.

Alps in Great Ice Age, 52.

Altamira Cave, 125, 127, 138.

America, Palaeolithic man in, 103, 104.

American monkeys, 29, 30.

*Amoeba*, 201.

Amphibians, origin of, 222.

Anau, excavations at, 173, 175.

Anthropoid apes, 29-35, 70 ; fossil forms, 65 ; migrations of, 72, 77, 143 ; origin of, 72 ; points of contact with man, 37-45.

Apocalyptic period, 282-284, 289.

Aralo-Caspian depression, 171.

Arboreal life, effects of, 43, 44, 71, 73, 77.

*Archaeopteryx*, 223.

Arnold, Matthew, 231.

Art, Aurignacian, 125-127 ; Magdalenian, 136-142.

Asia, Central, as original home of man, 76, 151, 171.

Atonement, doctrine of, 318.

Aurignacian art, 125-127 ; cultural phase, 56, 57, 90, 91, 119-128 ; fauna, 124 ; fossil remains, 120-124 ; industry, 124-125 ; origin of race, 143-146 ; religion, 137, 142.

Australian, aboriginal, 37, 62, 146, 149 *n*.

Azilian cultural phase, 91, 148-153.

Babylonia, 48, 54, 88, 89, 171, 173.

Balfour, Earl of, 183.

Baltic Sea, changes in, 150, 153, 154, 159.

Bateson, Prof. W., 234, 235.

Beddard, F. E., 32.

Bergson, Prof. H., 265, 267, 269, 274.

Berry, Prof., 87.

Bethune-Baker, Prof. J. F., 320 *n*, 328 *n*, 330, 334 *n*.

Biogenetic Law, *see* Recapitulation Theory.

Birds, origin of, 223.

Blewett, Prof. G. J., 6, 8, 270.

Boule, M., 90 *n*, 96, 107, 111, 123 *n*.

Brachycephaly, 98, 147, 150-152 ; in Neanderthal skulls, 108.

Brain characters in man and apes, 38, 39, 76 ; development in mammals, 68-76, 239 ff.

Brigham, A. P., 14, 15.

Bronze Age, 48, 134, 160, 161, 163, 165, 167, 173, 176, 178.

Brünn skeleton, 123, 131.

Brüx skeleton, 131.

Burial, Aurignacian, 142, 143 ; Mousterian, 114-117 ; Neolithic, 164-167, 175.

Campignian cultural phase, 91, 152-153.

Capsian culture, 145-146, 149, 150.

Cell theory, critique of, 200-202.

Celts, 177, 178, 180.

Chancelade skeleton, 132.

Charles, Prof., 281 *n*, 287 *n*, 291 *n*.

Châtelperron knife, 124, 125, 145.

Chellean cultural phase, 56, 82, 90, 91, 92, 104 ; fauna, 101 ; climate, 101 ; implements, 95, 99, 100.

Chimpanzee, 33-35, 39, 43, 45, 65, 77, 110, 143.

Chronology, Biblical, 48, 54 ; of Great Ice Age, 53-57, 63.

Coelenterate, dividuality in, 204, 205, 206, 207.

Coffin, Dr. H. S., 335.

Colloids, 16.

Combe Capelle skeleton, 123.

Commonwealth, British, characters of, 190, 192.

Conditional Immortality, 294-299.

Conklin, Prof. E. G., 181, 191.

Consciousness, 236 ; relation to brain, 265, 266.
Copper Age, 176.
Coup-de-poing, 99, 100, 112, 124.
Cranial capacity, apes and man, 38, 39, 76 ; Cromagnon race, 121 ; *Eoanthropus*, 96, 118 ; Mousterian man, 106 ; Rhodesian man, 109.
Creation, 8-10, 25 ; accounts of, 88-89, 263, 276 ; as kenosis, 25, 267.
Criterion of survival, 227-229.
Croll's theory, 51.
Cromagnon skeletons, 120-123, 124, 132, 144.
Crystals, growth of, 199.
Cult of the bison, 140.
Cunningham, J. T., 20 *n*.

Dancing, ritual, 137, 139, 142.
Darwin, Charles, 81.
Davidson, Prof. A. B., 280.
Dead, worship of, 116, 149.
Denudation, 14.
Dendy, Prof. A., 209, 213 *n*.
Denney, Principal, 289, 326 *n*.
Diet, change of in man, 78.
Disharmony, physical, 44 ; of skull, 124.
Dividuality, 200 ; in Protozoa, 201 ; in Coelenterata, 206 ; in worms, 208.
Divine mind, 23.
Dods, Prof. Marcus, 293.
Dog, 153, 157.
Dolichocephaly, 98 *n*, 124, 147, 150, 151.
Domestication of animals, 153, 158, 160, 173.
Double sepulture, 133.
Drummond, Henry, 27, 43, 254, 326 *n*.
Dubois, Eugène, 85-86.
Duckworth, W. L. H., 29 *n*, 34 *n*, 41, 86.
Dwellings, Neolithic, 158, 159.
Dysteleology, 242.

Earth, age of the, 48-50.
Egyptian fossil apes, 65, 70 ; races, 63.
Electrical theory of matter, 9.
Electron, 9, 198.
Embryology, human, 40-42, 204.
Energy, 9, 10, 16-19, 22, 264, 265.
English Channel, past history of, 58, 101, 157.
Environment, factor in Evolution, 15, 20-22, 71, 73, 76, 170, 225, 227, 228, 229, 230, 235, 236, 244, 268, 269, 296, 306, 314 ; fitness of inorganic, 10-14.
*Eoanthropus*, 93-99, 110, 118.

Eoliths, 80-85, 95.
Erigena, 270.
Ether, 9.
Evolution, 4, 13, 20-22, 27, chaps. ix., x., xi. ; and Jesus Christ, 311-319.

Faith, 4, 5.
Fall, the, 253, 312.
Fauna, during Ice Age, 60-62.
Feudal system, 184, 187.
Fishes, origin of, 220-222.
Fiske, John, 246.
Fitness of environment, 10-14.
Flower and Lydekker, 29 *n*, 34, 38, 39.
Fore-limb, development of, 69, 72, 74.
France, development of nationality in, 184, 185.
Fraser, Sir J. G., 89 *n*.
Freedom, 186, 189, 191, chap. xi., 269.
Freud, S., 2, 244, 298.
Furfooz race, 151, 169.

Gargas cave, 127, 138, 141.
Geikie, Prof. J., 52 *n*, 54, 56, 148.
Genesis creation narrative, 88, 89.
German people, 181, 182.
Gibbon, 31, 32, 33, 40, 65, 72, 74, 77.
Gibraltar skull, 107, 109.
Gladstone, Mr., 186.
God, and the World, 8, 10, chap. xii. ; as Love, 25, chap. xiv.
Gorilla, 33, 35, 38, 43, 65, 76.
Grace, 26, 270, 313.
Great Ice Age, 51-62, 156, 171 ; fauna of, 60-62 ; phases of, 52-57.
Gregory, W. K., 29 *n*, 45, 96, 104 *n*.
Grimaldi caves, 121-123.
Grosgartach, Neolithic village at, 158, 159.
Growth in crystals, 199 ; in organisms, 199, 200.
Guyer, Prof., 20.

Hairiness, loss of, 81.
Haldane, Prof. J. S., 19.
Hauser, M. O., 105, 123.
Heidelberg man, 92, 93, 95, 97.
Henderson, Prof. L. J., 10-14.
Heredity, 21.
Hesiod, 176.
Hominidae, *see* Man.
*Homosimius*, 72, 73, 78, 79, 80, 245, 246, 247, 249, 252.
Hunzinger, A. W., 306, 307.
Huxley, Julian, 211, 213, 214.
—— T. H., 28, 45, 106.
*Hydra*, 204, 205.

Immanence, divine, 272, 273.
Immortality, Aurignacian belief in,

142, 143; Mousterian belief in, 116-118; Neolithic belief in, 167, 215; relation to Individuality, 231-233, chap. xiii. ; in Old Testament, 276-282 ; in New Testament, 284-301.
Incarnation, central place of the, 311-319.
Indeterminism and life, 236 ; amongst Protozoa, 238.
Individual, definition, 198, chap. ix.; in Protozoa, 200-204 ; in Coelenterata, 204-208 ; worms, 208-210, chap. ix.
Indo-European people, 171, 177.
Infancy, death in, 233 n ; prolongation of, 246 ; characters of, 42-44.
Internationalism, 191, 194.
Iron Age, 176.

Jennings, Prof. H. S., 211, 238.
Jesus Christ, 7, 24, 25, 26, 259-261, chap. xiv. ; teaching on Immortality, 284-288 ; Resurrection of, 299-301 ; uniqueness of, 260, 305-308.
Johnstone, Prof. J., 199.
Jones, F. Wood, 42, 43, 67 n, 73.
Josephus, 283.

Keane, A. H., 36 n, 37, 39, 45, 165.
Keith, Sir Arthur, 63, 64, 65, 66, 80, 87, 90 n, 92, 93, 96, 98, 111, 121, 155, 156, 180.
Kennedy, Prof. H. A. A., 278 n, 288 n, 291, 320 n, 327 n.
Kenosis, 25, 267, 313.
Kent's Cavern, 101, 134.
Kesslerloch Cave, 134, 135, 136, 139.
Kidd, Benjamin, 21.
Kitchen-midden axes, 152.
Krapina skeletons, 108, 151.

La Chapelle-aux-Saints, skeleton, 106, 116.
Ladd, Prof. G. T., 234.
La Ferrassie, skeleton, 107, 116.
Lake-dwellings, 158, 173, 174, 175.
La Madeleine prehistoric site, 132.
Lamarck, 4.
Land bridges, 58, 77, 102, 143, 144.
Language as test of nationality, 182, 183.
La Quina skeleton, 107.
League of Nations, 190, 194, 195.
Leckie, Dr. J. H., 284, 295-297.
Le Conte, Joseph, 316.
Lee, J. W., 336.
Leenhardt, Prof. F., 237, 241, 248, 250, 251, 253, 262.
Lemurs, 29, 68, 70.

Les Combarelles cave, 126, 127.
Levallois scraper, 100, 112.
Life, 10-14 ; characteristics of, 16-20; early manifestations of, 16, 217, 218.
Lodge, Sir Oliver, 9.
—— Sir Richard, 184 n, 185.
Love, in God, 25, 270, 294 ; manifested in Jesus Christ, 260.
Lull, Prof. R. S., 35, 216, 217, 219, 220, 222, 223 n, 224, 244.

Macalister, Prof. R. A. S., 61 n, 62, 83, 90 n, 116-118, 124, 131, 134 n, 138, 144, 145, 149, 150, 152, 153.
M'Dowall, S. A., 269, 271, 272.
Macfadyen, Prof. J. E., 324 n.
Macfarlane, Prof. J. M., 17, 201 n, 217, 218, 225.
Macintyre, Prof. R. G., 280, 285.
Magdalenian art, 134-140 ; cultural phase, 56, 57, 90, 91, 132-142, 145 ; fauna, 133 ; fossil remains, 132, 133 ; industry, 133, 134 ; religion, 142.
Magic, 140, 142.
Maglemose deposits, 150.
Mainage, Prof. Th., 114 n, 139, 140, 142 144 n.
Mammals, characters of, 28 ; brain development of, 68-80 ; origin of, 223 ; primitive forms, 224.
Man, the religious creature, 3 ; antiquity of, chap. iii. ; origin of, chap. iv. ; place in nature, chap. i. ; points of contact with anthropoid apes, 37-44 ; racial divisions, 36-37.
Marett, R. R., 114 n, 141.
Marmosets, 29, 70.
Marshall, A. Milnes, 41.
Mathews, A. P., 16 n.
Matter, electrical theory of, 9.
Mauer mandible, 92, 93, 95, 96, 97.
Mazzini, and nationality, 187.
Mediterranean race, 169.
Megalithic structures, 163-165.
Mesolithic man, 47, 113, chap. vii.
Messianic conceptions, 280, 281, 324, 325.
Metchnikoff, E., 42 n, 44.
Migration, human, 112, 143, 162, 163, 170, 171.
Mill, John Stuart, 189.
Mind and energy, 10, 264-266 ; and brain, 265-267.
Mixture of races, 120, 131, 171.
Moffatt, Prof. James, 313.
Moore, Prof. B., 16 n, 17, 315.
Moral factor in survival, 231, 248 ff., chap. xiii. ; early moral standards, 252, 258.
—— order, 259.

Mousterian cultural phase, 56, 62, 90, 91, 92, 105-118, 119, 120, 131 ; climate, 102 ; fauna, 106, 113 ; fossil remains, 105-111 ; implements, 111-113 ; religion, 114-118.
Munro, Dr. R., 79.
Mutilation, practice of, 127, 143.

Napoleon, 186, 302, 303.
Nation, 179, 190.
Nationality, place and function of, chap. viii.
Naturalism, 13.
Nature and Grace, 26, 270, 313.
Neanderthal man, see Mousterian.
Negro, 36, 62, 123, 143.
Neo-Lamarckian factors, 4, 20, 21, 225.
Neolithic man, 47, 53, chap. vii. ; characters of, 147, 155 ; dwellings, 158, 159 ; fauna, 160 ; geography, 156, 157 ; industries, 161 ; implements, 161, 162 ; skeletons, 155 ; trade, 162, 163 ; religion, 166, 167, 174.
Neopallium, 67, 68, 241.
Neo-Weismannism, 20.
Nicolai, Prof. G. F., 181, 182, 196 n.
Nordic race, 172.

Ofnet cave, 149, 151.
Old Testament conception of Immortality, 276-282.
Orang, 32, 33, 43, 65, 77.
Origin of amphibians, 222 ; fishes, 220-222 ; of life, 16, 217, 218 ; of mammals, 223 ; of man, 65, 66, chap. iv.
Osborn, H. F., 10 n, 17 n, 22 n, 96, 226 n.

Palaeolithic man, 47, 53, 54, 78, chaps. v. and vi. ; characters of, 103.
Paramaecium, 200.
Paul, St., 7, 250, 271, 283, 299 ; teaching on Immortality, 288-292 ; and doctrine of Virgin Birth, 322 ; doctrine of Pre-existence, 325-326.
Penck and Brückner, 42, 53, 56.
Personality, divine, 273.
Perthes, Boucher de, 47, 100.
Piltdown skull, 93-99.
Pithecanthropus, 85-88, 93.
Platonic conception of Immortality, 231, 291.
Pleistocene, see Great Ice Age.
Pliocene man, question of, 63, 64, 83, 84.
Pottery, 147, 161, 163, 169.

Pre-existence, doctrine of, 323-328, 333.
Primates, 29, 64, 65, 67.
Pringle-Pattison, Prof., 22, 24.
Protestantism and development of nationality, 185.
Pumpelly, Raphael, 171, 173, 226.
Purgatory, 290 n.
Purpose in the world process, 21-23, 242.

Rashdall, Dr. Hastings, 326, 329 n.
Rayleigh, Lord, 49.
Read, Prof. Carveth, 78.
Recapitulation theory, 40, 42, 205, 243.
Regeneration, in organic kingdom, 205.
Religion, affected by the War, 2 ; character of, 3 ; of Aurignacian man, 137, 142 ; of Mousterian man, 114-118 ; of Neolithic man, 166, 167, 174.
Reproduction, in animal kingdom, 209-212.
Resurrection, development of doctrine, 280-283 ; of Jesus Christ, 299-301.
Retrogression in evolution, 235, 242.
Revolution, geological, 16 ; Russian, 1.
Rhodesian skull, 109, 110.
Robinson, Dr. Louis, 43.
Roman Catholicism and nationality, 185, 187.
Russia, Border States, 183, 189, 193 ; Palaeolithic man in, 136.
Rutot, A., 56, 82, 84.

Schoolmen, attitude to theology, 6, 8.
Schuchert, Prof., 15, 16 n.
Schwalbe, Prof. G., 87, 131.
Schweitzer, Prof. A., 329.
Scotland, Azilian culture in, 152 ; geological change in, 156 ; peoples of, 180 ; political development of, 185, 192.
Selenka, 42, 85 n.
Self-determination, 243 ff.
Sharman, H. B., 285 n, 286.
Shell-heaps, Danish, 152-153.
Sheol, 278-282, 283.
Sight, development of, 67-71, 239.
Simiidae, see Anthropoid Apes.
Sin, 253, 272, 273, 312.
Sinlessness of Jesus, 331.
Sirgenstein cave, 128, 129, 134.
Smell, development of, 67-69.

Smith, Prof. Elliot, 63 ; on development of mammalian brain, 67-77, 88, 96, 99, 110.
Sohm, Prof. Rudolf, 315.
Sollas, Prof. W. J., on eoliths, 83 n, 84, 146 n.
Solutrean cultural phase, 55, 56, 57, 90, 128-132 ; fauna, 130 ; fossil remains, 130, 131 ; industry, 131-132.
Speech, 86, 98, 247.
Spy skeletons, 107.
State, the, 190 ; as an organism, 213-215.
Stephen, Sir Leslie, 307.
Steps in evolution, 218, 219.
Stereoscopic vision, effects of, 70, 71.
Strepyan cultural phase, 90, 91, 99.
Suffering, 270.
Supra-nationalism, 191.
Switzerland and nationality, 182, 183.

Tabu, 115.
Talling, Dr. Marshall, 310, 318, 322.
Tardenoisian culture, 145, 150, 151.
*Tarsius*, 68-70.
Teeth in man and apes, 31, 39, 42 ; reduction in man, 44, 80.
Teleology, 21-23, 242.
Tertiary man, 63, 64, 83, 84.
Tertullian, 23.
Thames valley, 58, 101, 102.
Theism, 23, 265, chap. xii.
Theology, place of, in thought, 6-8.
Thomson, Prof. J. A., 21, 218, 236, 255, 266 n.
Tilbury man, 155.
Totemism, 142 n.
Transcendence, divine, 272, 273 ; in man, 272-274.

Tree-shrews, 68.
Trepanning, evidence of, 166, 167.
Trinity, doctrine of, 321, 326.
Tuc d'Audoubert cave, 137, 140.
Tunzelmann, G. W. de, 9 n, 267.
Tyler, Prof. J. M., 160, 163, 167, 176, 177, 228.

Uniqueness of Jesus Christ, 260, 305-308, 328, 329.
United States of America, 181, 187, 193, 195.
Universalism, 284, 290.
Uplift, geological, 14, 15.

Verbal Inspiration, 323.
Versailles Peace Treaty, 189, 194.
Vestigial structures, 44.
Vienna, Congress of, 186, 194.
Virgin Birth, 304, 319-323, 330, 333, 334.
*Volvox globator*, 202.

Wallace, A. R., 81.
War, the Great, 1, 2, 188, 191, 192, 193.
Ward, James, 256, 258.
Waterston, Prof. D., 96.
Will, as mind in action, 10, 243, 266 267.
Woman as inventor, 168-169.
Woodruff, Prof. L. L., 17.
Woodward, Dr. A. Smith, 90 n, 93, 96, 104 n, 109.
World, God and the, 8, 10, chap. xii.
Worms, dividuality in, 208, 209.

Yerkes, R. M., 239.
Youtz, Prof. H. A., 328.

# THE SPIRITUAL INTERPRETATION OF NATURE

*Third Revised Edition*

## By JAMES Y. SIMPSON, M.A., D.Sc., F.R.S.E.

PROFESSOR OF NATURAL SCIENCE, NEW COLLEGE, EDINBURGH

'This able book will be of great value to intellectual combatants who are interested in the practical synthesis of the scientific and the religious interpretations of Nature. . . . In order that the reader may have clearly before him the essential formulations of modern biology, Professor Simpson has devoted to this a large part of his book, and we wish to congratulate him, if we may, on his achievement of a difficult task. We have read his scientific exposition with great admiration; it is scholarly, lucid, and fair-minded. Particularly successful are the chapters dealing with the Factors of Organic Evolution. . . . There is much more in Professor Simpson's book to which we should like to direct attention, but perhaps we have said enough to indicate its value. It is evidently the result of many years of wide reading and careful reflection. In its clarity we recognise the experienced teacher, who has tried and tried again to get things clear. In its vivid picturesqueness the style has often reminded us of Professor Simpson's predecessor, Henry Drummond. While we do not happen to agree with all the author's conclusions, and ways of putting things, our appreciation far outweighs our criticism, and we recommend the book heartily to all who are interested in an able-minded way, alike in the scientific, the philosophical, and the religious interpretations of Nature.'—Professor J. ARTHUR THOMSON, M.A., in the *British Weekly*.

' "To recognise the spiritual aspect of evolution," writes Mr. Simpson, "is to believe in it as directed by an overruling yet indwelling purpose, a process with no breaks but of rare continuity and yet with 'increments'—these 'increments' being represented by such phenomena as the dawn of consciousness and the appearance of Christ in the world's history." This sentence sufficiently indicates the central thesis of the volume. It is written from a fulness of scientific knowledge, and with a power of exposition which will make it welcome to those who are concerned about the philosophical and religious implications of the current scientific doctrine.'—*Scotsman*.

'Dr. Simpson's volume will be a great help to theological students in all the Churches; it will be of service to ministers of religion; and it will be eagerly read by laymen who are often much perplexed by such questions.'—*Glasgow Herald*.

## HODDER AND STOUGHTON LIMITED

PUBLISHERS                    LONDON, E.C.4